UTOPIATES

A Publication of
the Institute for
the Study of Human Problems
Stanford University

Nevitt Sanford, Director

ATHERTON PRESS
70 Fifth Avenue, New York 10011
1968

UTOPIATES

The Use & Users of LSD 25

Foreword by Nevitt Sanford

Richard Blum & Associates

UTOPIATES
The Use & Users of LSD-25
Richard Blum & Associates

Copyright © 1964 by Atherton Press

Copyright under Pan American
and Universal Copyright Conventions

Address all inquiries to
ATHERTON PRESS
70 Fifth Avenue
New York 10011

Library of Congress Catalog Card Number 64–23746
Printed in the United States of America

Fourth Printing, 1968

CONTENTS

CONTRIBUTORS

RICHARD ALPERT, Ph.D., received his degree in social psychology from Stanford University in 1957. He has taught at Stanford University, the University of California, and Harvard University. Before becoming involved in the study of psychedelic drugs, he carried out research and published articles on academic anxiety, human motivation, personality development, elementary education, and mathematics education.

EVA BLUM, Ph.D., is a research associate at the Institute for the Study of Human Problems at Stanford University and associate editor of the *Encyclopedia of Problems of Alcoholism* there. She has been a clinical psychologist for the San Mateo County Mental Health Services and a consultant for research projects for the California Medical Association and the Stanford Research Institute. She has recently served as codirector of a cultural medicine and public-health study in rural Greece.

RICHARD BLUM, Ph.D., is a consultant to the Institute for the Study of Human Problems at Stanford University. He is on the faculty of the Center for Training in Community Psychiatry (Berkeley) and has been a lecturer in criminology at the University of California and a lecturer in psychology at Stanford. At one time he was director of research for the Medical Review and Advisory Board of the California Medical Association. He has directed research at the San Mateo County Mental Health Services and recently was codirector of a cultural medicine and public-health study in Greece.

EDWARD COMBER, M.A., is director of the Bureau of Criminal Information of the San Francisco Police Department. A lecturer in the School of Criminology at the University of California, he is a member of the Research Committee of the International Association of Chiefs of Police and has been state secretary for the Peace Officers' Research Association. He is also an instructor for the Institute in Training in Municipal Administration.

JOSEPH J. DOWNING, M.D., is program chief of the San Mateo County Mental Health Services and clinical associate professor of psychiatry and preventive medicine at Stanford University School of Medicine. He was trained in psychiatry at the Menninger Foundation and received epidemiological training at the U. S. Public Health Service Contagious Disease Center in Atlanta, Georgia. He served for five years as director of the New York State Mental Health Research Unit.

JOEL FORT, M.D., is director of the Center for Treatment and Education on Alcoholism (Oakland, California). He is a lecturer in the School of Criminology at the University of California (Berkeley) and a consultant on drug addiction to the World Health Organization. He has served on the medical staff of the U. S. Public Health Service Hospital in Lexington, Kentucky, an institution which specializes in the treatment of narcotics cases.

MARY LOU FUNKHOUSER, A.B., is a research worker on several projects dealing with the use of and attitudes toward mind-modifying drugs. She is a research assistant at the Institute for the Study of Human Problems at Stanford University.

KEITH KILLAM, Ph.D., is associate professor of pharmacology at the Stanford University School of Medicine. He is consultant to the Office of Science and Technology of the White House and to the President's Advisory Commission on Narcotic and Drug Abuse and a member of the Neuropharmacology Panel of the International Brain Research Organization. Before coming to Stanford, he was senior research fellow at the UCLA Medical Center.

TIMOTHY LEARY, Ph.D., received his degree in clinical psychology from the University of California in 1950. He has taught at the University of California, the University of Copenhagen, and Harvard University. Before becoming involved in the study of psychedelic drugs, he wrote two books and several articles on personality diagnosis and psychotherapy.

RALPH METZNER, Ph.D., received a B.A. from Oxford University in 1958 and a doctorate in clinical psychology from Harvard in 1962. He has published monographs and articles on learning theory and the experimental study of personality. In the past three years, his work has centered on the pharmacology and objective description of psychedelic drug states. Dr. Metzner is the editor of *The Psychedelic Review*, the scientific-scholarly journal for the new field of studies opened up by consciousness-expanding drugs.

NEVITT SANFORD, Ph.D., is professor of psychology and education and director of the Institute for the Study of Human Problems at Stanford University and scientific director of the Cooperative Commission on the Study of Alcoholism. Prior to joining the Stanford faculty in 1961, he was professor of psychology at the University of California (Berkeley). He is a former president of the Society for the Psychological Study of Social Issues, a former member of the Board of Directors of the American Psychological Association and of the Social Science Research Council, and a member of the San Francisco Psychoanalytic Society.

JEANNE WAHL, A.B., is a research worker on the staff of the D. C. Bail Project of the Georgetown University Law Center. She has done graduate work in the School of Criminology of the University of California.

WILLIAM WYGANT, JR., B.D., is Protestant chaplain to San Mateo County Juvenile Hall and San Mateo County General Hospital. He served as Protestant chaplain at Alcatraz Federal Penitentiary and has been a parish minister. He has received specialized training as a chaplain supervisor at the Institute for Pastoral Care. He has also been trained in psychiatric pastoral counseling.

FOREWORD

Every reader of the daily press and of popular magazines knows that LSD, the most powerful of all mind-altering drugs, is a controversial subject. The controversy has involved distinguished intellectuals and artists, university professors and their administrations, theologians and mystics, and, of course, official and self-appointed watchers over the public morals. Every editor of a newspaper or magazine knows that the subject is a sensational one. It has been possible to tie in LSD with stories of sex orgies, far-out communities of true believers, espionage, international smuggling and deportations, the subversion of the young, new kinds of religious experience, and, more specifically, with the dismissal of college professors, efforts to suppress freedom of inquiry, and resistance by the powers-that-be in science, medicine, and religion to something new and possibly threatening to the established order.

But it has not been easy to know just what all the fuss is about. Just what are the effects of LSD? What issues and problems does it pose? What is its significance for society? This book tells us what the issues are, and it goes a long way toward clarifying them. At the same time it shows that many of the arguments about drugs can be resolved by knowledge, for the book produces many facts highly relevant to what is bound to be a continuing public debate. The significance of LSD use for the individual and for society becomes clearer as one sees it in the perspectives provided here: one perspective derived from the extensive research of Blum and his colleagues and other perspectives offered by the contributing authors, each of whom presents a major point of view.

LSD belongs with the class of drugs including psilocybin, peyote, and certain kinds of mushrooms which, when taken orally, can produce impressive psychological experiences. Though there appears to be a wide range of response to LSD, commonly there are reports of sensory changes, extreme variations in numerous strong emotions, new perspectives about oneself, changed views of and feelings toward other people, changes from prior chronic situations, shifts in interest, and new integrative experiences which may be delusional or mystically religious.

Apparently the reports of LSD experiences have been sufficiently interesting, or perhaps distorted enough in the popular press, that important sectors of the public and the police have come to consider LSD as one of the "dangerous drugs" and to see the users of it as people interested in indulging their senses, gratifying their impulses, and generally kicking over the traces. In a very general sense, the controversy, as it is played out in the public domain, tends to line up on the one side people who are out to indulge impulses ordinarily inhibited in our society and on the other side people who would strive to maintain the moral code and to meet the requirements of law and order. But actually, the conflict exists inside each individual, for each one of us must control his impulses or act in such a way as to gain as much gratification as possible without running the risk of punishment by society or his own conscience. Thus it is that most people have ambivalent feelings toward the addictive or dangerous drugs. This very probably accounts for the absorbing interest that we, as a nation, have in the drug addict. The nation seems to be fascinated by our forty thousand or so drug addicts who are seen as alarmingly wayward people who must be curbed at all costs by expensive police activity. Only an uneasy Puritanism could support the practice of focusing on the drug addicts (rather than on our five million alcoholics) and treating them as a police problem instead of a medical one, while suppressing harmless drugs such as marijuana and peyote along with the dangerous ones.

• But as the authors make clear, the LSD movement is a different order of phenomenon. Those who advocate the drug's use are not, in the main, after kicks, nor are they interested in antisocial activity. These advocates, who include intellectuals, professionals, and scientists, claim that the drug offers great benefits to the individual—rich inner experience, freedom to be himself, a chance for further development of his personality, and a loving rather than a hostile or indifferent attitude toward other people. Some advocates claim that, when the drug is offered as a form of therapy in the right kind of setting with suitable preparation and aftercare for the individual, it can alter in a favorable way chronic conditions such as neurosis and alcoholism. It is claimed that revolutionary discoveries, such as LSD therapy is said to be, have always been viewed with a jaundiced eye by the "establishment" in science and medicine.

Opponents, also including intellectuals, professionals, and scientists, freely admit that the drug has important psychological effects with some subjects, but they doubt that the users of the drug are as loving, spontaneous, and effective as they feel themselves to be; they urge that the claims of the advocates are to be regarded with the same skepticism that would be accorded those of any convert. The opposition notes that there are grave questions about the ethics of offering the drug to young people who are not yet in a position to choose wisely and whose development might in fact be impaired or sidetracked; the opposition also notes that the advocates' claim of being scientific investigators is negated by the fact that they act as if they already had found the answers; and finally, that experimentation with a potent chemical substance ought not to be carried on outside medical settings.

There is no doubt that there are issues aplenty around LSD use and that there has been great need of relevant facts. Blum's approach to getting the facts is simple, but as far as the field of drug research is concerned, novel. His approach is essentially epidemiological. He has asked: Who uses the drug? What are the psychological-sociological, cultural, and subcultural characteristics of people who accept LSD? When and in what circumstances do they use it? What effects do they report? Answers to these questions were sought through interviewing—and follow-up—on a sample of LSD users and by interviewing a comparable group of nonusers who were asked to explain their abstinence and their attitudes toward users.

A major finding is that—up until now at least—LSD seems mainly to be used by professionals, intellectuals, or other middle-class people—in other words, by people who are successful, socially favored, respected, and generally conforming. The use of the drug by these people does not lead to behavior that is generally considered antisocial or immoral. If LSD use represents for them some kind of revolt, it is a quiet one.

At the same time, there seems to be a not inconsiderable trend toward LSD use among young people—people not yet established in major social roles—who use the drug for kicks, for something extraordinarily exciting, aesthetic, and euphoric. This group of users does not ordinarily have contact with mental-health professionals who have access to the drug, but they obtain the drug through black-market sources or make use of homegrown or purchased morning glory seeds.

• This is a point of great importance: The effects of taking the drug are heavily dependent upon the characteristics of the taker. They vary with the situation in which it is taken, with the subject's psychological state at the time, with personality and background, and with social and cultural group membership.

If the source of the drug is illicit and the setting is one in which the aim is to get high with a group of young people, then the effects will be similar to those achieved with the use of various other substances —orgiastic, artistic, or euphoric. On the other hand, if the drug is taken in a medical setting, the responses are more likely to be in the area of changed perspectives and integrative experiences. Within each of these settings there will be variations with personality and sociocultural factors.

People who use one drug are likely to use others as well; drug use can be an expanding phenomenon. Nevertheless, one man's meat is another man's poison. There is some reason to believe that there may be genetic factors that help to determine preferences for particular drugs.

But the contributors to this volume are more inclined to accent culture. They marshal evidence that the effects of any drug tend to be in keeping with the values of the culture or subculture in which it is used—or, if the user's wish is to express rebellion or dissidence, the effect will stand in opposition to the prevailing values. The same substance has different effects in different cultures; and the same effects may be achieved with different substances. There was a time when alcohol was hailed in much the same way that LSD is today, and a time when coffee was brought under the same kind of proscription that today holds for the opiates.

There has been a tendency in psychopharmacological work to accent the power of the substance itself, to design experiments for showing that one drug will affect this function, another that, and to assume that varying effects are due to the strictly chemical actions of the substance itself rather than to expectations, beliefs, social facilitation, and so on. The present work is a contribution to a growing body of literature which argues, from evidence, that drug effects cannot be considered apart from their context of psychological, social, and cultural factors.

It is further to be noted, as the authors stress, that we have in LSD use what amounts to a social movement. Those who accept the
• drug are held together by shared experience, and they engage in mass

communication and political activity when they deal with their opponents or try to get a hearing for their views. They exhibit the same kinds of differences within the group that are found in most social movements. They are, in some sense of the word, an in-group or an out-group, depending on how one looks at it, and they tend to cast their opponents in the role of suppressors. Most important, they have an ideology, one that accents the values of the inner life, of personal freedom, of mystical experience, and of love. The authors suggest that this ideology can be largely understood as a reaction against or, better, a withdrawal from major trends in contemporary society. There would appear to be no question but that the requirements for individual self-control and conformity with society are becoming more burdensome today. As work becomes more and more organized and complex, there are increasing demands upon the individual to be efficient and rational, to adapt himself to the organization or to the system of bureaucracy. At the same time, he is offered fewer opportunities for emotional expression or satisfaction. All phases of life become more standardized and impersonal—ordered to the requirements of an industrial civilization. There is loss of community feelings; work and play are sharply compartmentalized, festivals are commercialized. Leisure-time activities have become so highly conventionalized that they too must be under rigid control rather than offering a person genuine freedom to express his impulses or to be himself. More and more people "want out," and this includes, strikingly enough, as the study shows, people who have been successful in the society and have received the rewards that it promised them.

One could, then, understand the LSD movement as an attempt to regain values that tend to be dethroned in the system of today. Yet there appears to be a certain irony in all this. For one thing, those who take part in the movement do not resign altogether from the social system; on the contrary, they seem to carry on dutifully within it. One might ask how they can do this without accenting that impersonality that the LSD ideology disavows. Again, there would appear to be a certain inconsistency in a movement that seeks to revolt against technology through the use of one of its characteristic products, namely, a manufactured chemical.

But, as the authors point out, the LSD movement would not have started had there not been a need for it and a fertile social ground in which it could grow. There is no question but that the movement is accenting and helping bring to the forefront of the nation's attention values that have been sadly neglected. It has also posed ideological, moral, and scientific conflicts which are of considerable importance.

The needs, the value problems, and the conflicts in morals and life orientation are going to be with us for some time to come. So too will the expanding use and abuse of drugs continue to confront us. What we do about it and what will happen to us as a result are matters that we would all be wise to attend to. The contributors to this book are doing just that. They join with me in inviting others—citizens, scientists, physicians, mystics and ministers, lawmakers and lawmen, drug users and abstainers—to learn and think more about the phenomena of drug use and to begin to plan for social action. That action, which must be to define our course with reference to the handling of classes of drugs and classes of drug users, must soon be taken. When it is taken, it must be based on facts, not fiction, and it must be humane, sensible, and constructive.

Nevitt Sanford

BACKGROUND CONSIDERATIONS

[I]

Richard Blum

Mind-altering drugs are, with the exception of alcohol and the opiates, relatively new tools which a technological society has developed to control nature, in this case the nature of inner man. Their use, as manufactured products dispensed by prestigeful scientific healers, is compatible with Western man's trust in technology and its prophets. In addition, certain of these drugs are instrumental in the achievement of states of consciousness which are culturally approved as well as individually desired. Happiness, tranquillity, alertness, sleep, and relief from pain, fatigue, depression, or anxiety are among the approved ends of drug use.

One should not be surprised at the extensiveness of mind-altering drug use in the United States. Ours is a social environment which develops drugs and advertises them widely. It provides professionals to prescribe them and market places in which to buy them. It creates some of the misery which the drugs are meant to soothe. As an aggregate of values and judgments, it provides further stimulation to use by condemning misery as a bad thing, a state in need of correction. For a man to be unhappy is not only "wrong"; it can be taken as proof of his own personal fault or weakness.

The findings from various epidemiological studies of mental health show that there are quite a few persons who are in apparently chronic psychological distress. There are, no doubt, quite a few more who are temporarily upset. In addition, there are those who suffer a sense of futility or incompleteness rather than specific pain. These are the hollow ones, who feel the emptiness of themselves and sense the absence of vitality, optimism, spontaneity, and inner richness. The promise held out to them by life is unfulfilled. And those who have striven for much-heralded rewards and achieved them, only to find the crown of laurel an illusion—what about them? Should we be surprised that many among these people will seek out and extol each new and more powerful mind-altering drug as long as there is the hope or promise of benefit?

One speaks of the extensiveness of use and the rapidity of acceptance. What are the facts? No one is, as yet, sure, for no one has conducted an epidemiological study to learn how many Americans use which drugs under what circumstances. But prescription data are available, as are manufacturer's reports. And these indicate that hundreds of tons of consciousness-altering drugs are produced each year to be consumed by tens of millions of Americans—adults and children.

At least three sets of factors emerge to complicate drug use and to generate counterforces to the present expansionist trend. One factor is that many of the new drugs have dangerous side effects which produce physical or psychological pathology. Untoward reactions, ranging from minor states of confusion or a stuffy nose all the way to long-term psychoses and death, do occur. A second factor is that drug use appears not only to perpetuate, but to extend itself, leading, at least in some people, to habituation and, as new drugs are employed, to increased risk of addiction or an unfavorable response. But habituation itself is a bad thing only because it is believed to be so; it is a matter of morals and values. The issue is one of independence versus dependency, of the image of the whole man, resilient and resourceful, versus the image of the insufficient man, leaning on pharmaceutical crutches so that he may continue his movement down the road of life. The questions raised by this issue are by no means easy to resolve, either by science or ethics.

A third set of factors which oppose extended drug use are the responses of those not taking drugs, or at least of those not taking the same drug or taking it so often, to the avowed aims and observed reactions of the drug users themselves. The opposition is greatest to those drugs, and to those who take them, when drug use is associated with a lasting change in social orientation and activity. An example is found in the case of the barbiturate addict who clumsily feels his way through each day, his heavy tongue slurring the communication of leaden thoughts. Those around him are shocked and worried, perhaps even sympathetic, but they disapprove. Another case is the beat marijuana user, one who asserts his independence with a flourish of contempt, declaring his loyalty to his companions in staccato inhalations as he "blows pot" and declaring his nonconformist identity by wearing the costume and espousing the lore of the beats. Threading through the way of life of the "pot-head" beat is his disapproval of a society whose values, like the British tea tax in the American colonies, were levied without his representation. His war against society is conducted with a marijuana cigarette; it is a fairly safe combat because he may not tell the enemy that war has been declared. But the enemy, conventional society, is not without perspicacity, and its minions respond with irritable disdain and, if the evidence stands up in court, a jail sentence for the rebels.

Another illustration is the Navajo Indian in his lonely country shack who, the long night through, joins his fellows as they are absorbed in prayer, vigil, and contemplation while they eat peyote buttons. Their religious endeavors strive to reach the Great Spirit so that He may help them in their present trials and so that they may absorb some of his power and be greater than they were before. But peyote is forbidden, and in the darkness the arresting deputies swoop down on the tumble-down dwelling and cart the rapturous worshipers off to jail. In this case the deputies themselves are a bit ashamed, and the community, ambivalent, almost wishes that these humble people, seeking such quiet ends, had been left in peace.

The major disputes about drug use, as contrasted with public concern or alarm, are not over the sedatives, tranquilizers, energizers, stimulants, or analgesics, nor even over the intoxicants, such as marijuana and alcohol. The *disputes* center about the hallucinogens: peyote, mescaline, psilocybin, and "the king of drugs," LSD-25. It is about LSD that most controversy has arisen.

The LSD controversy is quite different from the debates that have raged about other drugs in recent years. There is a current debate about cigarettes, but the argument there is about the interpretation of results showing an association between smoking and lung cancer; the question is only, "How dangerous are cigarettes?" and, "Must I really give them up?" There is a debate about alcohol too, but it ranges not so much over the known dangers, but over the means of control: "How can we reduce the damage from alcohol?" and, "Who should take charge?" There is a very recent debate over Percodan, a painkiller. That debate has nearly torn one state legislature asunder, but the question is still only one of effects: "Is it really addictive?" and, "How much control on medical dispensing should be enacted?"

With LSD, it is not so much a question of effects, although these are still under study, but more of the rights of persons to use such a drug, the propriety of their aims and values, and the acceptability of the kinds of experiences and personal and social behavior which ensue. Fundamentally the question seems to be whether even a pluralistic and democratic society will tolerate the means and the philosophy espoused by what can be called the "drug movement" and whether it will tolerate that movement's challenge to contemporary values, especially when that challenge is raised by and diffused among *important* people. The movement's heralds are not the lowly, but are the very people who are expected to be models of the Protestant ethic because they have been rewarded by it and charged with the responsibility of communicating it—or selling it—to others. These important people are the intellectuals, or at least some intellectuals, and for them the drug movement is a revolt—the "silent revolution," some of its leaders have called it. And today we know what Lenin knew, but what wise and worldly Max Weber refused to believe—that, when intellectuals start a revolution, the rest of the society had better be aware that something is happening.

There are probably very few Americans who are not aware that something is happening, that the drug movement and LSD *is* an issue. With the clanging acclaims and denunciations, the national noise level has become a din. During 1962 and 1963, nearly every important national magazine carried a major article dealing with the drug itself. In addition many magazines and newspapers carried news and comments on the events associated with LSD use—most notably the activity at Harvard and in Mexico where psychologists and others using LSD were expelled. *Life* and *Playboy,* for example, have presented material with primarily favorable views of LSD and those who would use it to alter consciousness; *Esquire, The Reporter,* and *Look* have taken a much dimmer view.

While through 1962 and most of 1963 the outcome of the great LSD controversy was in doubt, by the end of 1963, one sensed the balance shifting. The International Foundation for Internal Freedom, an organization established by psychologists and others interested in furthering LSD use, announced, as its last act, its own demise. The reason given? LSD was becoming too hard to obtain. And why was that? Partly because the major manufacturer of the drug was reported to have placed further controls on a distribution already restricted to research and clinical experimentation. Furthermore, the Federal Food and Drug Administration (FDA), previously quiescent, began to seize contraband LSD supplies. In 1963, arrests also began to be made of persons charged with the illicit importation or sale of the drug.

There is no need to present the detailed history of LSD here. Discovered to be a mind-altering agent in 1943, it was at first considered to be a psychotomimetic with potential for research use in neuropharmacology, psychiatry, and psychology. By 1964, over one thousand studies of its nature or effects had been published. But in the 1950's, a shift in LSD interests occurred—a shift which reflected the recognition that it was indeed an hallucinogen, but that it did not produce, except by painful and unpredictable accident, a genuine psychosis. It was during the 1950's that professionals in medicine, psychology, and allied sciences began to use the drug for reasons that were not strictly scientific. They began to employ it as a psychotherapy adjunct, as a facilitator for creative or aesthetic experiences, as a source of "kicks" or euphoria, and to produce self-actualization, religious, philosophical, or other personal and social experiences deemed desirable.

It was when people shifted from using the drug to see what *it* was like or what *it* could do, to using it to see what *they* themselves were like or what *they* could do, that LSD *use* rather than LSD effects became an intriguing subject for investigation. It was this same shift which led to its becoming the center of controversy, for, as respectable people began to employ LSD purposively to change themselves or to change the nature of their experiences, almost immediately there was generated a social issue which reached into the core of individual and cultural values.

Some of the questions which surround that issue are:

The question of anachoresis: Is it right to turn inward and to glorify inner experience at the expense of ordinary outer (interpersonal, object-oriented) transactions?

The question of pleasure: Dare one allow others to indulge themselves in pleasure without restraint?

The question of rights: Can one allow a revolt to succeed, even if it presents no direct challenge to law, order, economics, or the power structure? Does a person have the right to decide for himself to use a drug for nonmedical purposes; in other words, is it legitimate to use drugs if one is not formally defined as being sick? Does one have the right to decide for himself whether he wants to change the nature of his consciousness?

The question of God's will: Does one violate the natural order or God's will if one tampers with one's body or mind, if one seeks to change balances which are "preordained"?

The question of risk: If it were proven beyond all doubt that some people do have bad reactions, what right does that give society to interfere with all of those who want to take the drug? Does one have the right to decide for oneself if one is willing to take a risk, or may the commonwealth properly protect one from oneself?

The question of punishment: How does one justify the punishment of people who have done things which are disapproved (drug use, sexual deviation) but which have not harmed others or themselves? Do we punish for effects or for wrongdoing?

The question of ecstasy: Is there room for ecstasy, for Dionysian extremism, in Apollonian America?[1]

The question of responsibility: Is it responsible conduct on the part of anyone to give LSD, the most powerful drug known to man, to another, knowing that a major shift in his life direction is likely to follow? Who is responsible, the one who offers or the one who takes?

The question of dependency: Is it bad to rely on things or persons so heavily that, when they are withdrawn, one suffers? Is the whole man, the admirable man, the one who stands alone? What is wrong with being habituated, even addicted, to a drug?

• *The question of reality:* Is LSD a glorious deceiver, a gilded mask for vanity, the great "I am"? Is it deception in a gelatin capsule? Is all that is revealed a monstrous delusion? Or if LSD does reveal truth, dare one block the pathway of the blessed? Should we not all tread that path?

The question of values: What if the movement is only a response to technology, bureaucracy, and collectivity? What if some of our most promising citizens do thereby renounce ambition, prestige, material success; what if they do protest a way of life? What remains for them to believe in? What remains for the rest? Can our culture generate a better way and beliefs more appropriate to the nature of man?

As LSD use has expanded, more and more citizens have begun to think over and sometimes have intense feelings about these questions. Some of them, reaching conclusions, found they shared an idea. From 1960 through 1963, the drug movement crystallized.

The movement is composed of people who have taken LSD and/or other hallucinogens and see in these drugs a tool for bringing about changes which they deem desirable. The emphasis is on the enhancement of inner experience and on the development of hidden personal resources. It is an optimistic doctrine, for it holds that there are power and greatness concealed within everyone. It is an intellectual doctrine, for it values experience and understanding more than action and visible change. It concerns itself with areas dear to the thinker: art, philosophy, religion, and the nature and potentials of man. It is a mystical doctrine, for it prizes illumination and a unified world view with meaning beyond that drawn from empirical reality. It is a realistic doctrine as well, for it counsels compromise and accommodation between the inner and outer worlds. "Play the game," it advises, "don't let the Pied Piper lead you out of town." And it is, explicitly, a revolutionary doctrine, although the revolution it proposes is internal, psychological, and by no means novel. It calls for freedom from internal constraints, freedom to explore oneself and the cosmos, and freedom to use LSD and other drugs as the means thereto.

The drug movement is certainly not the only movement to incorporate psychological and social interests in a drug-centered activity. The Ras Tafarian sect in Jamaica has a racial-religious-political ideology based on the use of marijuana. Among the metropolitan American beats there is a similar centering about marijuana, but their ideology is so loose knit and disillusionist that the beats are hardly an activist enterprise. And in the Congo, the dissident Kwilu Province tribesmen reportedly use marijuana as a source of stimulation and "invulnerability" before going into battle. In times past berserk Norse warriors employed the mind-altering amanita mushroom to inspire their fierce frenzy in battle. In the Middle East, coffee played a significant role; the coffee house was established for its use, and men gathered there to drink and talk. The coffee house became the center of new social forces, ones soundly denounced by orthodox political and religious interests. So resolute were these latter in their opposition to the dangerous drug of coffee and to the "mob" which drank it that, for a time, it was a capital offense to gather in or to own a coffee house. The evidence in antiquity is less clear, but one suspects that new drugs became the basis for sect activities if not for social change. It may have been that opium in ancient Crete (around 1800–1400 B.C.) took on a religious significance, and the use of wine in the Catholic Mass suggests that alcohol itself, at some point in history, must have been used to achieve ecstatic states.

Drug movements are not, then, new to the face of the earth. That historical perspective does not alter the present circumstances—and the fact is that there are dedicated enthusiasts who believe that *everyone* ought to take, or to have the opportunity to take, LSD. In opposition to them are antagonists, some dedicated and some merely skeptical, who think it would be better if only experimental subjects or no one at all had the opportunity to take LSD. It is the enthusiasm and the conflict which make the drug movement a prominent social issue.

Psychology and psychiatry have been especially torn by the disputes raised by the movement. There are two reasons. One is that many of the phenomena attributed to the hallucinogens are within the province of these disciplines; the other is that some of the leaders of the movement have come from these two fields. One battle looms over the challenge issued by movement leaders, reputable professionals in their own right, who charge that psychology and psychiatry have espoused orthodoxy. These professions, they say, are accretions of vested interests which pay more attention to tradition and self-interest than to potentially useful new methods of research and treatment. By the latter, they mean LSD.

A second professional issue is scientific and philosophical. It arises from the observation (in need of further testing) that a clinical research worker is likely to be aroused by the questions raised by the movement. His own position will be determined by his personality and values. His decision to take LSD or not probably rests, at least in part, upon these uncontrolled factors. So does his response to LSD should he take it. His use of and response to the drug will, in turn, influence his design of research and the fashion in which he interprets data. People who have had favorable experiences are likely to find in favor of LSD in their evaluations; the contrary holds for those who reject the drug or have not had ideological conversions in response to it. If these observations are valid, it would follow that one can predict the results of clinical research by knowing whether or not the investigator has taken LSD and, if so, under what ideological circumstances, that is, as a convert to the movement, as a preconvinced skeptic or antagonist, or as a scientifically desirable but socially rare bird, a drug neutral. Experimental results in that case would provide information about the experimenter, but not about his subjects.

These observations and the reasoning which accompanies them have led some movement investigators to contend that no adequate research can be done by those who have not taken the drug and had the "right" kind of experience with it. Some members of the opposition insist that no adequate research can be done by anyone who has taken the drug and had that "right" kind of experience. It is likely that future studies on investigators as well as subjects will lead to consensus; although, if one takes the debate on parapsychology as a parallel case, it can be a long, long time before that consensus is achieved. In the meanwhile, as long as both the movement and its opposition accept the basic premise that the LSD experience is the primary variable affecting the perception of truth, the former saying it is essential and the latter saying LSD prevents the possibility of such perception, neither side can offer the other irrefutable proof.

The contributors to this volume have tried to maintain their objectivity whatever their LSD experience. Five have taken the drug, nine have not. The volume itself aims to provide information about the natural history and consequences of LSD use, about factors associated with the acceptance or rejection of mind-altering drugs, and about the cultural, social, and personal conditions which bear on the many important questions posed by the drug movement.

NOTE

1. For a discussion of Apollonian versus Dionysian cultures or life styles, refer to Friedrich Nietzsche, *The Birth of Tragedy,* and to Ruth Benedict, *Patterns of Culture* (New York: Houghton Mifflin, 1934).

THE RESEARCH ENTERPRISE AND ITS PROBLEMS

[II]

Richard Blum

Research is rarely easy and research on living groups can be especially difficult. We had set out to learn about the use of LSD-25. We had hoped to learn about the drug movement which centers about LSD, about the psychological and social forces operating to interest people in taking the drug, and about the responses of law-enforcement people to this new activity. To accomplish our aims, it was necessary to become acquainted with persons who had had the opportunity to take LSD, with persons who had exercised this opportunity, and with police officers in drug-control work who were vitally interested in the problems posed by drug use. Once acquaintances were made it was necessary to gain the confidence of these individuals, to assure them anonymity, and to stimulate them to discuss their experience and the issues as they saw them.

We were fortunate to number among our own friends and acquaintances persons who had taken LSD and people in law enforcement. It was with them that our work began. Immediately two kinds of difficulties became evident—one methodological and the other methodological too, but involving deeper concerns of trust and our own position on issues. The methodological problem was essentially one of sampling. How does one know who has had the opportunity to take LSD? How does one know who is taking it now? The very nature of the act, imbedded as it is in private feelings, perhaps as part of the confidential nature of psychotherapy or in the precautionary conceal- ment of persons using illicit drugs, and associated with the tendency to ethnocentrism or "cultism" on the part of others, makes it impossible to find one's "cases" through any sort of public record or direct survey. One had to begin with persons with whom relations of trust already existed and proceed down a social chain, much as strangers in old Albania used to be conveyed from one district to another and handed over in safekeeping from one district headman to the next. Proceeding down a social chain, being introduced from one user to another, meant that our sample depended upon pre-existing friendships among users and upon the willingness of newly introduced persons to accept us with trust. It is a tribute to the good nature and intrinsic trustfulness of so many people that our movement down that chain was not halted and that so many strangers were willing to speak to us in frankness and intimacy.

But not everyone liked or trusted us. Perhaps some responded neg- atively to our intentions and some to our persons, whereas others were reluctant to cooperate because of understandable desires to protect existing activities from intrusion, from feared criticism, or from the possible danger of publicity and even prosecution. Not all those we met would speak of their drug use, and some who did, we have reason to believe, were not completely frank.

These problems of access differed from person to person, depend- ing upon such factors as their own patterns of LSD use, their status relationships to us, their loyalty to institutions which either approved or disapproved of our intentions or stated position, their trust in those who introduced us, and their personal attitudes on various other mat- ters—for example, on being interviewed, on revealing feelings, on the "academic" approach, and so on. One consequence was that, with one subgroup, we consistently failed. The various officials of what we have termed the religious-medical center were uniformly uncooperative and distrustful, refusing us access to themselves, their views, their data, and their LSD clients or initiates. This is not to say that their clients, that is, persons who took LSD under center auspices, were not accessible; we found them in other ways, again down that social chain. But the officials, those who played a prime role in establishing and running the center itself, would not—except for one exception, a most open and delightful person—participate.

Not only officials involved in promoting and dispensing LSD rejected us and our approach; many police officials took the same stand. In spite of the fact that one of the investigators had worked in and for police departments for some eight years and counts among his friends administrators in a number of departments, our reception was anything but warm in some jurisdictions.

One problem in police interviews was generated by the in-group feeling which characterizes some police personnel. Not unreasonably, many policemen feel themselves to be an unappreciated minority subjected to the irrational attacks of citizens who disguise their rebellious or criminal impulses under the guise of notions of police unfairness or brutality. Since the police have had many bad experiences at the hands of the public, one must be sympathetic toward the protective withdrawal which police groups sometimes undertake. But this means that many of those who have isolated themselves will be reluctant to speak frankly, especially if the inquirer is an outsider.

One policeman told one of the female investigators on our team, "Honey, you don't really think I'm going to cop out to you about any of this jazz, do you?" This rhetoric, facilitated by six Scotch and sodas, was nevertheless followed by very intense discussion, that is, "copping out," on the practices and issues involved. We learned, in that interview, that a previous interview had been conducted in a "bugged" room; this was known to the subject, but not to the interviewer, thus reversing the usual police-interrogation circumstances. Although none of us objected to the recording of what we had said, we certainly had to face the fact that what the subject had told us could only be designed for very official consumption.

"Why don't you chuck this jazz, honey, and be a woman?" This was the challenge to one of the team's pretty female investigators. Accompanied by flattering but persistent attempts at seduction, the comment points to a larger problem. The police have been so little exposed to social-science research—partly because of scientific disinterest and partly because of police standoffishness—that some lawmen feel uncomfortable under its probing, regardless of the aims of a study. Such men have not been trained to understand research goals and values as we know them, nor have they learned how to handle inquiries without uncertainty, embarrassment, and defensiveness. No wonder they wish to revert to more comfortable role relationships—man to woman in this case. More than that, as an eminently male fraternity, indeed as what might be called the last vestige of a warrior culture in Western society, police officers are often unused to dealing with women as professional persons or as equals. A woman may be placed on a pedestal or lured into a bed, but one does not easily sit down with one to talk about business matters. Business—police work—is for men. For a study in which women investigators are involved, these are problems of a psychological and subcultural nature which impede the free flow of inquiry and response. The immediate task is to recognize the likelihood of distortion in information rendered by interview and observation in the event that the sensitive police officer feels the researcher is an outsider.

Thus our results may reflect distortions due to sampling because the population of persons with LSD opportunities and experiences has characteristics and a distribution not fully known to us. Distortions are also introduced by the personal, social, and cultural factors affecting our relationships with the persons interviewed and their willingness to tell us what they did and believed. In the police data, there may be distortion due to uneven representation among the police departments asked to cooperate in the study. Beyond that we face the inevitable consequences of prior difficulties: the rather small size of the subgroups involved. In all, as part of the "natural-history" study, we contacted ninety-five persons who had, we thought, used LSD. As it turned out halfway through the interview, three had used psilocybin instead, and so, for the sake of purity, we excluded them from the sample. Our interviews took from one to six hours, not counting the hours spent in tracking down people and arranging the interviews. But a sample of ninety-two, when those subgroups which emerged as important were examined, became in fact five subsamples, ranging in size from twelve to twenty-four persons. And, of course, when it comes to describing behavior in these groups, one finds that people acted in various ways. The result was that groups became even smaller as one classified individuals in terms of one or another kind of behavior or self-report variable. For the most part, we described these groups in terms of the proportions engaged in one or another kind of activity and so on. For purposes of clarity and ease, we render these proportions as percentages, but we ask the reader to keep in mind that small numbers are involved. We have tried to avoid relying on these tenuous percentages for the substance of our conclusions.

In speaking of sampling distortion and the limitations imposed by small sample size, a very important question comes to the fore: How large is the total sample of persons who have had LSD experience or the sample of those who have had the opportunity but who have rejected it (from whom we drew our control group)? And what is the real size of the subgroups based on the circumstances of LSD use which we found it convenient to categorize? If a subsample of twenty does, in fact, represent a real "universe" of twenty-two, we can worry a bit less about actual numbers; if it represents a population of two thousand, we are in trouble. And the chances are that we *are* in trouble.

We have already said that there exists no handy roster of identified LSD "cases" in the epidemiological sense. Nor could we confidently undertake a door-to-door survey to improve this base—partly because we assume the number is too small and because too many "No, I haven't" answers might really mean "Yes, I did, but I won't tell." When we began the study, we hoped to interview everyone in a defined geographical area who had had LSD. Before we had finished we found ourselves extending our geography and abandoning our aim for a complete number. We moved from one limited local base to two metropolitan regions. Before that happened we had given up trying to reach everyone in one place who had had LSD. What population figures can we offer? Just a few. At the time interviewing began, the religious-medical center reported it had given LSD to one hundred and sixty people; we saw twenty of them. At the time of interviewing, our own informal black-market users group indicated that the regular number of habitués at its periodic parties was about forty. We saw twelve. Among twelve public-clinic patients, we saw eight. Among some twenty-seven private-therapy patients listed for us, we saw thirteen. As for those experimental users who had taken LSD in laboratories, we saw fifteen, but their actual number—across the nation—is probably thousands. The same is true for the sample we have termed the informal professional group, those medical and mental-health professionals and their close friends and relatives who have taken LSD outside institutional settings. We saw twenty-four of them; they estimate their own number—across the nation—to be more than twenty-five thousand! And so it is clear that we are in sampling trouble; but, since our available resources were limited, we could not extend the scope of inquiry any further.

One more methodological difficulty requires attention. The heart of our study was a scheduled interview, that is, a questionnaire which had open- and closed-ended questions which were presented to the subject. His replies and tangential remarks were recorded, and, if he had moved in an interesting direction, further questions not on the schedule were asked. Sooner or later one returned to the questionnaire itself. There were three kinds of exceptions to that technique. In the case of three LSD respondents who could not be seen in person, the questionnaire was filled in by the respondents without an interview. In the case of some of the controls, there was a face-to-face discussion or interview followed by the completion of the short-form questionnaire used with the control group. In these cases the completed questionnaire was returned by mail or handed back. A third group of exceptions involved about six of the informal black-market users. We were privileged to be invited to a bull session where a number of black-market drug users were present; it proved to be a long and informative evening during which we took advantage of spirited discussion to ask many questions and to listen to the sometimes heated debate which followed. But we did not feel we were in a position to arrange for individual interviews with some of these people, for we had not been introduced in a conventional way, nor had the aims of our inquiries been fully set forth by our host. Indeed, he seemed careful that we not learn the names or addresses of his guests, and their own uneasiness when one of us was identified as a criminologist was such that we did not care to push our luck. As a group, they told us much, but we sensed that, if we asked for more individually, we might jeopardize further frank discussion. Indeed, with two, we did try to set up such a formal interview, and they declined.

A different sort of problem in our study has to do with the communication of the content of personal experiences. It is hardly a new problem to psychology, but its presence requires discussion and leads us to now consider some of our findings. Many persons who have taken hallucinogens make the statement that their experience is ineffable; that is, what has gone on in their minds cannot be communicated to others; that no words exist to describe these internal events, and, even if there were such words, they would be devoid of significance unless the listener had himself gone through the same experiences. Operating on this assumption of ineffability, several competent LSD-using professionals challenged our sense and fairness in conducting an LSD study without having taken the drug ourselves.

As for the argument that words employed to describe the LSD experience are poor messengers of meaning, we are ready to agree, for the evidence is with the users. To anticipate later findings, it is clear that what one expects from LSD on the basis of prior information and personal predispositions, plus what one is told is happening by the administrator while one is taking the drug, are factors strongly influencing the choice of words used to describe the experience itself. People who expect a mystical-religious reaction are more likely to have one; people who want an expanding view of self seem to have a better chance of achieving it; people who are told while undergoing the drug reaction that they are seeing God do, in fact, seem more likely to report that vision. Yet, as one listens to each person, one feels that the phenomenological approach is not without merit and that the cerebral experiences being reported—the inner sensations, images, mood—are not so different from one another. We would elevate our impressions to the level of a postulate, indeed it was one of our initial hypotheses, to suggest that the unusual inner events produced by LSD are reported and even responded to differently, but that the inner sensations themselves may have much more in common than the language of the reporter suggests.

Ambiguous experiences are structured by learned expectations, strong motives, and situational cues. Further, language becomes a device to provide structure and to create a community of experience among persons having LSD. For example, one young man who had taken LSD said approximately the following:

> Really, when I first took LSD, I didn't know how to describe what had happened. It was intense and important, very much so, but there were no words for it. But after talking with others who had taken it, I could see that they were talking about the same thing. They did have words for it—"transcendental" was one—and so I started using those words myself. An interesting thing happened to my wife. After I gave her LSD she said very little about it. For a whole month she hardly said a word about her experience. But then I introduced her to some others who were taking the drug, and it wasn't more than a few days before she started talking a blue streak; you see, she'd learned how to talk about it from them.

This explanation describes how one learns a language which signifies to other users that one understands and has been through an LSD experience. The language is shaped by the culture of the speakers, in this case, by the particular subgroup with which the LSD user is socially affiliated and under whose auspices he has taken the drug. Drug language is as much a sign of "belongingness" and "togetherness" as it is a device for communicating the content of an experience. No wonder the person with LSD experience senses futility in talking with nonusers; to the latter, the words are neither signals for sympathy, nor are they understood as affirmations that one is a particular kind of person or a fellow member of an important in-group.

The trouble for the observer is that the reports of the LSD experience may have to be treated, when they differ from group to group, more as data for the study of comparative linguistics than as evidence for differing internal experience. We suspect reports carry both kinds of information; but distinguishing between that which is a function of an imposed linguistic structure and that which communicates internal experience capable of being validated by other measures is beyond our means at this point.

As for the original protest of some of the LSD *aficionados*, it is a genuine dilemma. One is scientifically contaminated if one does take it, one is guilty of insensibility if one does not. But the argument is not new. Perhaps in self-defense, for we agreed that no member of the study team would take any such drug prior to or during the study, we bring up the similarity between that argument and the one encountered when other groups are studied by persons not committed to the group in question. In the past, psychologists who studied psychoanalytic phenomena experimentally were warned not to do so unless they had been analyzed; otherwise they could only misinterpret and misunderstand. Unfortunately, as defensive as the argument really was, any review of psychological experiments in the field will come up with many outstanding examples of the correctness of the accusation. The author, when studying organized medicine, was frequently told that one could not properly study the behavior of physicians unless one was oneself "a doctor." The comment was usually made when the results of such study were seen as critical of organized medicine. It implies that it is much safer to hire researchers who are properly initiated into a group, groomed according to its tenets, and steadfastly bound by its obligations; such men can be trusted to be sympathetic. Indeed, within social science itself, one does not have to go far to find narrow provincialism and immediate criticism of one who would hoe another's garden; no matter that historians of science show that much creative work may come out of cross-fertilization. Our position is that behavior can be studied by means other than introspection; but we would not espouse behaviorism per se, that is, ruling out others' introspection. Indeed, in this study, we depend upon it, and our approach is, as we said, at least partly phenomenological. Perhaps it seems odd to have to make such a statement at this point in the twentieth century; nevertheless the position of some of our friends and acquaintances who use and study LSD is so strongly held that old issues in psychological science are brought to the fore once again.

We must grant that the complaints about language—its poverty, its tenuous validation for internal experience, and our lack of ability to check the adequacy of the experience categories implied—and about the unsympathetic response of nonusers may be correct. We grant, probably with all psychologists, that some way of climbing inside "the black box" and photographing its contents is much to be desired. But we deny that membership in every group is a necessary prerequisite for the study of that group, although we do not deny that such participant observation can be in itself an excellent technique.

Being a participant observer in drug studies poses problems of a special sort. Some people become psychotic after taking LSD and can stay that way for some time. No one would doubt that distortions might flavor the report of the psychotic participant observer. Some people become quite euphoric after LSD. A similar thing happened to Freud when he took and became a short-time booster of cocaine. Most people will grant that rose-colored glasses are not the instrument of choice for making psychological observations. Some people, after taking LSD, become depressed and/or suffer memory loss for parts of the experience. Retrograde amnesia may also occur. The absent-minded scientist may be a fit subject for a movie; we do not believe the absent-minded psychologist—or the depressed one—makes a fit or happy investigator. We think these arguments sufficient to account for our not taking LSD. This does not imply that everyone responds to LSD with distortion or disability. We know many whose perceptions remain clear and true. But in advance we did not feel we could predict our own responses and, for reasons of personal safety and scientific objectivity, decided not to take the risk.

If no one takes the drug, what can go wrong? Nothing, of course. The trouble is that in becoming affiliated with persons who are part of the drug movement—witty conversationalists, pleasant people, admirable alter egos, slick seducers, or proficient proselytizers—temptations arise. Luther wisely observed that, since temptations could not be eliminated, one must learn to withstand them. Some people do, and some people don't. Some newsworthy problems have occurred in the area of drug researchers sampling their wares and, in consequence, shifting their life directions. Their colleagues feel betrayed; their institutions are embarrassed; but the researcher-turned-user seems not to care, at least, not enough to return to his former life styles. In later sections we will examine the conflict in values which an LSD defection from former commitments reveals.

All of those working on the project were approached, at one time or another, by hopefuls wanting us to give them LSD. Since we had no drugs, it was not difficult to offer them only our regrets. All of us were also invited to take drugs by people we were interviewing. Most often we were offered LSD or marijuana. Sometimes a drink or two came first, then the promise of pleasant companionship, an offer of visions of joy, and finally out came the drug. "Come on, try it," "Don't be a square," "Certainly you're not one of *those* people, are you?" "When are you coming over for your LSD session?" The offers were generous, friendly, and sometimes insidious. A refusal could lead to an understanding nod, a shrug, or to expressions of disappointment, anger, and/or rejection of the interviewer.

Temptation is very hard to resist. As one reviews the histories of various teams engaged in research on mind-altering drugs, one finds a number of persons who have taken drugs. Some do so for genuinely scientific reasons, some for psychological ones, some to be good fellows. But untoward results may occur. Jail can be one of those results. As *Playboy* magazine noted in a marijuana review, there is little about the drug that is intrinsically damaging; it is certainly far less so than alcohol or cigarettes. But there is one thing definitely wrong with it, and that is that it is illegal. One can go to prison for two to ten years for conspiracy to transport or for unlawful acquisition of marijuana and similarly proscribed drugs on a first offense. For a second offense the penalty is five to twenty years.

Jail is a bad thing, and so is the decimation of friendship or of working relationships. Because beliefs about the propriety and significance of drug use are so strongly held, there will inevitably be recriminations if one investigator, or one part of a team, decides to take them and the others do not. Should those who abstain view the action of those who take the drug as a symbolic commitment to membership in a disapproved or illicit group or should the abstainers view researcher drug use as a betrayal of a commitment to remain "uncontaminated" during the research, there may very well be bitterness, and the research itself can be threatened or can go aground on the rocks of dissension. Clearly it is not just a matter of drug use itself; pharmacologists experiment on themselves with drugs quite frequently. It is the social meaning when drugs are taken or refused in social groups that matters.

The problem is a major one for social scientists, psychiatrists, and psychopharmacologists who would study people engaged in unconventional or illegal acts. Future investigators must keep it in mind and do their best to remember their commitments and to recognize that one can enjoy the company of one's research subjects without adopting their habits. It would be well, we suspect, for teams contemplating such work to examine themselves and their interpersonal dynamics thoroughly to detect hidden strains which might erupt and endanger the project, the team, or the security of the persons who are kind enough to cooperate in the study.

We can imagine that the presentation of the limitations of our own research, coupled with the more general warning about what might happen in drug studies if one is not careful, is hardly designed to encourage the reader who himself may be considering such investi-

gations. Nevertheless, let us affirm that the research itself was rewarding and exciting. The friendships made with drug users, members of
the control group, and policemen were important. The new points of
view which these people presented to us about life, about values, and
about the directions of American society were always provocative and
sometimes profound. Some of the issues they raise are central to much
in American life. We dare not ignore them.

SUMMARY

Gathering the sample of LSD users was done by introductions
down a social chain, from one user to another. Most were exceedingly
cooperative, except for the officials of a religious-medical center dedicated to LSD administration. Among police departments, less than half
of those approached were fully cooperative. Among LSD users and the
police, cooperation with inquiring social scientists varied by institution
and, within institutions or agencies, with the amount of administrative
support. Wide differences in individual response occurred among both
police and drug-using persons.

One problem in the study was both philosophical and social. LSD
users sometimes claim their inner experiences cannot be communicated,
so that no study of the LSD experience can be made except by taking
the drug for oneself. There is evidence that new users do learn a language from the "old hands" so that they can talk about the drug experience in ways that are meaningful and approved by the user group.
It is our conclusion that this language also helps to structure an intense
and ambiguous experience, that it signifies a commitment to the position of the drug-using group in question, but also that it can be used
for meaningful communication between an LSD user and those who
have not taken the drug. One of the hidden functions of the demand
that one take the drug before undertaking LSD research would appear
to be the initiation of the investigator into the drug-using group so that
his loyalty will be assured and his findings stated so as not to jeopardize
that group or its values. Much the same demand for loyalty and consideration is imposed upon an investigator by the police, although the
initiation there is not through drugs but through the development of
friendship ties over time. Although the investigator need not accede
to the demand for loyalty to an in-group, he does, through the promise
of anonymity and through reassurances, obligate himself to protect individuals and to be considerate of the values and feelings of the persons
under study.

A special problem in drug research is the possibility that research teams themselves may be subject to strain as individual investigators accept drugs and shift their interests, in consequence, from those of research to those associated with drug use per se. The acceptance of such offers may disrupt relations among team members, may impede research, and may place investigators in jeopardy of legal penalties for illicit drug use. This problem is a general one for any social-science team investigating illicit social phenomena; the history of LSD research suggests it is a particularly pressing problem in the study of that drug. It is recommended that, prior to undertaking any such research enterprise, the investigating team spend sufficient time in policy setting, group discussion, and continuing intercommunication, so that a group norm is established which can aid individual investigators in adhering to the established policies.

Social research on LSD use and police views is difficult but particularly rewarding because of the important psychological and social issues which are exposed during the course of study. It must be understood that such studies cannot be done without considerable personal involvement by the investigators—involvement which requires moral as well as scientific decisions.

THE NATURAL HISTORY OF LSD USE

[III]

Richard Blum, with Eva Blum
and Mary Lou Funkhouser

Examination of the patterns of LSD use reveals that the greatest amount of information is to be gained by the comparative analysis of the natural history of the several subgroups of users, these subgroups being defined by the conditions under which their members take the drug.

The chapter presents the findings from interview and observation on a sample of ninety-two persons who have taken LSD-25 one or more times. There are five subsamples as follows: an informal professional sample, a therapy-patient sample, the religious-medical-center sample, the experimental-subject sample, and the informal black-market sample. The plan of the chapter calls for a brief description of the subsamples, followed by a few comments on special aspects of their patterns of LSD use. A summary of the natural history is given for each subsample separately. A longer and more detailed section follows; it compares the subsamples one with another. That section is followed by a comprehensive summary.

THE INFORMAL PROFESSIONAL SAMPLE

The sample consists of twenty-four people who took LSD and who were themselves either medical or mental-health professionals or laymen who took LSD in the company of a mental-health professional. LSD administration was not part of psychotherapy, it did not take place in any institutional or formal setting, and there were no research or therapeutic goals which had been established by a formal social apparatus. Nevertheless, LSD use was sometimes described by sample members as "experimental" and as relevant to their professional interests.

Individual sample members reported that the first opportunity to take LSD was in 1956. Following that year more and more sample members were exposed to LSD and given continuing opportunities to try the drug. Examining the reactions to the offer of the drug, one finds that most quite quickly made up their minds to take it. There was no noticeable delay while they thought it over.

"Psychiatrist friends" most often initiated sample members into the use of LSD. Other initiators were work supervisors or employers, non-psychiatrist physician friends, teachers, or husbands. In every case the initiator had himself taken the drug before offering it to a novice. Often the initiator was in a status position superior to that of the person initiated. In this vein one should note that wives rarely initiated husbands but that husbands did initiate wives. One psychiatrist "gate-keeper" initiated one-third of the people in the sample. Only two persons initiated themselves; for the rest, LSD was a social event in which someone else gave them the drug and was with them during the experience. Most took LSD in a private home, either their own or that of an "experienced" LSD user.

Only a few (three) had tried any other kind of mind-altering drug before they look LSD. Afterward, more of them experimented with other drugs, so that, by the time of the interview, over half had taken drugs such as peyote, psilocybin, methedrine, and marijuana. Six of the twenty-four in the sample have continued to use these substances. Nevertheless, nearly all of them rate LSD as the best of the drugs taken. Three people said all of the hallucinogens were about the same in their effects. Very few of the people in this sample foresee much difficulty in procuring a supply of one or another of these drugs should they want them.

Most of the informal professional sample felt that LSD had improved their lives or persons. To demonstrate the kinds of changes reported, Table I below presents the self-descriptions by sample members.

The majority of the sample members had initiated or encouraged someone else in taking LSD. Those approached included friends and acquaintances, patients, research subjects, relatives, students, and persons under their religious guidance. For all their proselytism, there was

TABLE I

REPORTED CHANGES BY PERSONS TAKING LSD: INFORMAL

PROFESSIONAL GROUP $(N = 24)$

Internal psychological changes for the better	13
Improvement in interpersonal relationships	6
New and more satisfactory personal goals	2
Greater realism about goals and abilities	2
Reduced ambition, satisfaction over reduced goals	6
Satisfying changes in interests and perspectives	4
Enhanced aesthetic values or interests	3
Desirable changes in interests centering around the self; interest in growth and expansion	6
Desirable changes in interests sought in or about other persons or in oneself in relationship to them	3
Enhancement of religious values	3
Desirable changes in values about work and career	3
Desirable changes in philosophical-emotional values	2
Increased interest in physical activities, sports	2
Intensification, deepening of values already held	4
New interest in ESP, the occult	3

a consistent discretion about their LSD activities, a discretion which bordered on secrecy for many. LSD discussions were avoided in front of strangers. Part of the reason, they said, was because the drug experience is too private an affair, too much of an opening up of oneself, to expose before those not known to be interested or sympathetic. An analogy between the revelation of LSD experience and the content of psychotherapy was drawn.

On the other hand, there was also a very real concern about the reactions of society to their LSD use and interests. About one-third felt there were some "legal problems" associated with their informal use of the drug. A few were worried about public reaction. In contrast, several sample members were quite open and made a point of letting their associates know of their activities. Most felt that society did have hostility toward LSD users and that they might be the butt of prejudice.

The legal status of those who use LSD has been unclear to observers and to users themselves. LSD is defined by the Food and Drug Administration as a "new drug," which means that it is not available without prescription or on prescription, because it has not been shown to be safe and effective for the purposes for which it might be sold. LSD can only be legitimately sold to, acquired, and used by a research worker who has made application for and received a "Notice of Claimed Exemption" from FDA. To receive that investigational permit, he must submit and have approved a research protocol.

LSD use is illegal, under FDA laws, whenever it is sold to, acquired by, or given to a person who does not hold the FDA permit. Strictly speaking, the determination of illegality can only be made by the courts, so that, until there has been prosecution and conviction, the description of conduct as illegal is a presumption. Food-and-drug laws prohibit smuggling of LSD into the United States but do not prohibit its production here. Whether or not a "home-brew" LSD producer who took his own product would be open to prosecution, on the basis of provisions which prohibit unauthorized experimentation on human subjects, remains an open question.

Note that it is illegal to give the drug away except in pursuit of an approved research program. Should an authorized investigator deviate from his protocol to give LSD to his friends, he would be in violation of his permit. In theory, the FDA, upon hearing of the deviation, would rescind the permit after which time the investigator could not legally acquire nor administer LSD. However, until such time as the deviation was detected, hearings held, the permit rescinded, and perhaps an appeal made and ruled upon, the status of those giving and receiving the drug informally would be in doubt.

As a practical matter, by early 1964, no one, as far as the author has been able to learn, has been convicted on any count, civil or criminal, on charges of illicit LSD use. There are several cases before the courts in which the defendants have been charged with smuggling, conspiracy to violate the food-and-drug laws, and illicit sale of LSD. Since no prosecutions have been made for informal use and since FDA officials would admit that the "gray zones" in the law itself make enforcement decisions difficult, it is no wonder that many informal users of LSD, especially those in professional groups, conceive of their drugtaking as a perfectly legitimate activity. Black-market LSD users, on the other hand, mindful of the illicit nature of much of their drugtaking, are more likely to define their LSD use as unlawful.

Asked why nonusers might be critical of LSD use on other than legal grounds, some users suggested that it was simply a matter of lack of information about the drug. Others noted a general belief that those who use drugs are weak, inadequate, or lack moral fiber or wholeness. It was also suggested that ordinary folk fear the unknown, fear change, resent a challenge to the *status quo,* and fear loss of self-control. Some said that disapproval was sparked by the vested interests of orthodox religious groups who opposed mysticism and the metaphysical. An element of "dabbling in demons" as one revealed one's mind to oneself might frighten good Christians. The Puritan values were also blamed; some see wrongfulness in pleasure and sinfulness in dependency or in desires for escape or irresponsibility. Lack of ambition, seen as a consequence of LSD use, would also be reprehensible in Puritan eyes. A very few among the sample observed that the evangelical attitudes of the LSD users themselves generated counterresistance and that the cult features aroused suspicion and distrust.

The majority of informal professionals believed that they benefited psychologically from taking LSD. The benefits described were both mental and social. An adjective check list was employed to get more specific descriptions of self-change. Each person was asked whether or not an adjective applied to him at the time he took LSD and whether it described him at the time of the interview. Table II presents those results.

TABLE II

SELF-DESCRIPTIONS BY PERSONS TAKING LSD: INFORMAL
PROFESSIONAL GROUP ($N = 24$)

Adjective	Affirmative and unchanged	Change for better	Change for worse
Interested	16	2	0
Bored	0	1	0
Satisfied	6	2	1
Dissatisfied	3	4	1
Unfulfilled	7	4	1
Pleased with achievements	10	6	1
Pleased with self	5	8	1
Displeased with self	2	8	2
Happy	10	6	1
Depressed	0	5	2
Relaxed	8	6	2
Anxious	3	7	2
Empty-feeling	2	4	0
Too much to do	8	3	1
Things under control	11	3	3
Drifting along	0	1	3
Guiding my life	7	7	1
Trying too hard	3	8	1
Angry	2	5	1
Loving	6	10	0

From Table II, one gets the impression of individuals who are busy and alert, people subject to pressure and disappointment, but none of whom, at the time of first taking LSD, would appear to have felt themselves to be in dire personal stress. Since taking LSD, a fairly consistent one-third report self-improvement—most important in the direction of reduced anxiety, greater lovingness, greater ability to plan, reduced pushiness and ambition, greater relaxation, and reduced displeasure with oneself. A few see themselves as becoming more unhappy and distressed.

Replying to another question, two-fifths said that LSD made them feel much closer to people, not only during the drug experience, but afterward.[1] They described the change as a greater capacity for intimacy, warmth, and sharing. About half of the sample believed that their friends, family, or acquaintances who had taken LSD had experienced important personal or interpersonal benefits.

Summary

A sample of twenty-four persons who had received LSD from medical or mental-health professionals in informal settings was interviewed, except for three persons who filled out questionnaires. Psychiatrists with whom persons had friendship ties were the most frequent LSD initiators or "gatekeepers." The reasons for taking the drug most often set forth were curiosity and a desire for increased self-knowledge or self-enhancement. The majority of the sample stressed the pleasant aspects of the LSD experience, among which were the achievement of personal insight, improved interpersonal feelings, and sensations of relief and euphoria. Physical distress and loss of mental control were the worst aspects of the drug experience.

The majority of the sample had taken LSD more than once and would like to take it again. About half had had some other mind-altering drug besides LSD, most of them having expanded their use of such drugs after their LSD initiation. Nearly half would also be willing to try an addictive drug, but only for scientific reasons. The repetitive use of drugs, LSD and others, continues to be informal, taking place in homes or natural settings.

At the time of first taking LSD, most were leading normally satisfying and dissatisfying lives; many were highly successful in professional pursuits. After taking LSD more than half felt that their person or lives had improved; especially common was a feeling of increased self-satisfaction and reduction in tension and ambition. A few found themselves going downhill. Most persons in the group had sought to change their lives through psychotherapy or religious activities prior to taking LSD.

Some of the sample now find themselves spending more time with other LSD users, although most do not; nevertheless, the majority described LSD rejectors in unflattering terms ("rigid," "frightened," "defensive") and users in more complimentary ones ("seeking," "open," and so on). About half have proselytized for LSD; very few had "turned people on" to other mind-altering drugs.

Many were secretive about their LSD activities; some considered their behavior illicit. Most felt that society responded negatively to LSD use. The hostile reactions of others were attributed to lack of information; the notion that drug use implies weakness or lack of moral fiber; the fear of the unknown; resistance to change and response to threats to the *status quo;* fear of loss of control; competition from orthodox groups in medicine or religion or psychology, whose vested interests were in jeopardy; an opposition to mysticism or "dabbling in demons"; or a Puritanical opposition to pure pleasure, escape, aimlessness, or lack of social ambition.

The majority did not take a kindly view of law-enforcement people's attitudes toward or knowledge of the nonaddictive drugs. Only a few were neutral or approving of the role and work of the police. About half were also opposed to present narcotics legislation and enforcement procedures.

Regarding its background, the sample is highly educated, about equally composed of men and women, most of whom are between thirty-one and fifty and none of whom are judged to have any serious personality disorders.

THE EXPERIMENTAL-SUBJECT SAMPLE

Fifteen persons had first taken LSD as research subjects in a university, hospital, or other bona fide institutional research setting. The earliest LSD experience for a member of this sample was in 1950. However, most sample members had had LSD during or after 1959. Only one-third of the experimental subjects were naive in the sense that they had no knowledge of LSD before they took it. Most of these people, all of whom were volunteers, had friends or acquaintances who had already taken the drug; sometimes those friends were the experimenters.

Most expected to experience sensory distortions under the drug; their primary motivation was said to be professional or general curiosity or a desire for self-understanding. Most had a favorable response when they took LSD, usually described as a feeling of release, euphoria, or new awareness of heightened sensations. Like the two patient samples and unlike any other sample, the majority of the experimentals described their lives as very unhappy at the time they took LSD. Work and school troubles accounted for much of their misery.

About one-fourth of the sample had taken another mind-altering drug (peyote, marijuana, methedrine, mescaline, or the like) before volunteering to take LSD. After exposure to LSD in the laboratory, one-third went on to use it informally, thus moving from the laboratory situation to the friendly sociability of informal LSD use. The history of this group should be of particular interest to investigators in psychopharmacology. They show that friendship patterns influence who becomes a volunteer. They also show that some confirmed drug users may be among the volunteers, so that, among the prospective subjects for study, there may be fewer drug "virgins" than one might expect.

One-third of those taking LSD for the first time in the laboratory have gone on to take it informally afterward. Some have become regular users of the drug. A few sample members have gone beyond LSD to try other illicit mind-altering substances. This fact should also concern the laboratory investigator, for it suggests that he must be aware that the drug virgins he initiates may go on from his laboratory to extended informal drug use. The investigator may play a much greater role than he imagined in changing the social behavior and perhaps the life directions of his volunteers.

The majority of the experimental subjects report some beneficial psychological changes as the result of having taken LSD, although they have not reoriented their goals or interests. The majority had tried some other means of changing things before taking LSD—mostly psychotherapy. The amount of change most report in response to LSD is not great and, when asked to judge its effects on others, most say there are none. Most have not increased their association with LSD users, and only the experienced drug users among the sample tend to differentiate between LSD users and nonusers on psychological or other grounds. Half indicate they have influenced others to take LSD.

Although their own laboratory use of LSD has been legal, some are reluctant to discuss their experiences; they fear their jobs might be in jeopardy. About half believe the public to be hostile to LSD use, and most presume police hostility or ignorance about the hallucinogens. Most are also critical of present narcotics laws. The experimental sample is well educated; most are young men between twenty-one and thirty. None are rated as seriously disabled in any psychological sphere.

THE THERAPY-PATIENT SAMPLE

There were twenty-one psychiatric patients. All had taken LSD under the direction of one of three psychiatrists. Each of the psychiatrists was, in turn, part of the informal professional sample. The opportunity of patients to take LSD came only after their psychiatrists had taken the drug.

There are two subgroups in the therapy sample. Eight were patients in a public mental-health clinic attached to a hospital. They took LSD in the clinic. Five of these patients were diagnosed as alcoholics. Thirteen persons were private psychotherapy patients who took the drug in the home or office of their psychiatrist. Most of the clinic patients had heard little about LSD before taking it, nor did they associate with persons who had had it. The majority of the private patients, on the other hand, knew about LSD before receiving it. These subgroup differences reflect the well-known differences in socioeconomic class between private and public-clinic patients and serve to indicate the greater exposure to and interest in LSD information among middle- and upper-class people.

Both groups responded with heightened sensations, but the religious-philosophical effects reported by private patients were absent in the clinic group. Both groups were passively oriented, taking the drug as the physician directed in order to be helped with the personal problems that brought them into psychiatric care. Clinic administration was an impersonal affair; private patients received the drug in a social surrounding, in a home and with a spouse or friend present, thus repeating the experience in which their therapists, like other informal professionals, had first taken the drug. Clinic patients more often emphasized the unpleasant effects of the drug. Although both sets of patients describe their lives at the time they took LSD as being unhappy, the kinds of misery are much more dramatic among the clinic people, who are alcoholic, unemployed, and joyless; the private patients, although feeling displeased, lead lives which outwardly resemble those of the informal professional sample.

Most patients in both groups do not go on to take LSD again; of the few who do, all are private patients who move from medical administration out into the informal settings where they would then be classified as informal professional sample members. Most patients have not had other mind-altering drugs—except alcohol—either before or after the LSD experience.

Most patients feel LSD has benefited them, for the most part in their self-image or psychological adjustment; however, among the more seriously upset clinic patients, the improvements are more likely to be viewed as temporary. The private patient group members say that LSD has led them to change their life goals. Clinic patients still want a job, want to stop being alcoholics, or want to find some joy in life; they do not report life-goal changes. Similarly, private patients but not clinic ones speak of the improvements in sexual relations subsequent to LSD use.

None of the patients report spending more time with LSD users now than before their own drug experience, and most do not see any difference between people who accept and reject LSD. The majority have not proselytized, although about half would like to take LSD again. Most are reluctant to talk about their experience with "just anyone"; it is considered medically confidential, as would be any aspect of the personal difficulties which have brought them into therapy. None are concerned with any illicit drug activities of their own, and, whereas most do think of society as hostile to LSD use, most are neutral or sympathetic toward the role of the police in drug control.

In spite of their own reported good experience, only a very few of the patient sample are enthusiastic boosters of LSD as a therapeutic panacea; most see it as an adjunct, not a cure-all. One-third even doubt that utility.

As for personality disorder, severe disorder is judged to occur only in the clinic group, which is also rated high on distrust, overdependency, hostility, ego-control defects, and anxiety. The private patients were much less disturbed and showed fewer signs of distress on any of the rated variables.

THE INFORMAL BLACK-MARKET SAMPLE

Twelve persons were interviewed, observed, and rated. Their first LSD experience had been without benefit of either institutional setting or the presence of any medical or mental-health professional. Persons in the sample first began to take LSD in 1959 and have had continuing opportunities ever since. Persons in the sample were all acquainted with one another and were an active social group. One man had played a prominent role in introducing the group to LSD. He had given it to his friends, who had in turn initiated others, so that the total number of drug-using acquaintances who saw each other socially was, at the time of our inquiry, about forty. The females in the sample were all introduced to LSD by their husbands, lovers, or boy friends.

The "gatekeeper" of the group was in touch with older professional people who would fit in with the informal professional or religious-medical-center categories. At one time he had been in psychotherapy with a professional who had recommended marijuana to him. The young man's drug interests had expanded following that "therapeutic" event. We were not informed nor did we inquire about the sources of drugs used by sample members.

LSD was usually taken in a party setting. It was just one of a number of hallucinogenic or intoxicating drugs which were used. Everyone reported pleasant reactions or "kicks"—being "high" or having "freedom from troubles," for example. The majority also discussed aesthetic experiences; some were passive ones in which music or a painting was more appreciated; others were active in that users would paint, make montages or mobiles, or write. Some of the sample also spoke of their mystical religious experiences and most described unusual feelings of closeness and special appreciation of others. Upon occasion, we were told, these interpersonal delights became quite specific as the partying people took off their clothes and played romantic roulette. The intimacies might be rather public—on the front lawn, on the living-room floor, or with six on a bed. Given these varieties of play and euphoria, it is no wonder that a majority of the informal black-market sample said that orgiastic excitement was a feature of LSD use.

It is difficult to discriminate LSD experience and history from the use of other drugs by members of this group. Although nearly all of them felt that LSD produced the most dramatic results of any of the hallucinogens or stimulants, they did not treat its use as separate, nor were they always able to recall which drug they had taken on which occasion. The impression gained was that LSD use has been infrequent because "it is so hard to get." The combination of difficulty in obtaining LSD and its "superior" effects led to one special condition about its use. Whereas they might reimburse one another for costs incurred for other drugs (no profit-making was apparent), LSD was never sold. "Something this good I couldn't sell; it is a treasure; when I get it, I want to give to my friends (as an act of friendship)." Among the informal black-market group there were only two persons who declared their intention not to take LSD again; the impression was that all others would be willing to do so.

All of the people in the informal black-market group had had experience with drugs other than LSD. Most had had peyote and marijuana; some had had mescaline, psilocybin, Ditran, IT-290, and methedrine. Only two had taken LSD as their first drug; for the remainder, marijuana had been the drug first used. The majority employ one or another of these often, most taking marijuana several times a week—"Some people come home and have a cocktail; after work, I come home and have a joint." The other hallucinogens are used less often, partly because of an inadequate supply and partly because of the time required to take them—"It takes a whole week end for LSD; you take it Saturday morning and are high all day; Sunday you have to rest up"—and partly because of the social commitment involved: a party, outing on the beach, visit to a museum, or some other special activity.

Discussing the drug supply, one learns that peyote is easily obtained. One obtains it, they say, from a Texas cactus supply house. The buttons are then ground in mixing machines, prepared, and put in gelatin capsules. Marijuana is also obtainable in unlimited amounts; one buys it from friends who have been in Mexico; one buys it from peddlers; or one grows it in one's house or garden. The going rate for marijuana is $1 a joint or $25 a "lid" (a small King Albert pipe tobacco can).

As for the restrictions imposed on use, for the informal black-market group these are primarily external. Supply is the primary one—and this is associated with money. Awareness of their unlawful conduct does not inhibit the use of drugs, although it certainly leads to discretion and concealment.

As far as friendship patterns are concerned, persons in the informal black-market group spend increasing amounts of time with one another and decreasing amounts of time—outside of job requirements —with nonusers. The argot of the group clearly distinguishes between desirable and undesirable social companions on the basis of whether or not one uses drugs and subscribes to the doctrines of the group; subscribers are "good heads," "pot heads," or "pill heads"; nonsubscribers are "squares." The "squares," of course, refuse to take drugs— or, if they take them, refuse to respond by getting "high." Thus they are described as dull, conservative, or conventional. Users, on the other hand, are creative, free, curious, and may have other traits esteemed as virtues by the users.

Information on proselytizing is incomplete. It was our impression that men more than women had an interest in "turning people on," and, among the men, there were varying degrees of enthusiasm for it. Our impression was that most had played some role in initiating others —roles ranging from merely being present as users in a group to which nonusers were invited for their first experience, to the leadership activity in which nonusers were strongly urged to take drugs for the first time and then provided with those drugs. Who gets "turned on"? Wives, blood relatives, and friends. It is of interest that several users in their twenties described how they had introduced their parents to LSD and their younger teen-age brothers or sisters to "pot" or peyote. In this group, wives *had* to take drugs; it was a test of virtue and loyalty. And there was pride when a father or an aunt could be persuaded to join the inner circle. Similarly approval was forthcoming when young relatives came to drug use spontaneously; "I was really pleased when Kate came up from high school one night and told us she'd been turned on to 'pot.' Imagine, only fourteen and so mature and sophisticated! When I was that age, I was a real 'square.' "

As is apparent the primary requirement for the potential initiate is social proximity to the user. No profound psychological traits are prerequisites—only that one know and trust the person well enough to want him to "be as happy as I am" or "be turned on to a good thing." On the other hand, the initiators do say they hesitate to initiate unstable people: "I feel I have a responsibility when I 'turn someone on' to LSD; you want to be sure they won't go sour," and also, "You want them to have enough sense to know how to act; I mean to be discreet and not get themselves or anybody else in trouble."

As would be expected, all agree that their drug use is usually illicit and, for that reason, they must be secretive. They say they are careful not to discuss their activities with unsympathetic or untrustworthy persons and indicate that, should an unsuspecting stranger come calling while a drug party is going on, they make every effort to conceal their altered state of consciousness. Such an intrusion, of course, ruins the party and is embarrassing to the users as well. Although the informal black-market users stress their secretiveness and discretion, it was our impression that some were rather careless in their conduct and expressions with strangers. In contrast to some groups where being clandestine was at least partly denied (the religious-medical group, for example) but apparent in fact, these users insisted they were secretive while it was apparent—on the basis of conversations with nonusers who knew of their activities—that they were often remarkably frank.

Summary

Twelve persons were interviewed whose LSD initiation had been in an informal setting without any medical or mental-health professional present to administer the drug. People in this sample were an active social group who took LSD for aesthetic reasons, for novelty, for expanded consciousness, and for pleasure. None seem to have been searching for solutions to personal or interpersonal problems or for spiritual experiences. Most reported pleasurable effects, ranging to ecstasy and orgasm.

Most persons in this group had taken a variety of drugs before and after LSD; and LSD, although "the best," was only one of a number of mind-altering substances which were employed. The reasons for its use were not set apart from the use of other drugs, although it was granted to be the most powerful and effective and the most difficult to obtain of all the drugs employed. Among the other drugs commonly employed by sample members were peyote, marijuana, mescaline, and methedrine. Their general interest in drug use does not extend to the narcotics; sample members are strongly opposed to addictive drugs, and none have employed them.

Few report any personal or life improvements which they attribute solely to LSD; most appear to be pursuing already successful upward-mobile careers and do not complain vociferously about themselves or society. Most do attribute beneficial changes to mind-altering drugs as a class—mostly freedom from internal constraints and useless conventions and enhancement of creative and pleasure-pursuing abilities.

Persons in this group do spend much of their social life with like-minded drug-taking persons; they clearly distinguish between such "heads" and unlikable non-drug-using "squares." The differences are not, however, expressed in the jargon of psychopathology, but merely in terms of interests, values, and sociological factors such as age and status. Most are busy proselytizing among friends and relatives. Their drug activities are secret because they are acknowledged to be illegal and subject to social disapproval. Nevertheless, there was a remarkable freedom from hostility toward the police or any projected assumption of police counterhostility. Similarly, many called for strict controls on narcotics use and were sympathetic to present legislation. They saw no resemblance between their own use of nonaddictive drugs and the illicit conduct of narcotics users. Most of the group members were in their twenties; some of their affiliates in their teens; and the ages ran upward into the forties and fifties as group members introduced their parents to drugs. They were well educated, socially respectable, and ambitious as far as career goals were concerned. All but two appeared to make excellent work adjustments. None appeared to have serious personality pathology.

THE RELIGIOUS-MEDICAL-CENTER SAMPLE

Twenty persons took the drug under the auspices of a center established for the purpose of giving LSD. Under medical supervision, with avowed therapeutic and research aims, but with religious interests playing an important part in its establishment, the center provided LSD for a fee. Members of the sample took the drug either in the center facility or at the hands of one or more officials of the center in some informal setting. Not everyone in the sample had paid for their LSD; most had done so. The earliest center initiation had been in 1960; the more recent dates of the LSD experience for most sample members reflects the continued and expanding activities of the center.

LSD administration at the center was relatively formal and impersonal, according to reports of recipients. Some did not know anything about the person giving them the drug; most said it was given by either physician staff members or by the lay director. Usually several persons were present, sometimes as many as nine different people coming in and out of the room. Again, many of these were unknown to the subject. Very rarely did a subject bring a friend, spouse, or relative to be present.

Most sample members had learned about LSD and the center from social contacts; many hoped the drug would produce self-knowledge and other psychotherapeutic effects. Most had tried some other method of self-change before coming to the center. Most took the drug only once, although almost all reported wanting to take it again; the high cost of the drug at the center is one factor limiting repetition, for these people do not have access to supplies through informal channels. Most had had other mind-altering drugs as part of their LSD preparation at the center. Some had had marijuana before taking LSD at the center; others went on to the informal use of other drugs (marijuana, methedrine, and so on) after being initiated to LSD.

The majority of the sample described both pleasant and unpleasant reactions to the drug. For most, the unpleasantness was recalled as initial and transient. Frequently the unpleasant features were said to have been valuable, "part of the price of self-knowledge." Quite clearly, several people felt it was necessary to suffer to gain from LSD. The belief that suffering is a necessary requirement for salvation is extensive in our culture. It is found in psychoanalysis, in the Christian doctrine of salvation from sin, and in the Protestant work ethic which holds that good things do not come easily. One suspects that the welcome accorded to the painful facets of the center LSD experience is not unrelated to these larger themes.

Nearly all center sample members report self-improvement as a consequence of LSD use—often personal changes, spiritual benefits, and reduction in competitive or material concerns are cited. Although practically none of the sample had originally had any interest in having a religious experience through LSD, nearly half reported a religiously significant experience. Because of the heavy emphasis of center personnel on teaching the spiritual significance of LSD, it appears that one can respond to LSD not as the user had intended, but as the administrator of the drug intends. The failure of others to have such a response also demonstrates that there is nothing inevitable about such susceptibility to suggestion.

Most center sample members have increased their social contacts with LSD users and decreased them with nonusers; this is partly a result of attendance at discussion groups encouraged by the center. Many do subscribe to a personality typology of users and nonusers, the latter perceived in psychologically unflattering terms. Most have proselytized; most are secretive or discreet about their own experience; many are disdainful of nonusers. Most conceive of society as hostile to LSD use; and the majority are not sympathetic to the attitudes or understanding of the police with reference to the nonaddictive, consciousness-changing drugs. There is similar opposition to present narcotics laws. Center sample members are mostly college or high-school graduates in the thirty-one to forty age range; there are more men than women in the sample. The majority are rated as ethnocentric about drug use; many are overly suspicious. Most are judged to be free from serious personality disorders.

COMPARISON OF THE FIVE SAMPLES

The purpose of the present section is to compare the several samples of LSD users. One gains the impression of fairly consistent differences among them. One should not exaggerate the importance of differences in proportions which are reported. Apparent differences can be produced by sampling bias or by errors in reporting, observing, recording, or coding. The small size of all the subsamples involved requires care in approaching these comparisons. Nevertheless, it is interesting to see what patterns emerge.

LSD Availability

It is not surprising, for example, to see that the opportunities and settings for LSD use have varied with the occupations and affiliations of potential users. The first group to have access to LSD was research workers, and, quite naturally, one finds persons in the experimental group being given their opportunities beginning as early as 1950. As clinical research followed laboratory work, practicing professionals had access to LSD—and gave it to their friends and patients. The first LSD use in the informal professional group occurred in 1956, and very shortly thereafter, in 1957, its employment in clinical study on private patients began. Not too long after physicians had access to the drug for experimentation in private practice, it became available through informal channels; informal black-market users first began with LSD in 1959. The institutionalized use of LSD comes last; for patients in a hospital clinic, it was available (to our clinic sample) in 1960 and, in that same year, the religious-medical center began, with LSD administration as the central feature.

One can suggest that the growth of the black-market supply depended upon the relatively large number of physicians in private practice who had the drug; some of these, we must assume, have made it available indiscriminately, that is, not limiting its nonmedical use to their own friends and family. During these same years, as medical and nonmedical people experienced LSD effects, their interest increased and collective action emerged, such as the setting up of formal institutions for the sale and use of LSD. Thus the drug has become available in time to persons not themselves associated with medical and mental-health professionals—to some, through the association networks of the informal black-market group, whose well-educated members are certainly bound to know at least some physicians who might give them the drug, and to others, through the more formal and impersonal device of a center, where strangers may apply and pay for the drug.

As our study progressed a new developmental stage emerged; concern with LSD effects led to threats and action on the part of federal agencies and suppliers to restrict its distribution to physicians. The extensiveness of LSD use would necessarily have been reduced unless some new source of supply was generated. That new source rather quickly made its appearance. Supplies of the drug, apparently still widely available in Canada, were transported by individual travelers, according to reports of our informants, across the border to the United States. In addition, interested users learned how to produce LSD-25 in home laboratories.[2] A third source of supply, the natural LSD in morning glory seeds (monoethylamide) was discovered, and a run on nurserymen ensued. The publicity attendant upon this supply, well publicized by the press, led to experimentation by new groups of persons not ordinarily associated with either the informal professional or the informal black-market group. Although we have not systematically studied these emerging new groups, we have had access to them; some of them are composed of college and university students not previously involved in drug use other than alcohol and tobacco.

In a very short time, one has seen not only the expansion of use from essentially restricted and private to informal and public sources, but also the alarmed and restrictive "public" and agency reaction followed, in turn, by immediate LSD user counterreaction to the threat and fact of supply limitation. These counterreactions have, as already mentioned, taken the form of ingenious new methods of supply: international transportation (smuggling), home manufacture, and the use of "natural" garden resources. One sees parallels between these inventive responses to LSD-25 restriction and similar ones involved in the supply of other substances, narcotic drugs and marijuana, for example.

Expectations of LSD Effects

Just as LSD opportunities have varied with an individual's association with sources of supply and with the eventual provision of formal and informal channels for public distribution, so has an individual's social situation influenced what he has heard about LSD-25 and from whom he has heard it. Comparing our groups, we find, for example, that the experimental users most often had heard that the drug produced psychotic states and hallucinations. Their information was much in keeping with early descriptions of LSD-25—and early hopes for the drug's research worth—as a psychotomimetic. Even those taking it more recently learn of these possibilities from researchers still concerned with the investigation of "bizarre" processes by means of the drug. We must note that the link between subject and researcher in studies of LSD remains mostly part of an informal social system; that is, persons who volunteer for experiments most often do so at the urging of friends who are experimenters or of friends who had been subjects for experimenters. Initiation into LSD use in the laboratory setting is by no means a random affair but one closely tied in with association patterns in hospital and university communities.

The same is, of course, true for persons initiated into the informal professional and informal black-market groups. Friendship and kinship patterns are fundamental to transmitting information about the drug and in diffusing the drug experience to these groups. In both instances, what the LSD-experienced friends initially transmit is the knowledge that the drug produces heightened sensations. This same theme predominates in the information transmitted to therapy patients, but, in these cases, the transmitter is part of a formal rather than informal social system. The personal psychiatrist of private patients has, in every case, taken time to tell his patients what LSD does before he has given it to them; he has supplemented his discussion with literature. For public-clinic patients, the institution physician treating them as part of his clinical study of LSD therapeutic efficacy has, in the manner of so many public-clinic doctors, communicated little to his patients.[3] Sometimes he has given a simplified account of LSD effects—for example, one patient said her clinic doctor told her, "LSD was used by Indians to cure headaches"—and has given the patient a pamphlet to read.

As far as the information sources of the religious-medical-center people are concerned, these reflect the more formal nature of the center and its lack of a friendship net as a means of diffusion. The primary sources of their knowledge about LSD do include friends, but more often are casual acquaintances or associates (people at work, bosses, fellow participants in religious seminars, teachers, or speakers heard at public lectures). The main source, of course, is what they hear from center representatives or from those who have already taken LSD under center auspices; in effect, what the center holds to be the primary gain from LSD's combined philosophical-religious-psychotherapeutic experience. Center initiates, unlike other groups prior to LSD use, have most often heard of these potential LSD effects.

Motives

External factors—the varying sources of supply and differing degrees of intimacy or distance in social relationships through which drug information and drug opportunities are given—set the several LSD-using groups apart. But external physical and social features are not the only sources of difference. The distribution of motives and interests vary from one to another group. The motive most often cited by experimental users is curiosity. The same motive sparks the informal professional users. In contrast, the psychotherapy patients—in the case of public-clinic people—say that they have taken the drug because of a particular psychological problem for which they have sought a cure. Although they have learned that self-knowledge may be desirable in obtaining that cure, their primary orientation seems to be one of "riddance." Implicit is the fact that they have taken LSD because the doctor has told them to do so. It is like other medicines and, indeed, among clinic patients, we find LSD referred to as "the medicine," a usage encountered in no other group. (Private patients, on the other hand, occasionally do refer to "the treatment," but not to "the medicine.")

Self-knowledge is the most frequently mentioned motivating force among the religious-medical-center persons, a search which is reflected in their choice of words for LSD; it is called "the material," referring to "consciousness-expanding materials." The self-knowledge sought is of the self-expanding and "becoming" variety rather than the specific problem-solving sort. Finally, among the informal black-market people, one finds the most cited motive the desire for aesthetic enhancement, coupled with self-enhancement, curiosity, and, implicit but not always explicit, the search for a new kind of "high," "kicks," or euphoria.

It is sometimes suggested that drug use per se occurs as a response to life situations which are unhappy or intolerable. We asked sample members about their life circumstances at the time of their decision to take LSD. Their recollections, of course, are likely to be biased by a number of conscious and unconscious factors.

Only in the two psychotherapy-patient groups did the majority of persons remember their lives as being full of troubles and despair. The other samples described themselves, for the most part, as living ordinary lives without extremes of joy or misery.

The informal black-market group may be an exception. The number of persons giving us information was limited, but those few who discussed their lives at length said they were on top of the world. Their *joie de vivre* may be a function of errors in recollection or sampling, a matter of presenting an ideal image, or perhaps the happy circumstances of youth, for they are the youngest of the LSD-taking samples. Relying on their reports, one may conclude that the desire to enhance an already pleasurable state of being rather than a desperate need to escape misery may motivate drug use.

To return for a moment to the patient population, it is to be noted that the interviewers would agree with the clinic patients that the latter's lives really were miserable when they entered psychotherapy. On the other hand, the ratings of and reports about the private patients, admittedly measures which were relatively simple and subject to error, did not indicate that this group was discernibly more disturbed than members of any other sampled groups. What they felt about their lives and how the external circumstances of their lives appeared were different. The difference cautions us to discriminate between self-reports or subjective appraisals and the opinion of, or measures by, an outside observer. We shall have more to say about this chasm, which has long been a problem in psychotherapy evaluation, when we evaluate the reports about LSD effects.

Persons Present

Correlated with the differentiation of users by groups based on circumstances of initial use is the extent to which LSD administration is itself a social event involving other people. How many others may be present and what their relationship is to the initiate does vary from group to group.

Public-clinic patients received the drug, most often, with only the administering physician present. Private patients received it most frequently at the hands of the psychiatrist but, additionally, with a friend and/or spouse present. The "rule" of one psychiatrist is that observers from both sexes must be on hand. The range of persons present is much greater for the experimentals, depending upon the experiment itself, but most often there were two or three others besides the subject himself. Among the religious-medical-center people, having more than three persons present was the rule, although there was much movement in and out of the room during the sessions. The informal professionals and informal black-market group reported the largest number of persons present at the time of administration; the modal frequency for both groups is eight. It is nevertheless interesting to see how the more businesslike use of LSD in medicine or research tends to restrict the size of the onlooker or participant-use group, whereas, as one moves away from institutional business and structures in which dominant-subordinate role relationships are clear, the number of informally interacting individuals on the scene (or "making the scene," to use argot) increases.

LSD Reactions

One would expect that the kinds of reactions reported would depend upon factors such as personality predisposition, learned expectation, and situational demands and supports. Reactions are also known to depend upon dosage, but that is a quantum which we were unable to control. Examining our groups, we find at first glance that expectations tend to be borne out. The two psychotherapy-patient groups did most frequently report heightened sensations—just what they had been told LSD produced. So too the informal black-market people achieved aesthetic delights and the religious-medical group often reported mystical-religious experiences, again what most had been told to expect. The informal professional people expected a variety of effects, most often beneficial and enhancing ones, which results most felt they did achieve. The experimentals said they had learned LSD produced hallucinations and psychosis, but these are not what they report among important reactions; instead they describe release and relaxation.

By no means did people experience only the phenomena for which LSD was famed or those which they particularly sought. For example, unpleasant reactions occurred, but were not often expected. The informal professionals were bothered by physical distress, feelings of helplessness, or loss of control. The clinic patients felt self-conscious or were embarrassed by what they did or felt during the experience. The private patients suffered raw fear—of madness, of loss of control, of the unknown lying ahead. The religious-medical-center people went through what was most often termed the "initial horror," a pattern of psychic unpleasantness during the first part of the session consistently reported by this sample and by no other. That fact leads us to the conclusion that it was a by-product of the method of administration employed (see Chapter VII) by the center. Among experimentals the bad response most often cited was depression, a phenomenon closely linked to the pleasure of relaxation and release, if one posits a "releaser" phase which leads some persons to happy tension reduction and others to awful energy depletion.[4] Among the informal black-market users, the one bad effect was disappointment at the failure of LSD to meet their expectations—to produce the desired aesthetic, euphoric, or self-expanding sensations.

About half the people in the four institutional settings (clinic and private patients, experimentals, center) report they have had some unpleasant component in their LSD reaction. Somewhat fewer of those who have taken it informally report a bad reaction—38 per cent in the informal professional sample and 25 per cent in the informal black-market sample. The latter statistic reflects the comments of only a few persons so cannot be relied upon as a fair measure of actual reactions in that group. Nevertheless, the distributions as they exist raise some interesting possibilities. First, they follow the distribution of ratings of serious personality disorder (see end of this section) among sample members. Is there then, in fact, an association between unpleasant components in the LSD response and the presence of serious personality disorder? Second, one may ask whether the institutional setting, however benign, may not be tension-provoking in itself? Perhaps the presence of others who are in a formal status relationship to oneself creates some distress reflected in the LSD reaction. Or perhaps the orientation to LSD is such in the informal setting that persons are moved to conceal unpleasant reactions. It may be that the expectations of friends that one really will have a "good experience" operate more strongly upon one than the demands of strangers or institutional superiors, so that one is more likely to conform to group demands and philosophy. Certainly the data provide no evidence for important differences among the groups; we raise the foregoing questions for future studies.

On the basis of the distribution of expectations, settings, and effects, we do find evidence for the unremarkable predictions that any psychologist would have set forth, to wit, that (a) there is some relationship between what one has heard about drug effects and what one reports as experienced under it; (b) some effects are peculiar to particular groups and seem to depend upon how the LSD is given and upon how various props are used to produce a response presumably sought by the administrators of the drug rather than being desired by the user; (c) expectations are by no means always met and that in these cases one has an opportunity to infer the operation of "pure" pharmacological effects dependent upon the amount and chemical structure of the drug; (d) wide individual variations appear within each group and dictate the acknowledgment of response as a function, presumably, of physiological and personality variables setting one person apart from another; (e) there is no evidence that group membership or the atmosphere of administration can prevent unpleasant or adverse reactions to the drug, although we have reports from psychiatric clinicians who made on-the-scene observations that pathological interaction and the exploitation of the initiate by the initiator increase the likelihood of adverse reactions.

Repeated LSD Use

The proportion of sample members repeating LSD use is greatest among persons whose initial drug experience is outside any institutional setting or formal role relationship. We find only three (23 per cent), all males, among the private patients taking LSD more than once; each had his second experience once again at the hands of the psychiatrist. However, one of these patients has gone on to expand his use to informal administration, at the same time becoming an initiator by giving the drug to his wife. Among the public-clinic patients, none have taken LSD outside the medical setting, although five have had from three to ten medically administered doses at the hands of a psychiatrist. The religious-medical-center people took their initial LSD in a formal setting; only one of them went on to take LSD again. His second experience was also at the center, but his third round was taken in an informal setting not associated with the center. The members of the experimental group, on the other hand, have, in about one-third of the cases, taken LSD upon further occasions outside the original laboratory setting. Another one-third of that group had LSD more than once, but only as part of the planned research series. Among the informal professionals, we find 40 per cent reporting LSD use on more than one occasion, whereas, among the informal black-market users, a group least subject to institutional structure or formal role relationships of the doctor-patient sort, the estimated frequency of repeat use is 66 per cent.

In spite of the infrequency of actual repeat experiences with LSD, especially for those who took it first in formal (ritualized) settings, there is widespread interest in taking the drug again. Not quite half of the private patients and informal professionals say they want to take LSD again, half of the experimentals do too, and nearly two-thirds of the public-clinic patients and religious-medical-center persons want it. The greatest avowed interest is found in the informal black-market group, where we estimate (again suffering some liability in interview circumstance) that over 80 per cent will take the drug if they have the chance. Looking at these data, we conclude that, for all groups, interest in expanded LSD use exists and that more are desirous of taking the drug again than have actually done so. The group in which interest and action are most closely matched is the informal professional one, for its members not only have access to the drug but, being without the need for a formal setting, can easily arrange to take the drug in circumstances like those in which it was first taken. The groups showing the greatest discrepancy between desire and actual use are the public-clinic patients and the religious-medical-center people. In both cases, the majority want to take LSD again, but few or none have done so. They are dependent for a source of supply, the patients upon the clinic doctor, and the latter upon center personnel and the payment of $500 or more. These are the two groups in which supplier and user are socially the most distant, that is, not bound by ties of friendship or equal-status contact, and in which use has been most formal and anonymous. In these circumstances, the user has little power of persuasion or any levers in a shared obligation system by which he might set himself up for another LSD experience. To the extent that persons wanting to take LSD again in these two groups can make new social contacts through informal channels, they may eventually overcome their present frustrating position vis-à-vis the known LSD source. To do this will require a willingness to take LSD in a different setting—something about which some express considerable reluctance, believing, as they do, that the desired reaction will occur only within the setting in which the drug was first taken. We suspect that this belief is a function of (a) spontaneous conditioning, the pleasant effect associated with the surrounding, (b) of "teaching" on the part of administering personnel —especially in the center—who instruct initiates on the importance of setting and the dire consequences of taking LSD in an unsympathetic environment, and (c) of possible anxiety on the part of the user who, aware of some unpleasant emotional reactions to LSD, wishes to repeat the experience in the security of a setting which proved reassuring in the past—one in which some important emotional ties have been established with initiators. The experience may be a critical one, in which LSD-generated confusion, fear, dependency, joy, affection, and narrowed-but-intensified attention produce particularly strong feelings on the part of the initiate for those around him.

Use of Other Drugs

Examining the experience of people in each group with drugs other than LSD (and by "drugs," we mean here stimulants and hallucinogens taken to produce altered states of consciousness, not drugs medically prescribed), we find a pattern of wide use associated with informal consumption and limited use associated with institutional initiates. Among the informal black-market users, 83 per cent report experience with one or more hallucinogens or stimulants. The variety of drugs tried by this group exceed the range of any other group and include mescaline, peyote, psilocybin, methedrine, IT 290, marijuana, and Ditran. Forty-five per cent of the informal professional persons report they have tried one or more drugs other than LSD; methedrine and psilocybin are the most often mentioned. Of the persons in this group, only one had tried any drug before taking LSD (methedrine), whereas, after the LSD experience, 35 per cent began to experiment with other drugs; 25 per cent are continuing users (two of them are using psilocybin, a drug very much like LSD in its effects). Among the experimentals, more than one-fourth had tried other drugs prior to volunteering for LSD, a noteworthy feature in that it shows prior drug curiosity or interests as a characteristic of those who volunteer for LSD research and also suggests a source of "contamination" for experimentals who, in fact, may have begun drug use in informal groups and whose laboratory exposure could be only incidental to larger social patterns surrounding their drug use. Among those with that pre-experimental drug experience, two have continued to use drugs after LSD, taking marijuana and other substances. Two persons who had not had drugs prior to LSD began to explore a variety after their LSD exposure. Both of these individuals have gone on to take LSD repeatedly and, in addition, are now using marijuana and peyote. Three persons (20 per cent) took mescaline and psilocybin as part of the drugs administered in the laboratory. In all, among the experimentals, about half have had only LSD and about half (47 per cent) have had drugs other than LSD outside an institutional setting; among the latter, three (20 per cent) are current users. If one excludes the persons with drug experience prior to LSD, one finds that only 20 per cent of this sample has gone on to drug use after laboratory exposure to LSD.

Forty per cent of the religious-medical-center people have had other drugs not given under center directions. Fifteen per cent (three persons) say they had marijuana prior to going to the center for LSD; again we find a demonstrated interest in drug use characterizing a portion of those who seek out LSD in an institutional framework. Two of these marijuana-exposed persons continued with drug use (defined as one or more non-LSD drug experiences in the three months prior to interview) after taking LSD at the center. Among the majority of persons not reporting prior drug experiences before center initiation into

LSD, five (25 per cent of the total center sample) have expanded their interests after LSD, going on to experiment with mescaline, peyote, methedrine, and marijuana. In addition to consumption outside the center, 60 per cent of the center sample report having been given mescaline and/or methedrine as part of the center program; most report taking methedrine either at home or in the center to become acquainted with milder forms of altered consciousness, whereas mescaline is apparently administered with LSD to potentiate it. In any event, we find that expanded drug use, beyond LSD, characterizes the activities of about one-third of center people after they have had LSD at the center.

It is among the two patient groups that we find least experimentation with drugs other than LSD. Two of the private patients have done so, both taking peyote, methedrine, and marijuana. Both of these persons had begun their drug use prior to taking LSD. Both are currently using (illicit) drugs.

Among the public-clinic patients, only one has had drugs other than LSD. His exposure was to peyote, methedrine, marijuana, and heroin, but he is not now taking any of these.

Reviewing this information on drug use, and accepting the possibility of underreporting on illicit drug exposure and usage, it is clear that psychotherapy patients are the least "drug oriented," whereas persons using the drug informally (professional or black-market groups) are most "drug prone." Among the latter groups, at least half may be said to take LSD as just one of several substances employed to alter consciousness, or mood, without benefit of medical prescriptions or institutional controls. For these persons, the phenomenon of importance is not LSD use, but rather the general interest in producing mental changes through self-administered substances, often consumed in a very social atmosphere, which—if it came to a court test—might be found to be illegally employed. There is no evidence that these interests are attributable to LSD itself, although it is not unreasonable to suggest that for some, especially those taking it at the center, it was an important step along the way to expanded drug use.

For those people who are now taking drugs other than LSD, we find that the frequency of use varies in a not surprising way. The informal black-market users report a modal frequency of use twice a week; the experimentals, also a relatively young group in their twenties, say they average once a week. The rest say use is irregular depending upon their access to supplies and, presumably, circumstances. Certainly for those who do use the illicit drugs—and nearly all that are employed are illicit—supply is a major determinant of use frequency mentioned. This is the case for the informal professionals, the experimentals and the informal black-market users. What it implies is that their drug use would be more frequent if more drugs were available to them.

Although there are persons in the private-patient and religious-medical-center groups who also say that supply is the controlling feature of their use, a more frequent statement from these persons is that controls are internal; that is, without regard to supply, they restrict their own intake because of standards which lead them either to reject certain types of drugs or set to limits their use. Among the public-clinic patients, there is no one limitation cited more often than another; for the few persons with "expanded" drug experience, limitations are said to lie in the supply, in fear of loss of reputation or job, unwillingness to flout the law, or in personal value systems which exert control. It is to be noted that, even when personal standards are reported to inhibit expanded drug use, the psychological implication is that the desire for such use also exists; the conclusion is then that certain conflicts must exist within the individual with reference to his morals, self-image, or judgment, on the one hand, and his desire to experience altered states of consciousness, on the other. Such internal conflict as we presume does not rule out interpersonal conflict; we have a number of reports of social pressures by peers, employers, or husbands which run counter to the interests or values of initiates or potential initiates. The chances are that, in many cases, a simple two-sided conflict schema is insufficient and that many persons, users and nonusers, undergo internal ambivalence and a variety of conflicting external pressures.

It is unwise to invest too much trust in our measure of drug interest and preoccupation. Nevertheless, using the criteria of reports of thinking about, talking about, and planning drug experiences as such a measure, we find that such interest corresponds to expressions of desire to take LSD again, but not to actual experience of repeated usage. The majority of persons in each group are interested in or preoccupied with LSD; we offer both adjectives, for we are not sure which is the more accurate description.

Reported Changes after LSD

It is to be expected that mature persons, respected and successful, living in a culture in which "drug use" per se is viewed with apprehension and in which pleasure is something which must be "constructive," would find it difficult to justify drug use unless there was something about it which was noble and lofty, or at least in keeping with some approved values. LSD, then, must, like any missionary, "do good." Looking at the benefits said to be derived, we find many of them quite "proper" when viewed in this light: as a therapeutic tool, a means for enhancing values or expanding the self, a road to love and better relationships, a device for art appreciation or a spur to creative endeavors, a means to insight, and a door to religious experience. These value-consonant uses do not, by any means, rule out other effects, primarily reported to be release from anxiety or troubles, euphoria, heightened sensations, fantastic images or hallucinations, orgiastic excitement, and the like. Nevertheless, these latter "pleasure-principle" effects are not touted so much as are the "value-principle" effects when it comes to talking about LSD benefits or when initiators give testimonials to potential initiates. At these times, when talking about "what LSD has done for me," the emphasis is upon change for the good rather than pleasure for the moment.

We do find some differences among the groups in the extent to which people claim they have changed as a result of LSD. Nearly everyone (over 90 per cent) taking the drug in the informal professional and religious-medical-center settings contend they have benefited in their personal adjustments, that is, that they have had a satisfying internal psychological response to the drug. Somewhat fewer of the patients claim such changes, with about three-fourths of the private ones and two-thirds of the public-clinic people so contending. The group with the fewest reporting lasting positive personal changes is the experimental one. Unfortunately, our data are not sufficient to place the informal black-market people in perspective; the few stating their positions clearly did indicate they thought they had changed, although improved social relations were as often reported as inner psychological changes. On the other hand, it is our impression that the comments of many of the people in this latter group allow the inference that LSD itself, as just one of many drugs, is less often assigned the responsibility for the changes that do occur and, second, that people in this group, seeking aesthetic and immediate pleasures, think less in terms of lasting psychic alterations. We would place this group somewhere between the experimentals and the clinic patients when it comes to claiming positive change from LSD.

It is reasonable to think of readiness to take LSD in terms of some desire to change oneself in the first place; in that case, the gratification over LSD results would be in keeping with a wish antedating LSD use. Looking at persons in all the samples we find a consistent effort to induce self-change prior to taking LSD. Nearly everyone in the informal professional and religious-medical-center samples had tried psychotherapy, religion, medication, or the like before they took LSD. The same is true for three-fourths of the experimentals. By definition, all of the patients in both groups, in electing to undergo psychotherapy, evidenced such a desire. As for the informal black-market people, we are again short on clear statements. All of those who did discuss their interests indicated that they had been interested in self-change; some saw their education as a means to this end; others had been in psychotherapy, had participated in religious seminars, had meditated, and so on. We believe a safe estimate would be that the majority had sought self-change outside of drugs; in addition, it will be recalled that some had experimented with other drugs before taking LSD.

Readiness to Try Narcotics

What about other kinds of readiness, for new drug experiences, for example—for narcotic drugs in particular? The groups are by no means as consistent in this regard as they are on general self-change efforts. In the first place, one must distinguish between things which are seen as constructive—and here the majority would list LSD, as well as psychotherapy—and those which are simply productive of new experiences, pleasure, and so on. It is unlikely that any number of the well-educated and sophisticated people in these samples, excluding the not-so-well-educated public-clinic patients, would conceive of opium, heroin, or morphine as a foundation sustaining either the Protestant ethic or benevolent psychological changes. If they are willing to experiment with addictive drugs, it must be in the service of more immediate experiences—curiosity or "kicks." Given this assumption, it is not surprising that the informal users, those free of institutional and ritual controls and commitments associated with LSD, are the ones most ready to experiment with potentially addictive substances. The informal professionals express such a willingness in about half the cases. We estimate, without benefit of clear comments and substantiating code categories, that even more of the informal black-market people are also "ready." The patient groups, on the other hand, are not so venturesome; no more than one person in either expressed a willingness to move on to "heavy stuff." We should add that one public-clinic patient had taken heroin in the past, had not become addicted, and was not willing to try again, even though he had used other illicit nonaddictive drugs. Similarly, the religious-medical-center people are not venturesome, except for two of them (10 per cent). Of the experimentals, one-fourth indicate a willingness to try narcotic drugs.

Lest "willingness" be overinterpreted, we must make clear that the approach to narcotic drugs is not the same as that to LSD. Many people qualify their readiness for narcotics by talking of the need for adequate controls, assurances of safety, and some philanthropic purpose which would be served by their taking such drugs. They have in mind a medical experiment rather than back-alley "joy-popping." But the likelihood is that they could be persuaded to try it, provided they had sufficient trust in the person offering it. We would guess that such trust would be invested in a reputable research worker or medical professional. There is no reason to believe that many of the sample members are in jeopardy of being "hooked" by drug peddlers, mad scientists, or evil doctors. In fact, none have much interest in narcotic drugs, as far as we could tell; and while their general curiosity and interest in pleasurable new experiences, their past good experiences with drugs, and their trust in their former initiators do seem to put them in a situation of potential risk, we are willing to conclude that that risk is slight.

Growth of an In-Group

We have stressed that being introduced to and taking LSD is a social experience, that is, one involving other persons. The use of the drug, for many persons, strengthens their sense of affiliation with others whom they know to have used it. In consequence there can be formal meetings or discussion groups, increased friendly contact, and the development of a point of view shared by LSD users—a point of view which may have elements of "we-they" thinking about the user and the nonuser.

The extent to which contacts with LSD-using persons are increased and some consciousness develops of the LSD user as different from others varies remarkably depending upon the patterns of use, that is, membership in one or another of the sample groups. The patient samples, for example, report practically no change in their patterns of friendship and socializing before and after LSD. The experimentals in a very few cases (13 per cent) report that, after LSD, they began to spend more time with LSD-using persons and less time with nonusers. The informal professionals, in one-fourth of the cases, indicate that after first taking LSD they began to alter their social contacts, seeking out LSD users. On the other hand, among the religious-medical-center people and the informal black-market users, over three-fourths indicate an increase in social contact with users and a decrease in contact with nonusers.

In the case of the religious-medical-center people, it is important to remember that their changed pattern of socialization occurs in spite of the fact that most have not taken LSD a second time, that they were not bound by friendship ties prior to their LSD initiation, and that the LSD experience itself was under the formal and rather anonymous auspices of the center; center personnel were present, but other users were not. The social changes found in this group may be attributed, at least in part, to the center's encouraging its initiates to participate in continuing discussion groups after the drug experience. Encouragement begins as the person is coming out of his drug state; he is frequently brought to the house of another initiate, and there bonds of companionship are forged. Some of the center initiates have been attending discussion groups at one another's homes for at least twelve months. Others expand more informal relations, paying calls and partying together. Some have even gone so far as to plan to buy large houses in which three or four families may live together so as to achieve a degree of social intimacy and sharing which they report ordinary society denies them. Although not members of our sample, it is reported that some center initiates have gone ahead and set up group-living schemes, small urban Utopias in which housekeeping duties, meals, and recreation are shared.

In contrast to the social ties born of LSD use and center encouragement, which do not appear to require repeated LSD dosage, the ties of the informal black-market users are based at least in part upon their repeated use of drugs in company with one another and their dependency upon one another for a source of supply. In addition, they work together to prepare the drugs, as in the manufacture of peyote capsules or marijuana fudge. These drug-using activities are, of course, not limited to LSD, and, indeed, LSD is one of the least frequently employed drugs. This group, bound by ties of acquaintance, friendship, marriage, or blood prior to drug use and in which initiation itself was a social rite with many present and participating, is also affiliated for other reasons. Its members are nearly all young professionals or graduate students—or their relatives; they visit each other very frequently, and they share common artistic interests and social ideals.

Whereas it is easy to understand the clustering of the informal black-market users in the form of a genuine social group and the increased frequency of social contact among center people as they meet to discuss their ideas, insights, or emerging philosophies, it is not apparent just how the informal professionals escape the development of stronger group ties. We suspect that part of the explanation lies, in contrast to black-market users, in their independent access to drugs. As physicians and others in or close to medical or mental-health professions, they can secure LSD—or other drugs—more easily and from more diverse sources, supply houses, or professional friends. The legitimacy or quasi legitimacy of their LSD use, again in contrast to black-market individuals, does not require such development of techniques of secrecy, of shared justifications for unconventional or guilt-arousing actions, or of group-support societies which allow individuals to rely on one another to stave off the actual or fancied attacks of outsiders. It also appears to us, and these are impressions, that the informal professional people are in fact restricted by their professional success. Their work requires they maintain a number of social-professional contacts which cannot easily be disrupted without threatening their career patterns, and the demands upon their time are such that they cannot easily expand their present circle of acquaintances to include very many newly met LSD users. Here we must also note the growth of LSD use among persons already their friends and associates, so that, for many, mere continuation of old friendships is sufficient to include a considerable number of LSD users in their social circle. It is also to be remarked that the proportion of informal professionals expressing the desire to take LSD again and the proportion preoccupied with the drug is less than in either the informal black-market or religious-medical-center groups; we conclude that the proportion of professional people for whom LSD is centrally important is smaller than among these others and, consequently, there is less need for them to shape their lives about it.

The persons who take LSD and who are least likely to develop a genuine social group about it are the experimentals and the two patient samples. They are interested in the drug, and they do want to take it again, but most have not had it more than once. Why don't their interests lead them to affiliate with one another as a vital group? We suggest that it is at least partly a matter of orientation. The experimentals did not seek out LSD as an inspirational source; their reactions to it were quite moderate in comparison with those of other groups. The laboratory settings in which they have taken it have not been conducive to philosophical or psychic elaborations; the settings have been businesslike and without any aura of the mystical. Persons attracted to take the drug in this setting, with the limited expectations communicated by the experimenters, do not seem to be predisposed to or learn LSD's use as a grander substance. In addition, the experimentals frequently lack prior social acquaintance with users, are not affiliated in any social network through which LSD is spreading, and are therefore dependent upon the experimenter both for LSD supply and for introductions to other users. If the experimenter is not himself a social user of LSD, he will not be in a position to introduce users to such a social network; if he is, he may still refrain from doing so because there is no natural social stile which allows him to aid a laboratory subject to step over the fence of reserve and formality into the social life of the experimenter. This, of course, would hold true only for those subjects who are not recruited by the experimenter on the basis of their prior informal ties to him. In any event, we can see how the access to an LSD social group may be restricted for a laboratory subject both by the asocial nature of the setting and by the gatekeeper role of the experimenter.

Unlike experimentals, the patients are seeking something important from LSD, but they are doing so only on instruction from their psychiatrist (except for a very few private patients who seem to have sought him out because of prior knowledge of the psychiatrist's interest in the drug). Their exposure to LSD is within the conventional framework of medical care and the unequal status of the doctor-patient relationship. Neither patient group has prior acquaintance patterns among other LSD users, patient or otherwise, and so there are no established trails to follow in expanding upon their LSD experience. The acquaintances developed during therapy are limited; for the public-clinic patients, there has been acquaintance through group psychotherapy, but no encouragement for the participants to meet outside the hospital. Private patients have not, for the most part, had any opportunity to meet one another during therapy, nor have they had special chance to meet informal LSD users. Their psychiatrists control not only the LSD supply—and structure its use as subordinate to psychotherapy—but also control the communication-acquaintance channel. The psychiatrists do not step out of their formal role to introduce their patients to the informal professional circles in which they themselves may meet with other LSD users of their own status level. The same restriction on access to the psychiatrist's social life operates on the public-clinic patients, only more severely because of their much lower social status and more distant relationship to the clinic psychiatrists.

In review, then, we would suggest that factors which control the development of real social groups subsequent to LSD use—and center about that experience—include sources of drug supply; the degree of legitimacy of drug use; participation prior to LSD initiation in informal acquaintance networks through which LSD (or other drug) use is diffused; the extent to which the motivation to take LSD included a willingness or reflected a desire to change existing social patterns; the degree of intimacy and informality—the status difference—in the relationship between initiator and initiate; the willingness of the initiator to introduce the initiate into informal LSD social networks; the opportunity for acquaintance with other users provided by the setting in which the drug is first taken; the "learning" of the proper meaning and use of LSD, shared and social or not; and the extent to which affiliation provides support and justifications for acts or views which generate uncertainty, guilt, or social opposition.

The tendency to form views about differences between users and nonusers appears to depend upon acquiring a set of values about LSD use which includes some provisional theories of personality; these "we-they" views arise from particular kinds of social interaction. When we look at the most common descriptions of nonusers offered by persons who have had LSD, we find that the most frequent description implies disapproval of nonuse and personal superiority of users over nonusers. The terms employed, as well as the fact of in-group feeling, varies according to the category of user. The informal black-market users see nonusers as "squares," conventional, dull souls plodding down the rutted road of life. A "square" is a social type. It is easy to qualify for membership; one either refuses to take drugs or refuses to get "high" when one takes them. Like any typology, it suffers from inexactness for borderline cases. We became borderline cases one night during a bull session. The party was dull and constrained until about eleven o'clock, when two younger people, nonusing teen-agers, excused themselves. Immediately it became a "swinging" group, relaxed and happily chattering now that one no longer had to avoid talking about marijuana or sex. Two users who did not know us sighed, "Thank God the 'squares' are gone." The host then pointedly but kindly noted that we were not "pot heads," to which one of the newcomers replied, speaking to us, "Gee, I would never have known you were 'squares.'"

Among the informal professional, religious-medical-center, and private-patient groups, the most common description of nonusers is psychological; they are said to be defensive, rigid, intolerant, insensitive, cold, afraid, and so on—a trait constellation which implies that the refusal to take LSD is a good diagnostic sign for personality pathology. That a shared viewpoint which derogates the outsider has come to characterize those users who are participants in an LSD social in-group (the informal black market, religious-medical center and, to a lesser extent, informal professional) is not surprising; it is, however, surprising to find that these views are shared by the private patients.

The latter do not participate in informal groups centered about LSD. How do they arrive at an evaluation in common with one another, an evaluation which is the same as that offered by genuine in-group participants? In reply, we may note that they do have at least two experiences in common even if they do not know one another. They have psychiatrists in common (all of whom are members of the informal professional group), and they have an interest in LSD which has led them to read Huxley, DeRopp, Watts, to listen to Heard, and so on. We think they have learned from both sources. The psychiatrists may very well have communicated their views (intentionally or otherwise) which are drawn from the common stockpile of the informal professional group. In their reading and lecture-listening (radio, TV, and direct), they have also had a chance to pick up these ideas. Although these transmission routes may suffice to account for the denigrating diagnosis applied to the nonuser, we cannot rule out the possible empirical base. They may very well have observed their friends and neighbors, tested them, and found them wanting.

Neurotic character is *not* imputed to the nonuser by public-clinic patients. Their psychiatrists are also informal professional users; they have also read a little (but in the newspapers and popular magazines rather than in the works of the popular mystics) about LSD; they are also pleased with LSD and have had a chance to view those who are not so pleased; why the difference in public- versus private-patient evaluations of nonusers? We suggest two possibilities. One is that the public-clinic patients are, as a group, less verbal and less psychologically oriented. The diagnostic insult, so popular with those psychiatrically *au courant,* may not be at their fingertips. Second, they have been much more distant from their psychiatrists—distant in terms of background and status and in terms of frequency of contact. There are excellent studies[5] which show that class differences between patient and psychiatrist lead to reduced communication. We suspect it here and think that the psychiatrist did not bother to teach his patients his own view of nonusers, or if he tried, that he did not get it across. Conversely, we suspect that the patients had little interest in adopting the views of their status-distant therapist, so that they made no effort to identify with him or his social philosophy.

The experimentals are not so apt to call the nonusers psychological names. They do describe differences between the two groups, but most often list observed objective differences such as age and sex. Again we suspect that this is due to the absence of informal group affiliations, whereby one might indulge ethnocentric predispositions and/or learn a "theory" of drug use and nonuse. The fact that experimentals were not psychologically oriented in the first place, that is, did not seek LSD for soul-searching or socially reconstructive reasons, may also play a role in their relative disinterest in such matters. Nor is it likely that the experimenters had, or wished to pass along, any psychological theories of drug use which would cast aspersions on non-users; in consequence, the LSD initiation did not instruct the subjects in social philosophy or personality theory which implied praise for LSD takers and disapproval of nonusers. In the absence of such an orientation and the ethnocentrism accompanying it, it is interesting to note that the sociological observations made by the experimentals are consistent with our findings, especially about the experimental group; these people are younger and more often male than would occur in random population-sampling. They are also high-status, white, and Protestant, as some of the experimentals observed.

For a "good" there must be a "bad," and, if some people are "in," some others are "out." Exclusion and conflict are implied in the development of any ethnocentric group within a dynamic society. If nonusers are socially backward ("square") or psychologically unpleasant (rigid), it requires no great psychodynamic theory to predict that the dislike is complementary, that is, "they don't like us any more than we like them." Indeed the presumption of hostility on the part of the out-group can justify the formation and solidarity of an in-group and can also rationalize—whether or not it explains—the hostility of the in-group, a device well known to delinquents, paranoids, and others. And how do people who have taken LSD evaluate the opinions of others toward LSD use? More than three-fourths of the people in every group consider the surrounding society to be hostile or disapproving. It is the constancy of this view from one group to another which is surprising and which indicates that something more than ethnocentrism per se is operating. Were it simply a matter of reaction and counterreaction, or ethnocentric indulgence plus justifying projection, the genuine in-groups would be the stronger believers in outsider prejudice. But that nearly everyone in our sample presumes the same social view on the part of outsiders suggests reactions influenced by factors other than ethnocentrism. Either the sample members are reporting reality—what they have all heard or experienced—or they are feeling guilty or otherwise uncomfortable and are projecting to the outside world a portion of their ambivalence. These are not mutually exclusive possibilities; indeed, they are complementary ones.

It may be recalled that we discussed with our sample members their view of current narcotics laws. Our intent was to learn if there was any generalized sympathy for the drug-using underdog regardless of the drug being used and, at another level, to put their views into a larger perspective with reference to general attitudes toward the police and their work in drug-law enforcement. Most sample members who were willing to discuss it (and many said they simply had no information) disapproved of what they presumed to be law-enforcement people's views and actions toward marijuana, peyote, and LSD use, and, furthermore, the majority were critical to some extent of present narcotics law and policy. There was, however, no blanket condemnation of narcotics-control procedures; the group most critical were the religious-medical-center people, and those least critical were the informal professionals. In no group did we get an impression of identification with narcotics users; the protests heard were on the grounds of humanity and the need for medical control rather than punitive action. Our inference is that there is little or no sympathetic vibration with the addict qua addict; that LSD use, regardless of the aversion of society, is not felt to be akin to narcotics use by any stretch of the LSD user's imagination; and that he discriminates considerably between his activities and interests and those of the "junkie." Nevertheless, this does not stop the LSD user from exercising his time-honored American right of rebelliousness to presume that the police are "botching things up" or to express his humanitarianism in wishing that the unfortunate addict would be considered a medical rather than a police problem. It will be very important to keep the LSD user's point of view in mind when we come to the analysis of the views of policemen toward *them* in Chapter XII.

Proselytizing

Generally speaking, we may say that the majority of sample members enjoyed their LSD experience, insisted it brought about beneficial changes in their personalities or social relations, are much interested in the drug itself, spend a lot of time talking about it, and would like to take it again. A significant minority have taken it—and some other drugs—again, and many sample members have made LSD and the values associated with the drug—and those who use it—a focus of social activity. They are, in the Chamber-of-Commerce sense of the word, boosters. In addition, nearly all see society taking a view opposite to theirs, namely, discrediting the use of LSD. Given a booster faced with an unenlightened mass, what is likely to take place? Salesmanship. A missionary spirit.

Half or more than half of the sample members in each group but one indicate that they have tried to persuade others that LSD can work for them, that is, they have encouraged others to take the drug. The largest proportion (three-fourths) of initiates turned potential initiator is to be found among the informal black-market and the religious-medical-center people; informal professionals follow closely. At the other end are found the patient groups; about one-third of their members report proselytizing. The proportion of missionaries parallels the development of more exclusive social ties among LSD users, and we may take it that being a member of an LSD-using social circle and trying to persuade others to join that circle are correlated activities. There is some inconsistency between self-reports of salesmanship and interviewer ratings for active proselytizing; although interviewer ratings correspond quite well, proportionately, to reports in the religious-medical-center, informal black-market, and experimental groups, one finds that the interviewer felt the informal professionals and the private patients were more enthusiastic in their conversion attempts than they admitted. One can understand such concealment either in terms of constraints against admitting enthusiasm in an Apollonian society, in terms of the disapproval of being aggressive or "pushy," or in terms of being thought of as a kind of seductive drug peddler, a fantasy which some of our sample members were willing to admit to—at least insofar as they granted that others might think of them in that fashion.

That proselytism can be very important to the drug user is illustrated by the comments of informal black-market users:

> We've all "turned others on." As soon as you've been "turned on" yourself, you just can't wait to "turn everybody else on." You've got a list a mile long of friends who are just waiting there for what they've been missing. Man, everybody is getting "turned on."

or

> It's different when you're going to "turn someone on" to LSD. It's too precious and powerful to be careless about. It's so hard to get, you wouldn't give it to just anybody. But mostly it's because we've all seen the bad reactions that people can have; you know, when they get "the demons" or "the terror." You don't want to "turn anyone on" who will have a bad reaction. You don't want anybody who is going to fight it. You feel really responsible for them, and so you're careful.

Background Data

Except for the public-clinic patients, among whom there were no persons with higher degrees and only one college graduate, the majority in each group were college graduates. The majority of experimental and informal professional persons held higher degrees, as did nearly half of the religious-medical-center people. Informal black-market and experimental people were the youngest, and public-clinic patients the oldest. Most users were between the ages thirty-one and fifty. In all groups, Protestant religious backgrounds were predominant; the active religionists were found in the informal professional and patient groups, the agnostics and inactive Protestants in the other three groups. One finds a predominance of Anglo-Saxon family names. Males predominated in each group except the informal professionals, where there were about equal numbers of men and women. The highest proportion of currently separated or divorced persons was found in the private-patient group (39 per cent), and the fewest in the religious-medical-center and informal black-market groups (about 15 per cent).

Concealment of LSD Use

On ratings there was evidence of concealment about LSD use among all informal black-market persons and among three-quarters of the religious-medical people. About half of the private patients were reluctant to discuss their LSD experience with outsiders, as were 42 per cent of the informal professionals, and one-third of the experimentals. None of the public-clinic patients was reluctant to discuss his LSD use. We may conclude that the public-clinic people, regardless of their suspiciousness toward the interviewer, felt no shame or guilt about LSD use; we attribute this to the propriety of the setting in which they were given the drug and to their equating it with other medication given by a doctor. In every other group, at least some people were sensitive to possible disapproval from others should their own LSD experience or interests become known; this sensitivity increased in the social groups more centered about LSD. The illicit black-market users are not only sensitive to criticism, but also aware of their law violation in using other drugs; for them, concealment is essential.

Ratings of Drug Involvement

Interest in the expansion of drug use is inferred to be most common in the informal black-market group. About half of the people in the experimental, religious-medical-center and informal professional groups were rated as having already used, or being ready to go on to the use of, other (illicit) drugs. Insofar as these ratings accurately reflect interest and/or intent, they suggest a considerable number of individuals "at risk" for the violation of laws relating to the consumption of dangerous drugs (methedrine, peyote, marijuana, and the like). Only in the two patient groups and the experimental group was the rating of present or likely future drug-use extension limited to a minority. These are the samples whose drug use was controlled by a legitimate medical or research setting and was subordinate to psychotherapy and to the dominance of the physician or experimenter. While not controlling for motivation or personality difference, this finding does suggest the importance of legitimate institutions and formal relationships in controlling the extension of drug interests and, conversely, implies the failure of informal social groups to impose restraint on the expansion of drug interests and activities to illicit areas.

The ratings on habituation use the criteria of increased frequency and dosage over time. They are subject to errors in judgment, application of criteria, and information given by the persons interviewed. Keeping these cautions in mind, we find the raters citing evidence for habituation in one-fifth to one-third of the sample members in the informal professional, private-patient, religious-medical-center, and experimental groups. There were insufficient data for ratings in the informal black-market group, although it is clear that many of these people qualify for the title of "multihabitués"[6] in that they have used a variety of drugs over time with apparently increasing frequency. Only among the public-clinic patients do we find no evidence of habituation. As we employ the term, "habituation" does not imply physiological addiction, nor do we have evidence of suffering should LSD use cease.

Euphoria

Two more ratings are of interest. Euphoric response to LSD was inferred to have occurred in about half of the informal professional and religious-medical-center people, in three-fourths of the informal black-market and private-patient groups, and in only a fraction (14 per cent) of the public-clinic patients and experimental users. It would appear, should this rating be at all accurate, that a euphoric response to LSD is a function of expectations and setting as well as pharmacological effect.

Personality Disorder

On ratings of personality disturbance, we find the largest number of individuals with serious personality problems in the public-clinic-patient group (50 per cent). Only a few persons in four other groups (including the private patients) were so judged, while none of the informal professional people were rated as having serious personality disorders. Although this rating is crude and contaminated and does not attend to dynamics of any sort, its distribution in contrast with the findings on LSD preoccupation or interest, proselytizing, reported self-change, LSD social-group formation, expansion of drug interests, habituation, and so on clearly suggest that none of these latter emerge as a direct function of the severity of personality disorder.

According to our evidence, interest in LSD and other drugs and the expansion of drug use are not simple correlates of gross personality disorder. Quite the reverse; the group with the greatest maladjustments, rated either in terms of personality, objective measures of life troubles, or self-reports of life troubles, is the public-clinic-patient group. At the other extreme, the "best-off" groups in terms of these same measures are the informal professional and informal black-market groups. Among the clinic people, drug behavior is most controlled and least subject to illegality and expansion; in the informal groups, it is the reverse. We do not imply that personality factors are not important; we do state that social factors are influential and that the severity of personality disorder per se is not a variable which plays a very large role, unless it is an inverse one, bringing people under the greatest amount of medical institutional control and exposing them to comparatively little risk of expanded drug use.

Summary

A comparison of the several samples defined by the setting of initial LSD use reveals the following:

Opportunity and access. LSD opportunity and access varies according to profession and social contacts. Experimental workers and subjects in the sample first began taking the drug in 1950. It then became available to medical and mental-health professionals and practitioners who started taking it about 1956 in informal settings. Patients then began to receive it in psychotherapy, after which it became available, about 1959, to black-market users. The latter obtained it through social contacts with professionals. Finally, the religious-medical center was established, and, by 1960, LSD was available on a fee basis to the general public.

Threats and actions to restrict the flow of LSD to persons using it informally resulted almost immediately in the development of new sources of supply or of substitute drugs. New sources included the informal importation of the drug across international boundaries, the reported home manufacture of the drug, and the utilization of natural sources—for example, morning glory seeds and seaweed. LSD users also began to employ other hallucinogens such as peyote, mescaline, psilocybin, and the like and intoxicants or stimulants such as marijuana and methedrine.

Knowledge about LSD prior to use. Occupation and social contacts influence how much and what kind of information one has received about LSD before taking the drug. The year of opportunity is a variable as well. Patterns of work, reading, kinship, and friendship are fundamental to the kind of drug knowledge transmitted. Experimentals were likely to learn that LSD was a psychotomimetic producing sensory distortions; informal professionals and black-market people were likely to learn it produced heightened sensations, artistic or personal enhancement, and euphoria. Patients learned what their doctors told them— mostly that it was a psychotherapy facilitator. Religious-medical-center people, like public-clinic patients, had fewest contacts in a friendship net which linked them to LSD. The center people learned from acquaintances or public sources; those who heard about the drug from center officials learned that LSD produced religious experiences and personality benefits.

Individual motivation. The distribution of expressed reasons for taking LSD varied from one sample group to another; experimentals most often cited personal or professional curiosity, as did informal professionals. Patients took the drug because their doctor told them to and because they wanted to be "cured." Patients are the only ones who refer to LSD as a "medicine" and to the drug experience as a "treatment." The desire for self-knowledge sparked the center people; they refer to LSD as "the material" ("consciousness-expanding materials"). The black-market sample seeks artistic experience, self-enhancement, and above all, "kicks." Although there are overlap among the groups and multiple motives within individuals, one must attend to the user's kind of social circle and its many correlates as a shaper as well as a reflector of motives.

Sociability during initiation. The informality, number, and kind of other persons present when one is initiated to LSD and whether or not others are taking it at the same time also vary by initial setting. Clinic patients take it formally and alone with their doctor; private patients take it at the doctor's home office, sometimes with a spouse or friend present. Center people take it with center personnel standing by. Experimentals may or may not take it alone; but others present are research subjects and ordinarily not friends. Informal professionals and black-market users take it with friends. Sometimes, in the experimental setting, several persons take it together. Usually, in the black-market setting, a number of people take LSD at the same time. The more formal or businesslike the setting (research, therapy, the center), the fewer the people and certainly the fewer the friends around. The more informal and the more sociable the setting, the greater likelihood of simultaneous drug experience among those assembled—culminating, in the black-market group, which is youngest and freest, in the orgiastic use of the drug.

Drug effects. Responses to the drug vary by sample membership and by individual idiosyncrasy. There is a tendency for people to report the kinds of experiences which they have been told to expect. There is also a tendency to report the kind of experience which the administrator tells one that one is having.

Bad effects also occur, some of which are expected and some of which are not. The transient ones appear to vary with expectations, settings, and personality. The kinds of bad effects reported do differ from one sample to another; these seem intimately linked to initial expectations—for example, some experimentals expecting release report depression, which suggests release to the point of energy depletion. Center people report an initial horror, one they are taught is necessary for the passage to grace. It is less likely that expectations produce a bad response than that they help shape the translation of raw experience into words.

LSD repetition. The proportion of sample members repeating LSD is greatest among persons whose initial (and subsequent) drug experience is outside any institutional setting or formal role relationship. Although interest in repeating the drug is found in every group, only among the informal users is actual repetition encountered among the majority. Interpersonal and institutional controls and access to supply are influential. Many LSD recipients in institutional settings are hesitant to undertake informal (illicit) use even if able to develop contacts. The belief is encountered that the setting is crucial. To some extent, this belief is a matter of teaching on the part of administrators, who persuade initiates that their way of giving LSD is the only safe or successful way; the reluctance also may express uncertainty about altering intense and significant relationships with the drug initiator.

Other drug use. Those who have received LSD in institutional settings, in formal role relationships, are least likely to have experience with other mind-altering drugs. The free-and-easy informal black-market group has had the widest drug experience; psychotherapy patients are the ones least likely to have experimented with other drugs. For many persons associated with informal settings, there is a factor of general interest in mind-altering experiences; LSD is just one of several drugs employed as a means to that end. One cannot attribute expanded drug use to LSD itself, although for some, especially center users, that was an important first step. It is equally clear that use of LSD does not necessarily lead to the expansion of drug-taking activities. There is no inevitable sequence of drug use; the important factors appear to be personal predispositions, social contacts, and group modes, not any "demand quality" of the pharmaceutical preparation itself.

The frequency of the use of other mind-altering drugs also varies from one sample to another; the younger persons in experimental and black-market groups report the greatest frequency of use. Factors influencing frequency include supply, especially important to informal users, and inner controls or values, especially important to institutional users. It may be that the self-control or sense of propriety which institutionalized users say has been influential in reducing their use does reflect a greater conventionality among those people. Perhaps their moral strictures led them to seek LSD in a sanctioned institutional environment in the first place. On the other hand, the self-description may be a luxurious conceit which, in "sweet lemons" style, conceals their inability to find LSD anywhere else so that they might take it more often.

Preoccupation with the LSD experience appears closely associated with the presence of the desire to take the drug again. These expressions of interest and wish vary from one sample to the next. It is important to note that preoccupation does not correlate with actual repetitive use. That is interpreted as evidence of the restriction on LSD supply and of the operation of moral and interpersonal controls on its further use. One infers the presence of conflict within and between individuals about whether they should or should not repeat LSD. Were LSD to be easily and cheaply available, more persons would repeat the experience. With reference to narcotic drugs, no sample member shows any real interest in taking them. One patient, an alcoholic, in the past had taken heroin but did not become addicted and had no desire to take it again. The readiness to experiment with addictive substances nevertheless does vary by sample; persons in the informal groups are most often ready to try such a venture, persons in the institutional samples least ready. Although the lack of institutional restraint, the absence of internal controls against drug-taking, the trust in those who initiate them to drugs, and the presence of a general interest in altering the mind are all present in the informal sample members, there is no evidence of a desire to take opiates; and there is clear evidence that the "steppingstone" hypothesis of drug use (from nonaddictive to addictive) is not supported by a single case.

Social-group formation. LSD use is generally a social experience initiated in the presence of others. It can also become the center of social-group formation. The extent to which this occurs varies by sample. With the exception of the center people, the institutional initiates do not tend to restructure their social lives on the basis of LSD; among informal users, there is a greater tendency to do so, although, in the case of the black-market group, the social pattern merely reflects a prior social centering about drugs and the values represented in their use. Whether or not social groups based on common LSD experiences are formed depends upon the source of drug supplies; the degree of legitimacy of use; participation prior to LSD initiation in informal acquaintance networks through which drugs are diffused; the extent to which the motivation to take LSD reflects a desire to change existing life patterns; the role and status relationship between initiator and initiate; the opportunity for acquaintance with or access to other LSD-using persons; the "learning" of the proper meaning and use of LSD; and the extent to which affiliation provides support and justification for acts or views which have generated uncertainty, guilt, or a sense of social isolation or disapproval.

Proselytism occurs frequently. Its occurrence correlates with the presence of an LSD-oriented social group. Patients and experimentals least often report efforts to initiate others to LSD; informal black-market and center people do so most often. There is some evidence of concealment of proselytizing among private patients and informal professionals.

The extent to which a typology of users versus nonusers is formed also varies by sample. Persons exposed to "training" by mental-health professionals as part of their LSD experience and associations develop a "we-they" typology, employing essentially disapproving psychopathological terms to describe nonusers. Clinic patients and experimentals, both unlikely to be sharing personality theories with their initiators and least likely to be part of LSD-using groups, are also least likely to describe nonusers in uncomplimentary terms and users in flattering ones.

The social groups formed about LSD use need not have the same views and opinions. The prior orientation of the members, dependent upon education, occupation, social position, interests, and the like, and the existing loyalties to institutions and pre-existing groups determine that various LSD-using groups will stress different themes. LSD itself provides no common and constant experience which is reflected in uniform concerns among those taking it. The component social aggregates within the drug movement demonstrate diversity as well as agreement.

Changes in response to LSD. The report of beneficial changes in personal qualities or feelings and in social life is the rule, but the emphasis varies. Socially approved and "constructive" changes are much more often cited than enjoyable or pleasure-oriented ones. General changes are most often reported in the informal professional and center samples, least often among experimentals and black-market persons. Adjective check list improvements are most common among center people and private patients, least common among experimentals. With reference to adjective check-list changes for the worse, these are most commonly reported by patients, clinic patients foremost and private patients second. As for major life changes, most job-changing takes place among the two patient groups, most divorce among the private patients, most marriage and engagement among the young experimentals and, presumably, informal black-market persons. The greatest reduction in alcohol use is claimed by private patients and center people and the least by the alcoholics in the clinic sample.

It is not clear what factors contribute to real and perceived life changes reported as subsequent to LSD use. It appears that what one expects from the drug plays an important role; distressed people who do not expect it to be a cure-all (both patient groups) or who have little expectation of any psychological benefit on the basis of their prior knowledge (experimentals) seem to report least benefit. The patient groups, in the process of the most disruptive real-life changes, are also most likely to report undesirable changes after taking LSD.

Enthusiasm over the therapeutic potential of LSD varies considerably from one group to the next. Center people are most enthusiastic, whereas experimentals and patients are unlikely to see LSD as a dramatic therapeutic force. The evaluation of LSD's therapeutic potential obviously does not depend only upon the degree of initial psychic distress and the amount of alleviation of distress reported; it appears to be dependent in part upon enthusiasm and conviction.

Euphoria in response to LSD varies by sample. It appears most often among black-market persons and least often among patients and experimental users. A euphoric reaction to the drug is influenced by expectations and motivation, by the presence or absence of formal institutional controls in the setting, by whether or not others are also taking the drug, and by the theme of the gathering.

Personality and LSD use. There is no direct relationship between the frequency of gross personality disorder in a group and the amount of interest in LSD or in the extent of use of other drugs. The sample with the most seriously psychologically disabled persons, the clinic patients, had least interest in LSD and least extension of drug-taking to other substances, except for alcohol. One cannot say that LSD interests or use, or the use of mind-altering drugs in general, is simply a matter of personality disorder.

NOTES

1. Self-descriptions and observer descriptions can be at variance. Consider the findings of Morimoto (cited by H. A. Abrahamson in *Neuropharmacology: Transactions of the 2nd Conference* [New York: Josiah Macy Jr. Foundation, 1955]), who observed normal persons under LSD influence. He reported that, under the drug, there was a significant change in the interpersonal behavior direction *away, from, against* and *toward* others. There was a decrease in *with* behavior, defined as brotherly, friendly, reciprocal, or equalitarian, What was increased was avoidance, hostility, and seeking nurturance and support. On the Thematic Apperception Test, the subjects perceived reduced interaction and closeness; they experienced more difficulty in expressing emotion.
2. Whether reports of home laboratory production are true is a subject of debate. Some FDA enforcement agents insist no such production occurs; pharmacologists say it can be done but is difficult; knowledgeable professionals among the LSD users insist it is being done and that LSD is produced in vast amounts.
3. Lois Pratt, A. Seligmann, and G. Reader, "Physicians' Views on the Level of Medical Information among Patients," *American Journal of Public Health*, XLVII (1957), 1277–1283.
4. M. Ostow, *Drugs in Psychoanalysis and Psychotherapy* (New York: Basic Books, 1962).
5. A. Hollingshead and F. Redlich, *Social Class and Mental Illness* (New York: John Wiley & Sons, 1958).
6. S. Cohen and K. S. Ditman, "Complications Associated with Lysergic Acid Diethylamide (LSD-25)," *Journal of the American Medical Association*, CLXXXI (1962), 161–162.

LSD "REGULARS": CONTINUING USERS COMPARED WITH DISCONTINUERS

[IV]

Richard Blum, with Eva Blum and Mary Lou Funkhouser

It is the purpose of this chapter to contrast a group of individuals who are regular and continuing users of LSD with those who have taken it in the past, but who are not now taking or definitely planning to take the drug. The aim of the comparison is to elucidate the differences between LSD "regulars" and those who have ceased the use of the drug, at least temporarily.

Among the ninety-two persons in our LSD-accepting sample, there were thirty-two who had taken it more than once. There were eight more whom we suspected of repeated use, but for whom sufficient evidence of such use was lacking. There were an additional two who, at the time of interview, expressed the intention of taking LSD within a few days or weeks. If one combines these actual, tentative, and suspected repeat users, one finds that forty-two, nearly half of those who accepted LSD, have gone on (or plan to go on) to use it a second time. If one examines the statements of interest in taking LSD again, one finds that fifty-four (59 per cent) would like to take the drug, and another twelve are interested but not certain. Combining all those who indicate at least some interest in another experience (and excluding all those who say frankly that they do not know), one finds that nearly three-fourths of all the original LSD accepters have already repeated or might repeat LSD use.

In spite of the majority of LSD accepters' interest in taking LSD in repeated doses, only a minority of the sample may be characterized as regular users. The definition of a regular user is one who has taken the drug two or more times and intends definitely to take it again in the immediate future. There are thirteen persons out of the ninety-two who meet this definition of the regular user.[1]

INITIAL SETTING

Seven of these persons first took LSD in the informal professional setting, two in experimental setting, two in the religious-medical center, and two in private therapy. No informal black-market persons are represented here, although all eight of those who are suspected of repeated use are informal black-market persons. Each of the eight is believed to have taken and to be taking a variety of other mind-altering drugs. Each of the eight expressed a liking for LSD and a desire to take it whenever it was available. No patient in the public-clinic setting became a regular LSD user.

On the basis of the distribution, known or suspected, of LSD continuation, one concludes that regular use arises most frequently among persons whose initiation into LSD was in an informal setting. The institutional use of the drug, where administration was conducted in a more formal role relationship, where access to the drug was limited, and where more controls existed, results in less likelihood of continuing use. If one were to predict regular usage, based on the ex post facto data now at hand, knowledge of the initial setting of use would be one of the most important variables to identify. As a variable, it subsumes many correlates, for the pattern of use and the characteristics of users differ from one setting to the next.

The public-clinic patients did not in any case become LSD regulars and are therefore excluded from the continuer-discontinuer comparisons which follow. The reason is that knowledge of that setting provides sufficient information to enable one to predict their LSD conduct. One must keep in mind, however, that the clinic group ($N = 8$) was the smallest in the sample, so that it may be chance that none of these patients were in the regular-user group. For most comparisons of regulars versus discontinuers, the informal black-market group is also excluded. That is because the data on the conduct of that group are insufficient. Whenever it is included in a comparison, the fact will be indicated. The groups which are normally included in the comparison of regulars versus discontinuers are the private patients, informal professionals, religious-medical-center clients, and experimentals.

USE OF OTHER DRUGS

Eleven of the thirteen regular users have had experiences with mind-altering drugs other than LSD. Most had three or more different drugs besides LSD, typically peyote, mescaline, marijuana, or methedrine. The two persons who had not had experience with other drugs are both patients in private psychiatric care. Only two among the eleven with other drug experience had that experience prior to taking LSD. The rest had all had LSD first or had had LSD in combination with another drug as part of the initiation series, for example, with mescaline or with methedrine as a potentiator. Compared with persons who have first had LSD in the same settings but who are not now regular users, the regular users have had considerably more experience with other drugs; 85 per cent of the regulars have had other drugs, whereas 53 per cent of the discontinuers have had them.

Among the continuers, half[2] are also taking drugs besides LSD on a regular basis. In contrast, among the discontinuers, only 18 per cent are regular users of some other nonprescribed hallucinogen or stimulant. These figures quite clearly show an association between the continued use of one drug, LSD, and the continued use of other, milder drugs, some of which may be illicitly employed. The figures also demonstrate that when one quits LSD one does not necessarily quit taking other substances such as methedrine, peyote, mescaline, or marijuana. Nevertheless, the existence of a drug-interest factor, or a readiness to take mind-altering drugs in general, is more often present in the LSD continuing users.

As for the sequence of steps from one drug to another, one finds that most persons in both the regular-LSD-user and the discontinuer samples started with LSD. Sixteen per cent of the discontinuers had some other mind-altering drug first, and two out of thirteen (15 per cent) of the regular users had had some other drug prior to LSD. If one extends the analysis to the excluded informal black-market user group, one finds in that group a different pattern: All eight persons suspected of continuing LSD use were introduced to other drugs prior to LSD, whereas, among the black-market LSD discontinuers, of whom there are only four, two had had LSD as their first mind-altering drug. Both of these drug novices were women initiated by a husband or lover.

GROUP FORMATION

One would expect, in view of the special values associated with LSD use and in view of the negative response of at least some social elements, that regular LSD users would tend to cling together in groups. That is the case. Examining the comments of sample members about changes in their social life since taking LSD, one finds that regular users, more than others, have reconstructed their social circles so as to more often include those who have had LSD experiences and exclude those who have not. Sixty-two per cent of the regular users say their social lives reflect their changed interest patterns, whereas only 29 per cent of the discontinuers report that they now spend more time with LSD users. The difference between the two groups should not lead one to overlook the significance of the latter's 29 per cent; this figure shows that a rather sizable proportion of presently LSD-nonusing persons nevertheless congregate with users on the basis of their LSD interests—and the correlates of those interests. One should not be surprised if such a social grouping would lead to further drug experimentation.

The increased group-centeredness among LSD regulars is also reflected in the ratings of ethnocentrism. Sixty-nine per cent of the regular users, as opposed to 36 per cent of the discontinuers, are rated as ethnocentric in their attitudes. Though it is not always the case, the likelihood is that values associated with LSD, and the group using the drug, are the basis for the ethnocentric "we-they" contrast.

Unlike certain groups where membership is deemed a privilege by both insiders and outsiders, with the result that ethnocentric insiders erect barriers to membership, the LSD-using group, whatever the ethnocentric trends of some of its participants, does not erect barriers to membership. The entire notion of a movement is to enlist support and to enroll new battalions in the service of the new beliefs. One must anticipate that the LSD continuing users would be seeking enlistments, not reject potential initiates. Proselytism would be the result. Examining the ratings of the continuers versus discontinuers on the proseyltism variable, one finds that the regulars are indeed proselytizers par excellence; twelve out of the thirteen have played important roles in introducing others to LSD. One regular denies playing such a role, but other information suggests that he did. The 100 per cent proselytism among regulars is contrasted with 40 per cent among the discontinuers. Again, the latter statistic points up the LSD-centered behavior that can occur even among persons not now taking the drug.

To some extent the ethnocentrism and increased affiliation with other LSD users implies membership in a drug group per se, that is, in a self-aware congregation sharing the drug experience, the values associated with it, and perhaps the personality predispositions or reactions correlated with repeated use. Although the data do support such a view, there is also evidence to show that a strict "we-they" or insider-outsider dichotomy need not occur as a consequence of mind-altering drug use. For example, if one applies two observational measures, the use of argot[3] and the interpersonal ties reported, one arrives at an estimate that certainly no more than half, and probably less, of the LSD regulars would consider themselves members of any distinct congregation which is a drug-using, value-sharing, and nonconforming social entity.

But the number of self-identified members of a drug or "swinging" group among the discontinuers is fewer, in any event, than among regular users. Still excluding the informal black-market people, one would compare the maximum of 50 per cent "drugees," a phrase some of them use humorously about themselves, among regulars with about 25 per cent of the discontinuers who use the argot and report friendship patterns with other argot-using drug users. Again, the proportion of "drugees" among the discontinuers requires attention. Recalling that less than one-fifth of the discontinuers are presently using any (non-prescribed) mind-altering drugs (excluding alcohol), it is apparent that one can show the signs of membership in what an observer would call a drug-using group without having to take drugs or, at least, taking them very often. In other words, there can be people in the drug movement of LSD users and "pot heads" who are not active drug users at all.[4] Conversely there can be private drug users not associated with any group, although we suspect that, with LSD and marijuana, the latter are fewer than the former. What is implied is that association is a matter of beliefs, interpersonal contacts, and a way of life, not necessarily depending on drug use itself, especially not on regular use.

Once a person has signified his sympathy with the point of view expressed in word and deed by his acquaintances, signified it by taking the drug in a public ceremony which can very well be viewed as a *rite de passage,* once he adopts some of the language and expresses some of the opinions, then he is no longer a "square," even if the interval between his drug experiences is long. We do suspect that it must be viewed by everyone as an interval, that is, a "good head" must always say he is ready to take the drug again, although not necessarily immediately. Perhaps if a definite statement were made to the effect, "No, never again," then a falling out would occur.

One respondent told how he had been associating with a "swinging" crowd and had been pushed to take marijuana until it was necessary for him either to do so or to be cast out of the group. He admired the people in the group and wanted their continued approval, so he conformed, as would have been predicted.[5] His initiation with a whole "joint" was completed in full view of the assembled (thirteen or fourteen) multitude. He danced, capered, and donned outlandish garb. Those present nodded approval and later spoke of the "great things" that "pot" had done for the new initiate. The respondent confided to us that he had been very careful not to inhale so that he would not experience any pharmacological effect; he had no intention of becoming intoxicated. His behavior was a drama by which he conveyed the spirit of his conversion to the group; his "high" had been a pretense. But his initial resistance and initiation conduct were symptomatic of fundamental differences. Within a matter of months he parted company with the group because of more basic disputes over morality, propriety, and the friendship obligations.

As somebody in the group put it, approximately:

> The first time you really refuse to blow "pot," you're through. Using drugs is the final measure of a man. It's the moment of truth. But if you do go along, it's not just sharing drugs. You've got to share your wife with some of them too. There's one guy, he's a "professional rapist"; he sleeps with every woman, every wife, he can get his hands on in the crowd. Only two I know about have refused him. He'll just stand up and say he's going to sleep with so-and-so, almost always somebody's wife—and he does. Hell, his wife had a baby that wasn't his, and he doesn't care. But there was one guy who cared. X went after somebody's wife. The husband found out; he couldn't help it, since they sit around talking about it in front of each other. Anyway that was one husband who would have none of it. He went after X with a gun. Luckily for X, X was out. You should have seen what he did to X's house. Holy cow! Bullet holes, doors torn off the hinges, some of the stuff set on fire. No, it isn't just drugs. You have to go along with the whole bit, the whole scene. If you don't or can't, why, you're out.

Drug-taking can symbolize the renunciation of old values, or at least of conventional ones, and the acceptance of new ones. The pharmacological reaction to the drug itself need not be the primary reason for drug-taking, and the reaction that does occur need not be of great concern to the group. What is important under these circumstances is that affirmation, or conversion symbolized in drug-taking, extends to enough important areas of value and conduct so that the associates in drug use can get along without disruption. Persons in the drug movement can get along quite well and maintain friendships with those not using drugs as long as other values are shared. Conversely, if drug-taking is not accompanied by actual agreement on matters of how to live and what to believe, associations will be disrupted. The drug experience is not in itself a cement which can bind people together who are not in fundamental agreement. It does appear to be a funnel through which persons with converging interests may move rapidly and intensely into channels and associations they would not otherwise have experienced.

It is in this light that one must view the development of a user's language, whether it be marijuana argot or intellectual mysticism. It will be recalled from Chapter II that many LSD users describe their experience as ineffable. What is uncommunicable only becomes communicable if a new language is taught, or if old words are given new meanings, and if the listener is presumed to "know" what is meant by virtue of his having had the same experience. In Chapter II, a case was cited in which a regular user had described how he had been unable to talk about LSD until he had learned the proper vocabulary from other experienced users. His wife had the same problem, reportedly being silent about her experience until she had contact with other users and developed a new way of talking. She also read among the popular mystical writers and from them developed a sense of what to say.

The experience of being taught a language in association with other users must be taken as more than instruction in communication. It is instruction in approved words and approved experiences; it is instruction in a point of view and in the necessary qualities for an approved associate.[6] The language that is learned can be used to structure the pharmacological response to a drug, giving that experience sense and meaning that may not have been in it at the time it occurred. It has already been shown that what one expects from a mind-altering drug (based on information) and what one wants from it (motives, interests) affect the kind of experience reported. So too will the attitudes of those around one affect that response during the experience as people are taught to "recognize" what is happening to them (see Chapter VII). And naturally, what one is taught afterward about what happened will affect the interpretation of the drug experience; "Oh yes, from what you say I can tell it really got to you,

you *did* have a transcendental experience." Such comments are not only instructive, helping the person define and describe his response, but they are also approving or rewarding and, as experiments on conditioning have shown, approved responses are repeated.

In speaking about the learning of an LSD language and learning the philosophy of the drug movement as steps in the commitment to an identifiable group, we speak with perhaps more definiteness than the facts warrant. The notion of a "group" is an easy one to employ but must be used with caution. Groups are, in fact, very hard to identify as viable social objects. A group is a convenience in the mind of an observer; it need not have any identifiable existence in the minds of any of its "members." Much is written these days of roles and groups and identifications and the like; but one must be careful before elevating conceptions to the solid state of "fact." For example, among the persons identified by their associations and argot as users of LSD, marijuana, peyote, and the like, persons having many views in common and spending time with each other, persons who take drugs together and commonly sense the hostility of a disapproving world, one would think there would be no difficulty finding a group. There is no difficulty as long as the group is defined by time and place, for example, twelve informal black-market users gathered at X's house from seven o'clock at night until two the following morning. Even that is too definite; one person there was not a drug user at all; two went home at eleven o'clock; two came at one o'clock. One was recently introduced and nobody, not even the host, knew his name or anything else about him except that he was a fellow "pot head." And that knowledge was strictly hearsay. The visitor might really have been a cop.

There is no group referred to in this entire study which has a fixed and constant membership enduring over time, whose members all know one another and among all of whom there would be any agreement, or even vague idea, that they constitute an identifiable social entity set apart from other social entities. The "continuing drug users" (drawn as they are from the different samples) are a category that we have constructed; as a social fact, they do not exist, for they do not know one another and certainly may not think of themselves in the way we have found it convenient to describe them. The informal professional sample we have described also does not exist as a real group either. Its "members" live as far as five hundred miles from one another, have never met, and will probably never meet. If they did, they would identify one another in various ways, one of which might or might not be as fellow LSD initiates.

ORIGINAL MOTIVATION

Continuers and discontinuers may also be compared with reference to their reasons for taking LSD. Some differences would be expected, since differences in motivation have already been shown to characterize the various samples specified by the circumstances of initial LSD use. Rather than deal again with the content of reported motives, it is interesting to examine the variety. Continuers consistently describe themselves as having been motivated by several interests (or more accurately, their statements have been coded to show several different themes): curiosity, self-exploration, therapeutic desires, religious-mystical interests, professional concerns, and so on. Discontinuers generally report only one or two reasons for taking LSD; the regulars report three.

One may interpret the results in terms of the present feelings of LSD users that the drug has, quite literally, done more for them, by providing satisfactions in several different areas. Or it may be that continuing users are more interested in the drug or are more verbal people and discuss their behavior with it at greater length with the interviewer, thus increasing the likelihood of several motivational themes emerging. Or one may interpret the results to suggest that, at the time LSD was taken, those who later became regular users hoped for more out of the drug and were, at the time, searching for fulfillment in the sense that their multiple interests were not providing a sense of satisfaction or completion. On the other hand, it is possible that their interests were simply more broad and complex than were those of persons who later discontinued LSD use.

RECOLLECTED DRUG RESPONSE

Examining the reported nature of the first LSD experience, anticipating that those who had a bad experience would be less likely to continue, one finds that, among the regulars, three out of thirteen (23 per cent) say some part of the first experience was unpleasant; one indicated it was entirely unpleasant. Among the discontinuers, 62 per cent recall unpleasantness in their first experience. One cannot exclude the possibility of selective recall or of amnesia; indeed, in following several subjects, it was apparent that short-term memory failures which appeared clinically to be like those encountered in organic brain dysfunctions did occur.[7] On the basis of these reports, there is reason to believe that although the majority of LSD initiates experience some unpleasantness, those who continue to use the drug either did not have an unpleasant drug reaction or have forgotten any distress.

CHANGES ATTRIBUTED TO LSD

With reference to reported self-change, as measured by the adjective check list, between the time of LSD initiation and the present, there is little difference between the two groups in the proportion of recollected initial conditions; an average of half of both groups described themselves over-all as being troubled, overwhelmed, or unhappy at the time they decided to take LSD. There are rather large differences on particular items, the regulars more often describing themselves at the time of LSD initiation as being displeased with their achievements, having too much to do, not having things under control, and not being loving. Discontinuers, on the other hand, more often complained they were bored or were just drifting along.

As far as the LSD-induced changes are concerned, there is a slight tendency for the regular users to believe more strongly that they have improved or progressed from a state of initial distress or displeasure than the discontinuers do. An average 68 per cent improvement on all items of original distress (twenty adjectives) is reported by regular users as opposed to 62 per cent improvement by discontinuers. The greatest amount of improvement reported by regular users, compared to discontinuers with recollected distress in the same area of function, occurs with reference to moving from being dissatisfied with self to being satisfied with self, from feeling unfulfilled to feeling fulfilled, from feeling empty to feeling vital, from having too much to do to having a reasonable amount to do, from having no sense of self-guidance to having control of one's destiny, from being angry to being no longer angry, and from not being loving to being loving. The last item is the most important; most regulars had felt unloving before, but all of them now feel they are loving people. Only a minority of the discontinuers had felt unloving to begin with; and of those only a few felt themselves to be changed by LSD. The beneficial changes in response to LSD more often reported by the discontinuers were relief of boredom and reduction in anxiety.

On the basis of self-descriptions, one is led to conclude that regularity of use of LSD is associated with a considerable sense of self-improvement in a number of areas, especially those implied by the terms self-satisfaction, self-direction, and emotional richness and equanimity. The changes in response to LSD reported by discontinuers are also considerable, but, comparatively speaking, put less emphasis on the expansion of inner life and direction and put more emphasis on the elimination of distress. One should not overinterpret what are really (numerically) rather slight differences between the groups. Perhaps—at least for some persons—when among the many changes felt to occur, anxiety is successfully eliminated by an LSD experience, an individual will then proceed without any repetition of the drug experience. Perhaps when anxiety is not eliminated, but when emotional richness, spontaneity, and self-acceptance are believed to depend upon the drug, repeated use of LSD will occur.

Such a theory about the role of anxiety in producing continued LSD use is at odds with traditional psychological notions of learning through satiation or of motivation simply as tension-reducing. It is the discontinuers whose anxiety has been reduced, or perhaps eliminated for a time, through LSD. And it cannot be said that they took LSD because they knew it would be tension-reducing. Nevertheless, LSD appears to have reduced anxiety, and they stopped using it. But for the regular users anxiety has less often been reduced; and we postulate that it is this phenomenon which accounts, in part, for the repetition of the drug. If anxiety is partly reduced, then one can hope for better next time, while, at the same time, continuing anxiety spurs one to continued action. One is reminded of the self-stimulation of the brain in humans as reported by Heath.[8] One patient frantically pressed the button, not because it produced orgasm, but because it was an attempt to reach the orgiastic end point, the beginnings of which had been initiated by original button-pushing. It was a situation of partial pleasure and frustrating high tension which was associated with the most frequent self-stimulation of the brain. In a second patient, button-pressing produced irritation but was continued. Why? The patient said it was because an elusive memory was "almost" recalled as he stimulated his brain. Thus, in both of Heath's patients, the highest frequency of repetitive behavior was associated with frustration or "seeking" for something which was desired, but which was never achieved.

It is in that connection that one is reminded of the technique employed by one religious-medical center in preparing its clients for LSD. It will be seen (Chapter VII) that CO_2 is given, and, according to our interpretation, anxiety created. The CO_2-induced anxiety creates a dependency bond between client and initiator, which facilitates "teaching" of the center's LSD point of view and enhances the motivation of the client to continue with the center and its LSD program. The induced anxiety dissipates over time; its residue is a very strong conviction and considerable ethnocentrism among center clients, but little repetitive use of LSD. On the other hand, where anxiety is previously present and felt as a function of personality conflict or life stress and where LSD use only partly eliminates that distress, there will be repetitive use of the drug.

What is implicit in that hypothesis is that, when partial or temporary gratification (feelings of pleasure, maturity, richness, and so on) is obtained through LSD but when anxiety itself is not eliminated, then this combination of anxiety and delight will impel the individual to repeated drug use. When other gratifications or beneficial changes occur and anxiety is reduced by one or a series of LSD experiences, then the individual no longer hurries to take the drug, even if other areas of function are still seen as distressing. One can further speculate that the interaction of long-term and immediate LSD responses is important. If the initial LSD experience is at least partly unpleasant, but that experience leads to anxiety reduction, there would be reasons of aversion as well as reasons of reduced need to account for nonrepetition. On the other hand, when there is no unpleasant experience during LSD, when it leads to very considerable inner satisfactions, but when anxiety has not been entirely eliminated, then for reasons of both pain elimination and positive gratification, LSD repetition might be sought.[9]

On objective changes, albeit self-reported, regarding work, marriage, and sex, one finds no difference of any consequence between the regular and discontinuing samples. Most have not changed jobs, and most have not changed marital status. Somewhat more of the continuers report improvements in sexual relations (46 per cent as opposed to 34 per cent), but the actual number is small. One surmises that the somewhat better sex life may be correlated to reduced tension and to greater "lovingness," taken quite literally.

When one considers the emphasis on enriched inner-life experience reported by the regular users and the more general reduction of interest in the hectic material world and contrasts these statements with actual reports of job change, two points are raised. One is that the real job changes are considerably fewer than what one would be led to expect by persons really converted to contemplative mysticism through a drug experience and association with other like-minded souls. That raises the question of the extent to which the orientation of the contemplative mystic has been taught but the way of his life has not been realized. Recalling the emphasis of at least some of the LSD users on Zen, Tibetan Buddhism, the reading of Eastern works and those of Huxley, Heard, Watts, and others, might not one expect more real shifts from intellectual to contemplative pursuits? Obviously, some of these individuals must be living in two worlds at once, religiously or philosophically speaking. But to which one is their long-term commitment, after all? Perhaps the teaching of the mystical experience before, during, and after LSD, as evidenced in the adoption by the intellectuals of the mystical language and their self-descriptions, has made only a superficial impression. Perhaps they have learned the words but remain committed in action to dollar bills, professorships, and one-man shows.

Or a conflict may exist between two genuine interests—an inner contemplativeness or artistic concern and an outer sensitivity to the demands of the world. One regular LSD-using respondent expressed it by saying,

> I have more real feeling now . . . but I can't spend too much time in the other [inner] world; I can't be led out of town by the Pied Piper. I've got a degree to finish—I might just say "screw it." What I really dig is art and music and poetry. But every time I have to study for exams I quit taking drugs almost entirely. I see the dirty job of getting through school as incompatible with the view of life that comes through taking drugs. That view, well, more ecstasy in life, is open, spontaneously creative, sensual. . . . Ordinary people become like gods and goddesses. But there's a barrier. You can't forget that drugs are illegal. You never stop worrying. And if you dare relax, then you aren't cautious . . . and taking drugs takes time. . . . But my work takes time too.

Another discrepancy appears when one compares the individual's descriptions of unchanged work habits (as opposed to changed work interests) with the rater's evaluation (based on direct observation and information gained from others who know the person) of work ability. For example, none of the regular users report any job changes for the worse in the period since they have taken LSD. Nevertheless, what they say and what others see is not always the same. One, for example, had been working before but is now hospitalized in a psychiatric center. A second whose work requires very aggressive interpersonal contact says he is relaxed now and no longer a "go-getter." A third person, whose employer was interviewed, said he was "shocked at how sick X seems to be these days"; X's "sickness" was the reaction to frequent mind-altering drug use in which memory loss and decreased attention are observed.

In the sample being compared here, six persons are rated as having shown signs of reduced job efficiency. Of these whom we describe as suffering some incapacitation for work, the three above are in the regular group; three others are in the discontinuer group; the proportions are 23 per cent affected in the former and 5 per cent in the latter. One cannot be sure that all these persons with reduced work effectiveness have become that way since taking LSD, although our information strongly suggests that this is the case with the regular users. One cannot affirm that it is LSD alone which accounts for the reduction in work effectiveness, for these individuals are taking a variety of other drugs along with LSD, and one of these other drugs, or more likely all of them in combination, might very well account for the effects observed. It is also necessary to keep in mind that there may be an underlying psychological factor or disability which both interferes with work and predisposes one to multi-drug use, as well as the more apparent hypothesis that, at least for a few persons, continued drug use predisposes the user to work difficulties and/or psychological deficit (in memory, attention, judgment, energy, or the like).

OTHER RATINGS

On the ego-control scale, half of the discontinuers are rated as overcontrollers, one-third as adequate controllers, the remainder (17 per cent) as undercontrollers. The regular users are the reverse; only 17 per cent are overcontrollers, 41 per cent are adequate controllers, and 41 per cent rated as undercontrollers. If the ratings are accurate, then the persons who stop using LSD are a group quite capable of withstanding frustration, of delaying gratification, and of rigidly—or adequately—controlling themselves. Although the majority of LSD regulars are also capable of postponing and planning, an important minority, very nearly half, are impulsive, find it very difficult to withstand frustration, and do not easily put off their pleasures. A characteristic such as this would account for why at least some of the regular users have returned to the employment of LSD, whereas many of their colleagues, apparently equally interested in taking the drug again, have not been in such a hurry to repeat it. Undercontrol is most certainly consistent with the frequent use of a gratifying substance or, in keeping with the theory of anxiety advanced, with the impulse to repeat a partially gratifying or otherwise incomplete experience—or a partially frustrating but at the same time satisfying one.[10]

On the trust-distrust continuum, there are also differences. The continuers are rated as being much more trusting of the acts and intents of others than the rater would deem reasonable. "Trusting" is considered in terms of naïveté, optimism, blandness, discounting of exploitative or aggressive intents in others, acting in such a way as to expose oneself to danger by relying on the protection of good will of strangers, and so forth. Thirty-eight per cent of the continuers were rated as overly trusting, as contrasted with only 9 per cent of the discontinuers so rated. At the other end of the scale, 23 per cent of the continuers were rated as overly suspicious, as contrasted with 43 per cent of the discontinuers. These differences may very well reflect one of the consequences of the reduced competitiveness and tension and increased relaxation and occupation with inner experience which LSD users have described in themselves. It may also account, in part, for the greater liking expressed by the interviewer for the continuers in proportion to the discontinuers. Interviewers rated themselves as liking 62 per cent of the continuers, as opposed to 45 per cent of the discontinuers; they rated themselves as disliking 15 per cent of both groups. In several cases, the interviewers spoke of feeling "protective" or "nurturant" toward the overly trusting LSD continuer.

The behavior which raters regard as overly trusting and self-endangering to the LSD user may also reflect "lovingness." Recall that continuers more often report they are still anxious but are also more loving. What a rater calls overly trusting may be what the continuer feels to be "loving"; certainly trust is implicit in love and, as we have seen, does evoke counteraffection in the interviewers themselves. But recall too that the LSD regular, in spite of his feelings of warmth and spontaneity, still is troubled with anxiety. Perhaps his overly trusting attitude or generalized lovingness does not occur without awareness that it might place him in jeopardy from those who are still living in a more competitive jungle world. Or perhaps the lovingness and overtrustfulness are also a way of dealing with anxiety, mostly by suppressing it in favor of hope and optimism, a technique which has the flavor of Pollyanna or hysteria about it. A related possibility occurred to a psychiatric observer, one who himself had taken LSD. It was his suggestion that LSD reduced the signals which provoke one to being anxious—that it produces rose-colored glasses which can lead the wearer to overestimate his own safety or misread the interpersonal omens about him so that he sees favorable signs where none are.[11] If that were the case, the trust of the LSD regular would be a response to the drug which inhibited ordinary distance, control, anxiety, and distrust and allowed the release of spontaneous, affectionate feelings and human warmth, presumably feelings to be drawn from the storehouse of idealism or kindness within the person.[12]

On the ratings for gross personality disorder, five among the thirteen regular users (38 per cent) are judged to have moderate or serious disturbance; among the discontinuers, only 2 per cent are so judged. If one supplements the discontinuer sample with the black-market and clinic-patient groups, one finds only 16 per cent so rated. It is to be kept in mind that these ratings may be unreliable and contaminated.

PHARMACOLOGICAL RESPONSE: HABITUATION

It has been shown that there is a wide variety of individual response to LSD depending upon personality, expectations, setting, affiliations, dosage, and so on. There certainly is no inevitable response to LSD which follows one course. There certainly is no guarantee that the initiate will have a pharmacological experience which, by itself, impels him to commit himself to the drug movement or to internally generate its values. It is a potent drug, the most potent known to man, and most people will have *some* response to it, a reponse which has a fairly predictable range of later interpretations and which, we assume, is not without considerable intensity, ambiguity, pleasure, or displeasure at the time it occurs.

Because so many people say they want to take the drug again and because some do repeat it, the question has been asked: "Is it habituating? As defined here, habituation includes three criteria: Over time, do people who take LSD tend to take it more often, to increase the dosage, and to report less effect if dosage and frequency are not increased? That is, do they show tolerance for the drug? Some laboratory studies answer this question in the negative.[13] What is worthy of mention here is that some continuing users do not, at least over the three years (modal) that most of the continuers in this sample have been taking LSD, report any increase in dosage or frequency. But over half do. The remainder say that the intervals are similarly spaced over time and the dosage is nearly constant. On the other hand, two-thirds of those reporting do indicate frequency and dosage have increased and that there is a form of tolerance; that is, the initial overwhelming effects of LSD are not usually repeated in later experiences. (Many repeat users find this change satisfying, indicating that with reduction of wild sensory changes more of the essence of the experience is enjoyed.) Another point to be kept in mind is that, although LSD dosage may not be increased, the use of other drugs can be expanded, so that the frequency and/or dosage of mind-altering drugs in general, but not LSD in particular, may be increased over time. Recall that half of the regular-user sample uses other drugs; if one includes the black-market group, the proportion rises to considerably more than half.

Although over half of the regular users are rated as increasing

LSD dosage and frequency, only one-seventh (14 per cent) of the discontinuer sample give information suggesting that their use of LSD followed an upward trend. What is interesting here is the apparent fact that an individual may increase his LSD dosage and frequency for some time and then discontinue the drug—in other words, that the standard signs of habituation can be detected in the history of persons who do not become identified as regular LSD users. It is also clear from the foregoing that not all regular users, as defined here, show the signs of habituation as conventionally defined.

EUPHORIC RESPONSE

Among the regular users, three-fourths described their LSD experiences in euphoric terms, or displayed such emotions in their discussion, or were described by others who had been with them during the experience in terms that led the rater to describe their response to the drug as having a euphoric component. Among the discontinuers, a little less than half (42 per cent) were rated as experiencing a euphoric component in their drug experience. The suggestion is that the experience of euphoria is associated with continuing drug use. Nevertheless, what raters see as euphoria can be called tranquillity or mystical joy by users. The evaluation certainly varies with the point of view. The ratings also imply that the pharmacological effect need not be euphoric in all persons.

BACKGROUND FACTORS

Access to LSD is by no means easy. It may well be that one of the reasons that some of the interested discontinuers are not in the regular-user group is that they cannot get the drug. Even medical professionals may have a difficult time obtaining LSD unless working on bona fide research projects, unless, of course, they have access to black-market supplies, either homemade or imported. If continuation is partly a matter of supply, one would expect mental-health and/or medical professionals to be the group with the greatest opportunity for obtaining the drug. Are there proportionately more such professionals among regular users than discontinuers? Among the thirteen regulars are three (23 per cent) mental-health and/or medical professionals; among the discontinuers, 18 per cent are professionals. The number is so small that the difference cannot be considered important. If, however, we were to revise it on the basis of the information gained just as the study ended (and as this was being written), suggesting that two more professionals who had been categorized as discontinuers were in fact regular users, one would then have a revised figure of 33 per cent among the regulars versus 16 per cent among the discontinuers.

Ten of the regulars are male, three female (77 per cent and 23 per cent); among the discontinuers, the proportion of males to females is 63 per cent to 37 per cent. The differences suggest the possibility that males may be more likely than females to become regular users.

The modal age range for both regulars and discontinuers is thirty-one to forty, but the proportion of younger persons is higher in the regular-user group. Three out of thirteen regulars (23 per cent) are thirty or under; only 9 per cent of the discontinuers are in that range. Again, the numbers are small. Nevertheless, one can keep in mind the possibility that younger persons are more likely to become regular LSD users. Were the informal black-market group members to be included, most of whom are under thirty, there would be a preponderance of youth among the continuing users compared to the discontinuers.

SUMMARY

Nearly three-fourths of all persons who have had LSD express an interest in taking it again. About half have had it at least twice, but only a minority can be characterized as regular users of the drug. The size of that minority varies depending upon the certainty required of the data; the range is from 14 per cent to 25 per cent. Regular use is most likely to occur among informal users—those with access to a supply, with no internal moral censors constraining them not to take it, no institutional role relationships to monitor their conduct, and the presence of a general interest in and widespread experience with a variety of mind-altering drugs.

Most regular users began their drug interests with LSD; at least half are now taking drugs other than LSD on a regular basis. In contrast, among those who have discontinued LSD use, less than one-fifth are regular users of some other mind-altering drug. But it is still apparent that discontinuing LSD use does not mean one abandons other drugs as well.

Most regulars have reordered their social lives in order to spend their time with fellow drug-users; most discontinuers have not done this. Furthermore, most LSD users, but not most discontinuers, are rated as ethnocentric, with drug values as the core of the "we-are-superior" viewpoint. All of the regulars are proselytizers as well; but not all are members of a self-identifying, socially distinct drug group. Conversely, some of the discontinuers who are not now using drugs are members of a genuine congregation of self-identifying drug-users. One may maintain membership in a genuine drug group without frequent drug use, providing one has signified an initial affirmation or conversion through a public drug-taking initiation and continues to espouse the point of view of the group.

With reference to drug effects, regulars less often report a bad initial reaction to LSD. They claim, compared to discontinuers, more beneficial effects from the drug, especially in self-satisfaction, self-direction, freedom from pressure and overcommitment to work and goals, and increased "lovingness." There is some evidence that regulars experience less relief from anxiety through LSD than do discontinuers.

Several regulars are rated as showing reduced capacity for work and, far more than discontinuers, as demonstrating ego undercontrol. They are also more likely to be rated as trusting and naive. More regulars than discontinuers have experienced euphoric responses to LSD.

More than half of the regulars do show signs of habituation, but quite clearly LSD does not necessarily lead to habituation. Some discontinuers have increased frequency and dosage but then stopped use of the drug.

There is some suggestion that medical and mental-health professionals, men, and younger persons are the most likely to become regular users of LSD.

NOTES

1. Just as the study ended, we learned that two others who had told us they were not continuing users nevertheless were. Both were informal professional sample members.
2. Keep in mind that "half" of thirteen is, in this case, only six people. (One of the respondents gave no information.) However, if one were to add to this group of LSD regulars taking other drugs the near-certain eight repeaters from the informal black-market sample and the two more informal professionals who we now believe lied to us, then the sample of regular drug users becomes an *N* of twenty-three. More than half of the regular user group so defined also use other drugs, in contrast to the minority of discontinuers so doing.
3. There are two kinds of drug language which are observed. One is associated with the younger, nonconforming, but nevertheless upward-mobile groups. Their jargon includes words from musical, beat, and criminal sources. Among our sample, these words implied association with marijuana users, although not necessarily so. These are the "pot heads" and "swingers" of our sample. The other kind of drug language is associated with the intellectual and generally conforming, socially arrived, persons. We limited "argot" to words associated with the former group. Illustrative terms, their meanings in parentheses, include: "high" (the euphoric condition produced by the drug), "turn on" (to be given or to take the drug), "contact high" (to have a sympathetic or vicarious

reaction by becoming high just by being in the presence of someone taking the drug), "cool" or "to cool it" (to be or do something in an approved, successful fashion), "joint" or "stick" (marijuana cigarette), "pot" or "grass" (marijuana), "lid" (a container of marijuana), "hung up" (to have a problem, be stymied), "come down" (to come to the end of the high). By way of illustration, the terms often used by the intellectual LSD user include "transcendental," "Zen," "oneness," "guru," and so on. Their language is clearly drawn from Eastern and Western mysticism.

4. One individual, for example, was closely associated with an LSD-user group. He spent his time with them, shared their views, demonstrated the "we" feeling, and so on, yet he had never taken LSD. He suffered from a severe chronic illness, and his physician had prohibited him, warning him of a risk of death, from taking LSD. Thus one may have the attributes of a drug regular without ever having had LSD or any other mind-altering drug.

5. E. Walker and R. W. Heyns, *An Anatomy for Conformity* (Englewood Cliffs, N.J.: Prentice-Hall, 1962).

6. Becker reports this phenomenon among novice marijuana users whereby ambiguous effects, or even unpleasant ones, are reinterpreted on behalf of the new smoker by experienced users who tell the novice that what is happening to him is pleasing. See H. Becker, *The Outsiders: Studies in the Sociology of Deviance* (New York: Free Press of Glencoe, 1963).

7. Experimental findings are relevant here. G. D. Klee ("Lysergic Acid Diethylamide [LSD-25] and Ego Functions," *Archives of General Psychiatry,* VIII [1963], 461–473) tested memory impairment during the LSD experience and found that "definite impairment of many aspects of memory was demonstrated. There is no doubt that memory is more severely impaired with higher doses of LSD, but subjects are difficult or impossible to test under larger doses." Klee also reports amnesia can surround the drug experience. In a personal communication, Leo Hollister reported that, in two separate studies in which a self-rating mood scale was used during the drug experience and a questionnaire following it, he found a curious discrepancy. Self-descriptions of the experience were uniformly unfavorable; people saw themselves as less friendly, less energetic, less clear-thinking, more aggressive, more jittery, and more depressed. Following the drug experience, the most frequently checked adjectives on the questionnaire were almost uniformly favorable; the experience was described as interesting, pleasurable, satisfying, and beneficial. The discrepancy, according to Hollister, suggests selective recall.

8. R. G. Heath, "Electrical Self-Stimulation of the Brain in Man," *American Journal of Psychiatry,* CXX (1963), 571–577.

9. It is interesting in this regard to note L. J. Meduna's remarks (*Carbon Dioxide Therapy: a Neurophysiological Treatment of Nervous Disorder* [Springfield, Ill.: Thomas Publishers, 1958]) about CO_2 anesthesia and his citation of Kluver's observation of mescal intoxication. Both describe a *presque vu* phenomenon, in which the subject speaks of an indescribable and fabulous experience which is almost but not quite apprehended, a vision promised, but which eludes. It may be that an incomplete sensation has prepotence in the brain, leading to attempts at resolution. This is exactly what Gestalt psychologists referred to when talking about the tendency to "completion," an illustration of which is found in the Zeigarnik effect. F. D. Sheffield (F. D. Sheffield, T. B. Roby, and R. A. Campbell, "Drive Reduction vs. Consummatory Behavior as Determinants of Reinforcement," *Journal of Comparative and*

Physiological Psychology, VII [1954], 349–354) has demonstrated how incomplete drives or drive states in animals are regnant and reinforcing.

10. There are two other possibilities: One is that continued drug use tends to reduce ego control; the other is that the rater-interviewers, suspecting that very consequence, biased the ratings in the direction of their expectations.

11. See D. P. Ausubel's theory (*Drug Addiction* [New York: Random House, 1958]) about euphoric responses to the opiates as being a function of a raised perceptual threshold for pain, the inhibition of anticipatory anxiety associated with pain, and the minimization of seriousness to the self with which pain sensations are regarded.

12. Lest there be an overstatement of one side of the case, it is necessary to note that the wives and friends of LSD continuers described the LSD regulars' behavior as, at times, irritable, pushy, difficult, unreasonable, thoughtless, cruel, or the like.

13. Sandoz Pharmaceuticals, *Annotated Bibliography Delsyd LSD-25 (d-lysergic acid diethylamide)* (Hanover, N.J.: 1958), addenda 1–5.

REJECTION AND ACCEPTANCE OF LSD: USERS AND CONTROLS COMPARED

[V]

Richard Blum, with Eva Blum
and Mary Lou Funkhouser

In reviewing the natural history of LSD use, one is impressed with the rapid expansion of the size of the group which has taken the drug. Many individuals seem to be ready to have that sort of drug experience and, afterward, some become enthusiastic proselytizers. But their efforts to persuade others to take the drug do not always succeed; there are many individuals who are unwilling to try LSD. One is immediately curious. In what ways do those who resist taking LSD differ from those who are willing to take it? It is possible that these differences, if they can be isolated as variables, might be found to play an important role in impeding or facilitating the diffusion of other mind-altering drugs, alcohol or marijuana, for example. In the meantime, if one can set forth the variables which influence the acceptance or rejection of LSD, one has added to the understanding of the natural history of its use.

We expected that resistance to LSD, defined as the refusal to take the drug when it was offered or a failure to pursue an opportunity to take the drug in circumstances where it was available, would depend upon four general sets of factors: the kind of information the person had about LSD effects in relationship to the kind of life experiences he was interested in having; the relationship of the potential receiver of LSD to the one offering it, including the evaluation of the latter by the former in terms of dominance, obligation, trustworthiness, and admiration; the life circumstances of the potential receiver in terms of general life satisfaction and distress; and the personality of the potential receiver, with special reference to ego control, flexibility, feelings of trust, and invulnerability.

Interviews, observations, questionnaires, and participant interaction are productive research tools but do not provide a rigid experimental test of hypotheses. However, the hypotheses advanced have been of a rather general nature, and we think the method of inquiry fits the questions. The data do support a finding of consistent differences between persons who accept and reject LSD. Furthermore, drug-accepting behavior does appear to vary in the predicted direction with the kind of information a person possesses, with his or her relationship to the potential initiator in terms of power and status, with the personality of the person with reference to anxiety, ego control, and trust-distrust, and with the life circumstances of the person. More than these, a variety of other differences emerged which should be of considerable interest.

Before reporting the findings, it is well to spend a moment on the control group employed. Its selection involved the same problems found in trying to obtain an LSD-using sample. We looked where we could to find people who had had the chance to take LSD and who had refused it. The best source of information was from LSD users themselves; they spoke of those who had rejected the drug. We inquired among persons already interviewed and among our acquaintances for leads to control subjects. In the end, we obtained a sample of forty-seven controls. We cannot contend that they are representative of all controls; we have no way of knowing how many people have had LSD offered to them, nor have we any way of knowing the characteristics of that population.

CHARACTERISTICS OF THE CONTROL GROUP

The distribution among the controls of the setting in which LSD was first offered approximates that of our LSD user sample, except for the absence of a group of persons who were offered LSD in psychiatric treatment. We are not sure whether such a group exists; we suspect that it would be very unusual for a bona fide psychiatric patient to refuse to follow the instruction of his therapist to take the drug. Although noncooperation in medical care is common, we suspect that noncooperation in psychiatric care would not tend to be expressed by a refusal to take a drug often claimed to be a short cut to treatment success.

Among the forty-seven controls, fourteen (30 per cent) had been offered LSD in an experimental setting (hospital, university, or the like), fourteen (30 per cent) had been offered it in the informal professional setting (at the hands of a mental-health professional in a home or other informal place outside of any institutional or patient-healer role relationship), fifteen (32 per cent) had been offered it in an informal black-market setting, that is, the potential initiator was a nonmedical person offering it in a social situation; and eight (19 per cent) were acquainted with a staff member or knew about the religious-medical center and were aware that they could purchase LSD there if they wished to do so.

Because there are no LSD-refusing patients in the control group, we shall exclude the LSD-using patients from the LSD-accepting group as we compare the two on various experiences and viewpoints. What this means is that a control group composed of forty-seven persons being offered LSD outside traditional medical care is to be contrasted with seventy-one persons being offered and taking LSD under much the same circumstances as those under which the controls refused.

Comparing the two groups on general background, we present the general characteristics in Table III.

The foregoing table shows that the majority of LSD accepters and controls are highly educated, white, Protestant, and Anglo-Saxon. The accepters are somewhat younger, religiously more active, more likely to be single, and more likely to be male. One cannot be sure whether these differences reflect sampling errors or are real reflections of membership characteristics.

It is our strong impression that the male-female differences are real, for, in every LSD-user setting, there were fewer women than men (and the women who were there were usually less enthusiastic about the drug than the men). The age difference between controls and accepters primarily reflects the heavy concentration of twenty-one- to thirty-year-olds in the experimental user group. Most of these experimentals have been offered and taken the drug within the past few years. In the control group the opportunities for experimental use of LSD took place comparatively more often in the past, between 1950 and 1959. In both cases one is led to the surmise that experimental subjects are most likely to be approached while still graduate students or while working as young professionals. As for the married-single differences, these probably reflect the younger age of the accepters. It

TABLE III
CONTROLS AND LSD ACCEPTERS COMPARED ON
BACKGROUND CHARACTERISTICS

	Controls (N = 47)	Accepters (N = 71)
Education		
High school diploma or less	11%	9%
Some college or bachelor's degree	29	36
Master's, law, or doctoral degree	60	55
Age		
21–30	15	31
31–40	51	43
41–50	28	17
51–60	6	7
61–over	0	1
Religious preference		
None	51*	35*
Protestant	38	43
Jewish	9	10
Catholic	1	6
Mystic-private-universal	0	6
Derivation of surname (in the case of wives, of husband's surname)		
Anglo-Saxon	75	61
Race		
White	100	100
Marital status		
Married	85	58
Divorced or separated	13	21
Single	2	1
Widowed	0	
Sex		64
Male	43	36
Female	57	19

* Most professed agnostics, atheists, and religious nonpractitioners in both samples came from Protestant backgrounds.

is well to note that several of the accepters now listed as divorced were married women at the time they took LSD.

INTRODUCTION TO LSD

Like LSD initiates, controls are most likely to report having been offered the drug by someone in their circle of friends and acquaintances. Husbands are less often mentioned by the control wives (*N* = 2) than by women accepters (*N* = 5 or possibly 6) as having proposed, offered, or recommended the drug to the wives. About the same number of husbands in both groups have had LSD—eight husbands of control women, seven husbands of accepter women. Among the married women in the accepter group ($N = 10$) one sees that five (50 per cent) were initiated by their husbands. Among controls, on the other hand, few were offered the drug by husbands. One infers that husbands play a prime role in introducing wives to LSD. If the husband asks the wife to take LSD, she is likely to do so; if he does not ask her to take LSD, there is less likelihood of her taking the drug, in spite of the fact that she will be exposed to a number of other persons who are taking it.

In both cases where the control wife refused to take LSD from her husband, a divorce followed. In both cases, the wife blamed the divorce on the husband's LSD interests. In one case among the accepters, the wife took the LSD as requested by the husband in an effort to effect reconciliation, but a divorce followed nevertheless. In another instance, a wife who took LSD but basically disapproved of it had a strongly negative reaction to her husband's interest in the drug and to his behavior under its influence.

Among the male controls there is no case in which the wife took LSD and then offered it to her husband. In the two cases of accepters in which the wife took LSD before the husband, there is one in which the wife introduced the husband to the drug.

Reviewing the role of spouses in LSD initiation, it is our conclusion that the husband is a "gatekeeper" for LSD. If he takes the drug and asks his wife to follow his lead, she is likely to join the ranks of the initiates. If he asks her to do so and she does not, there are likely to be marital strife and ultimate divorce. His insistence and her refusal may be symptomatic of general strife in the relationship, or it may be attributable directly to feelings about LSD itself.

Turning now to another hierarchical or power relationship which influences LSD acceptance, one finds in the control sample three persons (6 per cent) who have been offered LSD or advised or influenced to take it by some superior of theirs in an institutional role relationship (employer-worker, teacher-student, and so on). In the accepter sample, there are twelve persons (17 per cent) who took LSD under some urging or direction from an institutional superior. (Recall that these figures exclude all the patients, for no patients are included in this rejector-accepter comparison.) If one adds the medical patients to the foregoing comparison, one finds that 35 per cent of the accepters have been influenced to take LSD by someone in a superior institutional role relationship to them, whereas only 6 per cent of the rejectors had been influenced to take LSD by some institutional superior.

The conclusion is that an important factor in LSD diffusion is the power or the status of the initiator vis-à-vis the potential initiate. When a person in an institutionally responsible or superior role offers the drug to one with less status or power, whether the person be student, employee, wife, or patient, the chances are considerably greater that the drug will be accepted.

One very interesting exception to the rule of LSD diffusion from dominant to subordinate occurs when children using LSD initiate their parents and even aunts and uncles into use. It has already been indicated that proselytizing does extend down kinship lines; husband to wife, occasionally wife to husband, older brother to younger sister, and cousin to cousin. There are also cases in the sample where parents have initiated their children, but these have always been young children (pre-teen) and young parents (pre-forty). There is no case in which older parents have "turned on" older children; but there are several cases in which children in the twenty-one to thirty age bracket have "turned on" their parents. It is a very important conversion, and those doing it are enthusiastic about how "loving" the family has become. Sometimes there is a disappointing result. "Dad didn't get much out of it, although I was very proud of him for taking it." One wonders if, in a youth-oriented culture, the parents are trying to keep young with their children. Perhaps it is democratic or permissive child-rearing; one must not only approve, one must join in with the grown children in their important activities. Or perhaps the parents are apprehensive of the consequences of refusal or rejection, not wanting to expose the family to the ideological divisiveness which might follow.

PRIOR INFORMATION ABOUT THE DRUG

When one looks at the years in which LSD was offered, one finds twice as many opportunities for the controls in the years between 1950 and 1960 as for the accepters in those years. As noted previously, this reflects the greater youth of the experimental user sample, but it also suggests that more rejections occurred during a period when the LSD "atmosphere" was different—that is, before the drug movement was really under way and before it was widely heralded as a boon to mind and spirit. In the earlier days it was viewed as a psychotomimetic, which would be less attractive to those seeking personal benefit.

Is such an assumption borne out by the controls' comments? The most frequent things which controls said they had heard about LSD prior to its being offered was that it produced hallucinations, model psychoses, perceptual disturbances, or precipitated irreversible personality changes, including long-term psychotic reactions. Others spoke of unpleasant effects: confusion, loss of control, anxiety. In all, the expectations of an unpleasant LSD effect outweighed pleasant or neutral expectations by a ratio of 4:3. Contrast such expectations with those of LSD accepters, whose ratio of unpleasant-dangerous to pleasant-beneficial effects is quite the reverse: 1:4.5. It appears that the kind of information people have about LSD prior to being offered the drug does play a role in their decision. This apparent rationality is modified, however, by the fact that what people report now as having been their expectation in the past can hardly be guaranteed to be accurate. In the first place, there is the possibility of selective perception. Those wanting to take the drug for another reason can attend to the good reports; those wanting to avoid it can attend to the bad. Similarly, in retrospect, one's memories serve as justifications for past actions and present positions; the accepter group justifies what it has done by saying it had been told the drug was a good thing, the rejectors by saying they had known all along it was a bad drug.

MOTIVES AND LIFE CIRCUMSTANCES

In reviewing the comments of accepters, one will recall that general knowledge about or expectations of the drug had no one-to-one relationship to the reasons for taking it, that is, to the particular motives reported. It is the same with the controls. Although most of them say they knew the drug produced unpleasant or psychotic effects, only a fraction ($N = 5$, 10 per cent) said they rejected LSD because they feared these effects. The reasons most often offered for rejection were (a) lack of interest in change (41 per cent): "I'm not adventurous," "I accept life as it is," "I don't need a new experience," "I don't want to 'grow,' " " 'kicks' aren't for me"; (b) fear of loss of self-control (26 per cent); (c) a general set against drugs of any kind (15 per cent): "I just don't like to take drugs, not even aspirin"; (d) uncertainty about LSD dangers (15 per cent): "not enough is known about it yet," or "it might be dangerous"; (e) lack of time (13 per cent): "I'd rather do something else with my free time"; (f) lack of confidence in those who offer LSD (10 per cent): "I don't trust them," "they're amateurs." Other reasons for rejecting the drug include the advice of a physician or psychiatrist not to take it (8 per cent), knowledge of an unfavorable LSD reaction in a friend or relative (8 per cent), reluctance to try anything new (4 per cent), reluctance to have a private experience among strangers (4 per cent), fear of addiction (2 per cent), moral inhibitions (2 per cent), and so on.

Reviewing these statements, we find three major themes. For one large group, LSD is a very unusual kind of experience, which they do not want, primarily because life is seen as satisfying or because other familiar pleasures are preferred. For another group, there is fear of loss of control, either over themselves or over their environment; and finally, there are those who think in terms of unusual dangers—what the drug can do to harm them. Contrast the disinterest, distrust, and awareness of danger among controls with the motives of the users, predominantly stated to be a desire for self-change or new self-knowledge, the expression of curiosity or interest in the new, or the enhancement of aesthetic or sensual experience.

As one might expect, the controls report greater acceptance of life as it is, are readier to perceive danger in the environment, and are less "driven" by dissatisfaction to experiment with dramatic novelties. Comparing the life circumstances as reported by controls at the time of their first (rejected) LSD opportunity with life as described by LSD accepters at the time of their first acceptance, one finds that nearly three times as many (42 per cent versus 15 per cent) of the accepters describe their lives as miserable or unsatisfying at the time of the LSD offer. In contrast, 65 per cent ($N = 30$) of the controls as opposed to 42 per cent ($N = 25$) users report life as satisfactory, "normal," "settled," or the like. The same proportion in both groups, about one-sixth, report their lives to have been *very* satisfactory at the time of the LSD offer. This finding supports our initial surmise that life dissatisfaction would be associated with greater readiness to try a life- or at least mind-changing drug.

It is worthy of note that, although the reported sources of life satisfaction differ little for the two groups, among the users, five persons (9 per cent) find alcohol among life's grandest joys, whereas none of the controls mention alcohol as having been among their major sources of satisfaction. Because of these differences, one can consider an association between felt life distress and a general readiness to take mind-altering drugs, of which alcohol and LSD would be but two.

Both groups were asked what they remembered as the major sources of distress at the time LSD was made available to them. The controls emphasized external difficulties; the accepters internal ones. For example, the controls spoke about job uncertainties, work interruptions, or troublesome in-laws. The LSD accepters discussed problems which they felt to be their *own* fault, problems inside. Only 15 per cent of the controls described themselves as dissatisfied with themselves or suffering from internally generated distress. A few cited difficulties which may or may not have implied self-failure (lack of interest, lack of goal achievement, and so on). Thirty-six per cent of the accepters talked of intrapsychic problems, sometimes complaining of several different kinds of difficulties. Fourteen per cent complained of their own feelings and inadequacies in social relationships ("I'm lonely," "I'm oversensitive"), 14 per cent of symptomatic psychological problems (lack of spontaneity, anxiety), 11 per cent of feelings of inadequacy and dissatisfaction, 10 per cent of major psychological distress, and so on. Among the controls, the proportions reporting specific themes of internal distress are: symptomatic distress 6 per cent, self-dissatisfaction 6 per cent, and frustration 6 per cent. None reported major psychological disturbances or inadequacy in social relationships.

ORIENTATION

These differences are important. Not only do LSD accepters remember themselves as having been more often unhappy with life, but they see themselves as the major contributors to their own misery. That is consonant with the theme of the drug movement itself. The emphasis on internal freedom is to free oneself from one's own inner liabilities and limitations and to make one's life and self better by capitalizing on one's inner resources. As one man put it, "The big problems in life are inside your head; not outside. It's not society that needs changing, it's oneself. People will let you do all you want to, at least in the privacy of your home; it's to reach that point where you can have those inner experiences that matters."

In contrast, the controls appear to have been less miserable with life and with themselves. They see themselves as having gotten along better with themselves and with others. When something does go sour, it is not oneself that is to blame. What is implied is not only a difference in contentment, but in orientation. The LSD accepters are more self-preoccupied, self-punitive, and introverted.

One might also be tempted to suggest that the users are more psychologically oriented and perhaps more "insightful," assuming that one accepts the current doctrine that people brew most of their sufferings inside their own heads. Yet, if we examine the professional affiliations of the two groups, we find proportionately more mental-health professionals among the controls (22 per cent) than among the LSD accepters (17 per cent), and, if we examine the proportion who have sought psychotherapy in the past, one finds that, although 50 per cent of the LSD sample have been in therapy, so have 44 per cent of the controls. We take it then that being unhappy and attributing it to oneself is not simply a matter of psychological sophistication; rather, we must propose that the inward-focusing unhappiness of the LSD accepter reflects either unresolved psychological distress or, equally as likely, a philosophical or characterological turning inward.

EXPERIENCE WITH OTHER DRUGS

Some of the controls distrust drugs of any kind; more do not want the kind of changes mind-altering drugs bring. Must we conclude that the control group are pharmacological virgins? Almost, but not completely. Only six (15 per cent) of the forty-seven controls report the use of such drugs (excluding alcohol). Five persons (11 per cent) have had marijuana; two have used methedrine; one peyote; and one, previously refusing LSD, subsequently did try morning glory seeds (which contain LSD). It is clear that the rejection of LSD need not mean the rejection of all mind-altering drugs. However, the controls are drug free in contrast with the user group; 12 per cent of the former compared with a minimal 65 per cent of the latter have tried drugs other than LSD. In order of popularity among accepters (sometimes the choice depends upon the decision of an experimenter or center official rather than the choice of the individual), are mescaline (39 per cent), marijuana (30 per cent), psilocybin (25 per cent), peyote (24 per cent), and methedrine (24 per cent).

Only three of the controls (6 per cent) are currently drug users. They use marijuana with regularity (up to seven times a week), and one also uses peyote. Current or continuing users of drugs other than LSD among the LSD group members, in contrast, number nineteen (29 per cent of those responding to our inquiry), while eleven (20 per cent) are continuing to take LSD itself. If we combine the total number of persons in the LSD group who are regularly employing one or another mind-altering drug, we find there are at least twenty-two persons (33 per cent) of the accepter sample doing so.

There are differences between the two groups with reference to mind-altering drug use in general; are these differences reflected in expressed readiness to experiment with addictive drugs? Eight per cent of the controls indicate they would take heroin, for example, but they specify conditions of experimental control. Thirty per cent of the accepter group say they would be willing to try heroin, although 15 per cent specify an experimentally controlled, scientifically useful employment. There is then a greater readiness to try uncontrolled narcotics in the accepter group, but, we would stress, there appears to be no real interest in such substances in any sample member.

We conclude that a general set or readiness to take drugs distinguishes between LSD accepters and LSD rejectors. Only a minority of the controls have taken any mind-altering drugs; a majority of the users have taken several. Readiness does not imply regularity of use, but there is an association between the number of different drugs taken and the presence of a pattern of continuing use. In the controls, experimentation and regularity are minimal; there is only a fraction of continuing drug users, mostly using marijuana, whereas, in the LSD groups, at least one-third are continuing drug takers.

As we indicated, one control group member took morning glory seeds and will likely go on to take the real thing. His action reflects the existence, among the controls, of a few individuals who lose their initial reluctance to take LSD and do become users. Another person was interviewed as a potential control, but at the time of interview expressed an interest in taking LSD if he could find some that was inexpensive. We did not include him in the control group, for he had had marijuana and methedrine, and it was clear that he would soon be moving into the LSD-user group. He did so within a few months. A third person, a control wife, became an LSD taker under the influence of her husband just as the study ended. There were three other persons who were interviewed about whom no decision could be made as to which group they belonged in, and so they were excluded. Each had had either psilocybin or IT-290. One fell into the informal professional group, another into the informal black-market group, and a third was a private psychiatric patient. The two informal group members had wide drug experience (peyote, marijuana, methedrine, psilocybin, and the like), had had repeated doses of one or another hallucinogen, and were continuing users of marijuana. But they had never had LSD. Unlike control group members, they had never rejected LSD; rather no one had ever offered it to them. They were quite willing to take it if they could find it. In behavior and history, these three persons closely resembled the others in the LSD-accepter group (defined by circumstance of initial drug use).

We mention these excluded interviewees here to demonstrate that patterns of drug use are not specific for LSD, but rather that any of the hallucinogens may be used and that the natural history of that use is much the same as for LSD. The qualification is that LSD, as pharmacologically the most potent, is the preferred drug and the one about which most institutional ritual and meaning has developed; therefore, the values centering about LSD are signally important.

REPORTED CHANGES AFTER LSD

One of the outstanding features of LSD use is the frequency with which those who have tried it report that it has worked beneficial changes.[1] Are such changes limited to the LSD group, or do controls also claim to have experienced life improvements, even without LSD?

Let us first examine the adjective check-list items in which retrospective self-descriptions are offered for the time when LSD was first offered in comparison to the present time. Taking eleven items indicative of unhappiness and distress, there is no difference between the groups in the average reports of such distress at the time of the LSD offer. An average 40 per cent of controls and users describe themselves as unhappy or displeased. The difference is that, among the users, 67 per cent say they have improved since taking LSD, while among the controls an average 39 per cent improvement is reported. On seven adjective check-list items dealing primarily with dissatisfaction or satisfaction with activities and life direction, the two groups are about the same; an average 28 per cent users and 33 per cent controls indicate initial displeasure with activities. Again, but to a lesser extent, users report more improvement than controls; an average 59 per cent of the former and 51 per cent of the latter. On these reports, then, we find the two groups relatively evenly matched in descriptions of distress. Users see themselves and their lives as having improved since taking LSD more than do controls over a comparable time period.[2] In terms of kinds of changes, controls see greater improvement in life activities and goals than in personal feelings and behavior; users report the same (greater) improvement for both inner and outer conditions.

What about the other side of the coin? Surely all life changes are not for the good; what do the interviewees have to say about things that are getting worse? In all, the report of things getting better outweighs reports of things getting worse by a very considerable margin for both users and controls. The most frequently cited declines are also much the same for the two groups; the difference is that the controls more consistently report the bad along with the good. One-fourth say that, unlike the time when LSD was offered them, they now have too much to do and that things are no longer under control. Twelve per cent are displeased with their achievements in life, and 13 per cent say they are now depressed, whereas in the past they were not. Among the users no more than 10 per cent ever report any decline or worsening. Nine per cent say they now have too much to do; 7 per cent say things are not under control, and 9 per cent say they are now depressed, whereas pre-LSD they were not. We are not sure whether "drifting along" is pleasure or pain; we suspect that it is not seen as a decline; in any event, 10 per cent of the users say that pre-LSD they were striving and pursuing, but are now "drifting with the current."

Examining more general comments on changes since the initial LSD opportunity, one finds a consistent emphasis among the accepters on improvements in themselves (83 per cent) and social relations (28 per cent), which is greater than that claimed by controls (62 per cent for psychological changes, 17 per cent for social improvements). Similarly, the users more often say they have come to have increased aesthetic interests (16 per cent), greater religious concerns (20 per cent), and a better philosophy (19 per cent), compared with an average betterment in interests of only 3 per cent on the part of controls. In the matter of goals, a rather different picture emerges; nearly half (47 per cent) of the controls report they have clarified or set new life goals, whereas only 20 per cent of the users have set new, clearer, or more ambitious goals. More striking, 31 per cent of the users happily say they have lessened their ambition or become less goal oriented; none of the controls indicate they have become less striving or have abandoned (external) goals altogether.

Turning to reports of observable life change, one finds a few differences between the groups. One-fifth of the users and one-third of the controls report having changed their jobs—and more of the controls are pleased with the change than are users. Divorce rates have been the same (one out of every ten marriages), and one-third in each group say sex is better than ever. Weight gain is more often reported by controls (28 per cent as opposed to 11 per cent), while alcohol consumption is said to have been reduced more in users (22 per cent) than in controls (11 per cent). Six per cent of both groups say they drink more liquor now. Users more often say they sleep better or need less sleep (21 per cent as opposed to 13 per cent); and nearly half of the users say they have less muscle tension, compared to one-fourth of the controls so reporting.

Reviewing these three sets of self-reports, each subject to error and selective perception and reporting, one may conclude as follows:

(a) Users are much more likely than controls to describe themselves and their lives as having improved since the time they were first offered LSD. Users are consistently less likely to report any downward trends.

(b) Controls report greater improvements in external affairs than in internal ones; similarly, they are more likely to report dissatisfaction or strain in association with external events. In particular, they report increasing overwork or frustration over failures to achieve; such concerns trouble the users much less often.

(c) Users are more likely to report changes for the better in matters of aesthetics, religion, and philosophy. Almost no controls report changes in these interest areas.

(d) The two groups have a very different orientation to goals. Externally focused, the controls in many more instances have clarified, altered, substituted, or expanded their goals and ambitions. In contrast, one-third of the users report reduction in (external) goal-striving and the abandonment of high-level ambition. No control reports any turning away from striving, power, and other worldly goals.

(e) Assuming the accuracy of reports of objective changes, one finds more frequent and more satisfactory occupational change among the controls. They do not so often report reductions in muscle tension or the dramatic relaxation that users claim. Controls are more likely to report weight gain and are less likely to say they have cut down on alcohol intake (but keep in mind that some users, but no controls, originally placed tremendous importance on alcohol as a pleasure source). We assume that the activity-oriented controls care more about work and respond sensitively to the varied events in the external world. They do so at the cost of tension, overeating, and the use (although we have no evidence of overuse) of alcohol. LSD accepters, more inner focused, contemplative, or benign, are less likely to be caught up in work and goals, are removed from the fray, and report as one benefit considerable tension reduction. As long as they enjoy this distance and the effects of LSD, it seems that they are less likely to rely on overeating or alcohol for gratification.

(f) We suspect that the comparative failure of the LSD users to report personal defect, decline, or dissatisfaction smacks of overoptimism, if not of downright denial. On the basis of clinical observations on some of the "improved" LSD users, it is our impression that euphoria, denial, and selective amnesia must be entertained as variables affecting some overly positive self-descriptions.

The clinical observations which we report in (f) above would be better replaced by objective measures in some future study. There are, however, some indirect data which may be interpreted in either of two ways: either as supporting our own clinical position, which finds LSD-user self-descriptions to be unrealistic or as demonstrating how the author, as a nonuser, shares a similar observer bias with other nonusers when it comes to evaluating LSD effects.

The data are derived from the fact that many of the control group were acquainted with—or married to—persons who had taken LSD. Sixty-two per cent of the controls ($N = 29$) were well enough acquainted with accepters to venture descriptions of LSD effects. Before presenting what they observed, let us note what the LSD users themselves had to say about what they had seen among their acquaintances who had taken LSD. First of all we note that being critical or not perceptive of change may itself be a function of the circumstances of LSD use. Experimentals and informal professionals were more often skeptical of LSD effects. Religious-medical-center users and private psychiatric patients rarely were. Black-market users were never skeptical. Among persons who had taken LSD to oblige an experimenter friend or who did it to please an insistent husband but who sought no self-change nor any approval by a group of persons who were convinced of LSD benefits, we found no tendency to refrain from skepticism.

Out of forty-five LSD accepters commenting, six (13 per cent) said they knew of no real changes in personality, lives, or outlooks among users, several commenting further that users had illusions of change only. Another seven (15 per cent) described only bad effects, for example, "loss of sense of responsibility" or "group paranoia," while 9 per cent spoke only of neutral matters ("they change jobs"). In contrast to the skeptical one-fifth (several of the above codes were overlapping), 80 per cent of the users did see positive changes in other LSD takers.

The observation of LSD effects is quite the reverse among controls. Thirty-eight per cent said there were no real changes; some noted that users had illusions of change. Forty-nine per cent had observed primarily undesirable changes; for example: "He was inadequate before he took it, and more so afterward"; "he was happier at first, but then he became withdrawn"; "he became less productive."

The differences in perception of LSD effect are dramatic. Eighty per cent of the users say their acquaintances have changed for the better; 69 per cent of the controls say their acquaintances have changed either for the worse or not at all. The issue raised by these differences—which would become even more dramatic if one removes the marijuana users and the potential LSD takers from the control sample and excludes the one-shot experimentals and obliging wives from the user sample—is of great consequence. How can the intelligent and honest individuals who comprise both groups, many of them mental-health professionals or otherwise skilled observers, differ so greatly on their evaluations of LSD effects? It is not likely that the two groups have been watching singularly different samples; because of the nature of our down-the-chain sampling, many of them are acquainted with one another and are, in fact, describing the same individuals. Are people looking at different events? Perhaps, yet both conceptualize changes in the same terms; psychological adjustment, social relationships, and interest areas. Such categories used in common by no means rule out different orders of data and different referents for the abstractions; perhaps the users attend to the things they value (relaxation, religious experience, understanding, and the like), whereas controls look at matters of greatest importance to them (achievement, involvement, and activity). Is what is observed distorted by prior expectations, emotional feelings about drug use, a need to justify one's beliefs and position, or desire to convince the listener? Quite likely, but which group is distorting?

One suspects it is this awareness of how differently LSD users and controls do view the LSD experience that makes the debate over the qualifications of the investigator in hallucinogen studies a matter of such intensity. In Chapter II, that debate was noted—how users contend only investigators who have had LSD are qualified to study it and nonusers contend that only nonusers are free from bias. It is not an academic matter, for as one reviews the literature of psychological-psychiatric studies on LSD, one rather quickly detects which writers employ the drug and which writers have rejected it.[3] The problem of observer bias is not eliminated even when psychological tests are employed or when psychotic reactions are counted. We find ourselves, for example, very dubious about some of the "tests" which have been developed strictly for studying LSD effects; we even find ourselves in disagreement with colleagues in the simple matter of counting the frequency of psychotic reactions in the same sample of LSD-taking persons. Ultimately the research issue should be capable of resolution as controls and observations are refined; but we doubt whether the cultural and psychological issues involved in the selection of hypotheses, samples, and levels of data, in the intepretation of results, and in the general view of drug use will be capable of resolution through careful methodology alone.

VIEWS OF "THE OTHERS"

The opposition implicit in the views of the user and nonuser groups is further demonstrated by their descriptions of the characteristics of LSD rejectors and accepters. These descriptions also demonstrate the greater emotional intensity of users as they view the accepter-rejector dichotomy. In the first place, more controls than users decline to comment on differences between accepters and rejectors. Over half of the control group (56 per cent) either cannot or do not wish to describe differences between these two "types" of people or say there are no differences. Thirty-seven per cent of the users avoid comment, and none of those who do comment say there are no differences.

Of those users who do comment ($N = 45$), about one-third (29 per cent) describe LSD accepters in favorable terms ("freer," "tolerant," "emotionally responsive"), whereas 57 per cent use words which we term neutral (although there is likelihood they carry a favorable implication, for example, "searching," "looking for answers," "not willing to be adjusted to a life without understanding"). Only 11 per cent of the user group describe accepters in unfavorable terms—"less emotionally stable," "passive," and so on. Describing drug rejectors (the controls), users never utter flattering descriptions, whereas over half (56 per cent) use unfavorable phrases such as "rigid," "afraid," "defensive," and the like.

Like the users, the controls who discuss the differences ($N = 24$) most often describe accepters in favorable or neutral terms; 13 per cent are clearly approving, and 59 per cent use words which we term neutral but which may well imply approval, for example, "looking for more self-understanding," "less 'hung up,' " "less competitive," "less oriented to society's goals." Nearly one-third of the controls imply disapproval of the users, saying they are "insecure," "fanatic," and the like. Rejectors are never described in glowing terms; 17 per cent speak of them neutrally as "older" or "more settled," and 13 per cent are critical. "They're 'squares'—constricted and afraid."

In sum, one finds nearly all of the user group (86 per cent) describing LSD accepters with implicit approval or understanding, while the majority (72 per cent) of controls are also at least understanding and noncritical of LSD accepters. It is true that proportionately more controls than accepters are critical of users, but critics are a minority among both samples. The acceptance of difference by the controls is not returned by the users; more than half of the LSD sample indulge in ethnocentric judgments by disapproving of the "squares." Indeed, neither approval nor neutrality is expressed toward the LSD rejectors by any commenting member of the LSD sample; all who describe the nonusers are critical.

We conclude that LSD users are more conscious of difference between themselves and nonusers than are the controls. Further, the users are more likely to praise themselves and to be critical of nonusers. In the control group, the majority are approving of or neutral about users, and only a minority praise their own traits while downgrading those of the users. This consciousness of difference and increased emotional polarization of the social world by users into a good "we" and a bad "they" is, we suggest, evidence for in-group feeling on the part of LSD users, coupled with hostility toward outsiders. Whether that hostility originates in earlier life experiences and emerges, either cathartically or symptomatically, after taking LSD and joining the drug movement or whether it is in response to drug movement membership and subsequent awareness of rejection and disapproval of drug use by society cannot be said.

VIEWS OF SOCIETY AND THE POLICE

Whatever the understanding that the majority of controls express of those who use LSD, the controls join with the users in agreeing that the rest of society is hostile to the employment of psychedelics. Sixty-five per cent of the controls and 81 per cent of the users so state. It is not surprising that users more often report social prejudice against them than do controls. In any event, if we take the judgments of both these groups and couple them with the comments of the police and parole sample, we may take it that LSD users are objects of antagonism. We should not wonder that they respond with protective group formation and counterhostility. They would be in error, however, to believe all nonusers are "the enemy," for the majority of persons who make up the control sample are, as we have seen, not in the ranks of the accusers. It is likely that the in-group member who feels liable to persecution by any outsider does not take time to discriminate potential friend from potential foe any more than the quail waits patiently to learn if the approaching man is a hunter or friendly bird watcher.

The police symbolize, to many, the power of society to enforce its convictions, if not its prejudices. Do the users differ from the controls in their appraisal of the attitudes of the police toward various aspects of drug use? They do, but curiously enough the controls are more likely to characterize the police as unduly hostile, punitive, or intolerant vis-à-vis marijuana, for example, than are LSD users. Seventy-two per cent of the controls who venture an opinion ($N = 35$ out of 47) and 46 per cent of the responding users ($N = 59$ out of 71) take that position. Other differences are unremarkable; the users more often accuse the police of an ignorant failure to discriminate between classes of drugs (19 per cent versus 9 per cent in controls); about the same number in each group (one-sixth) agree that the police are just doing their job.

Less than half of either group venture to estimate the police officer's views toward LSD. The majority claim no knowledge and make no guesses. Of the minority who do estimate the police position, the most frequent guess is that the police are punitive, intolerant, and hostile. Not found in the control group is the belief voiced by six users that the police are not disapproving, but only wish to keep things under sensible control or ignorantly fail to discriminate among classes of drugs. Not found in the user group is the belief of three controls that law enforcement differentiates by offender class and that no LSD user who is shaved, white, and wearing a clean shirt will ever be arrested. Nor do we find among users the disapproval voiced by two controls who contend the police are exceedingly lax and that they should but do not know about the widespread use and effects of LSD.

It is also quite possible that the beliefs about police hostility represent the projection of moral disapproval of drug use which neither users nor controls can admit directly. Later, in Chapter XII, it is suggested that police officers may project their own revulsion over drug use on to the public. But here one finds a very tolerant, indeed sympathetic, public putting the hostility toward drugs on the shoulders of the police. If the police are more than a public conscience but are, in fact, a projection for private consciences as well, one can infer that the non-drug-using controls are, in fact, restrained from drug use because of moral strictures. As tolerant intellectuals and accepting mental-health professionals, they may find the direct sentiment of moral disapproval inadmissible; but that inadmissible private sentiment can be attributed to the police who are, after all, expected to be the guardians of morality.

With reference to opinions about present narcotics laws, there is practically no difference between the two groups. Over half of each sample strongly condemn the present punitive approach. About one-fourth think that controls are needed, but that revisions in the direction of treatment and humanism are required. About one-sixth say stricter controls should be instituted.

On the basis of the remarks about police attitudes and present laws, we must conclude that a majority of persons in both samples feel that present narcotics legislation is both unwise and inhumane and that police views of nonaddictive drugs are more punitive than rational. Furthermore, it is apparent that a negative estimation of police views is not limited to the user group but rather seems to be common among the educated, urbane individuals who make up both groups.

There is certainly little evidence of strong support for suppressive drug control among these people, regardless of their own use or nonuse of drugs. Indeed, the users are less likely to say they believe the police are extraordinarily punitive toward nonaddictive drug users than are controls. Why this is so is a good question. Perhaps users have more experience with the police and know them better. We think this is very unlikely, for most subjects claimed little knowledge of police officers or their work. Perhaps some users hesitated to voice the fears they had, perhaps thinking that LSD use could be made to appear more "respectable" (to use the words of one eminent LSD user) by contending

the police were not, in fact, opposed to its use. Perhaps the acknowledged professional affiliation of the writer—in a school of criminology
and as a police consultant—made some persons reluctant to speak
frankly.

In any event, the agreement between users and controls shows that
negative views of the police need not be a function of membership in a
drug-using group which feels itself surrounded by a hostile society.
On the contrary, the evaluations of drug-law enforcement and enforc-
ers appear to be dependent upon membershsip in the social and occupational strata from which both the user and control samples have been
drawn. The lack of sympathy for the present program of suppressive
drug legislation and for any hostile or suppressive approach to drug
control among these persons who, we believe, represent an intellectual
elite, poses several serious issues. It is clear that there is a chasm between these individuals, many of whom are well qualified to pass judgment on drug effects and means to control behavior, and the present
drug-control philosophy as they see it embodied in law. This means
that the law not only fails to have their support, but that they do not
feel optimistic about being involved in its improvements.

Another issue is raised by the frequency of a negative evaluation
of the attitudes and knowledge possessed by the police. Users and controls both fail to give the police the credit for knowledge and humanitarianism which many of them deserve. In this case the view of the
intellectual appears unconsidered. It would benefit by increased contact
with the police themselves. This latter end is frustrated by the sometimes mutual distrust, by different orientations to life and sometimes
to values, and by actual differences in social class and contact opportunities which restrict face-to-face interaction between intellectuals and
law-enforcement personnel.

The attitudes toward law and authority held in common by controls and users point to something which might otherwise be overlooked in a section which attends to the differences between drug
accepters and drug rejectors. In spite of the real differences in drug use,
work values, inner versus outward orientation, inferred in-group solidarity and out-group disdain, both samples are drawn from the same
stratum and are much more alike than different. Users and controls are
nearly all successful, socially integrated, well-educated, moral, law-
abiding, artistically and religiously concerned, psychologically oriented,
psychiatrically well (at least not severely disturbed) individuals. In
addition, the majority are white, Protestant, Anglo-Saxon Americans.
This is indeed a rare group of people, measured by normative standards.

COMPARATIVE RATINGS OF CONTROLS
AND ACCEPTERS

Controls and LSD accepters were rated on several variables. The ratings suffer from contamination, since the rater knew the status of the interviewee vis-à-vis LSD, from a failure to establish prior reliability among interviewers and from a failure to be tested for validity against some "hard" measure.

Ethnocentrism

The interviews led to the conclusion that at least some LSD accepters had formed an in-group which claimed spiritual or psychological superiority over outsiders. Proportionately more LSD users are rated as moderately or severely ethnocentric (45 per cent) than are controls (31 per cent); nevertheless, it is a minority of persons in both groups who are so rated. The conclusion must be that participation in the drug movement need not lead to consciousness of superiority to others; and although there is some evidence that LSD group membership can lead to increased ethnocentrism, the "we-they" attitude occurs among the controls as well.

Anxiety

LSD users contend that they are "easy" and relaxed and that the consequence of drug use has been a drastic reduction in tensions of various sorts. Controls, according to their own self-descriptions, had been less often relaxed to begin with (when LSD was first offered), and the passage of time has much less often brought them relief; indeed, we noted how, for some of them, external strains have increased. The ratings tend to support the self-descriptions of the LSD users. Evaluated on the basis of manifest anxiety (nervousness, restlessness, speech pressure, nail biting, and so on), the majority of both groups are rated as free of manifest anxiety. One-third (33 per cent) of the controls are judged overtly anxious; only one-fifth (22 per cent) of the users are so rated.

Fear of Loss of Self-Mastery

LSD accepters sometimes accuse the refusers of being frightened of "letting go." Controls themselves spoke of their distrust of drugs or, rarely, reluctance to undergo new experiences. At the beginning of the study we had wondered if a fear of loss of self-mastery, that is, loss of control, might not more often be found in controls. The rating, again subject to contamination by interview content and the rater's own expectation, supports such an hypothesis. Half (48 per cent) of the LSD accepters were judged to have no evident fear of loss of self-mastery, while only one-third (33 per cent) of the controls were so rated. It may be that more LSD users are, in fact, willing to "let go" than are controls. This difference in percentages, reflecting rather small numerical differences (twenty-three out of sixty-two users, seventeen out of forty-four controls) must not lead one to overlook the fact that at least half of the persons in both samples were determined to maintain conscious self-control.

That control-oriented disposition is reaffirmed in the rating of ego control. The two groups did not differ on the ratings for the adequacy of ego-control mechanisms. What is striking is that nearly half in both groups (44 per cent users; 48 per cent controls) were rated as overcontrollers.[4] About two-fifths in each group (37 per cent users; 39 per cent controls) were rated as adequate controllers; undercontrollers comprised 18 per cent of both samples.

What the ego-control ratings suggest is that many persons in both samples put a very considerable premium on self-control, planning and delay, impulse restriction, and general prudence and caution, sacrificing spontaneity and vitality in the process. Viewing the demands a competitive, future-oriented, Apollonian society makes, it is no surprise that so many persons who have adapted quite successfully to it and to its roles have done so by building up rather massive control and frustration-tolerance mechanisms. It is our surmise that overcontrol is a class-related phenomenon which is one of the risks of middle-class acculturation. It is not inevitable, as the presence of highly successful adequate controllers in both samples demonstrates. Nor does its presence forbid LSD use; one can understand the motives of overcontrollers who are longing for a return to spontaneity, inner vitality, or a carefree withdrawal from the demands of an overplanned life. What is interesting is that LSD use, even though it does appear to produce relaxation, inward turning, and some abandonment of the hectic world of ambition, does not produce any basic change in ego-control apparatus. Changes in feelings, interests, self-perception, and kinds of involvements do occur; but the psychic apparatus of the individual, built up over many years of exposure to the Protestant ethic, does not seem to be altered.[5]

What we judge to be overcontrol is not unrelated to the capacity for trust. Again on this variable we find no difference between the two samples, and again we find a rather high proportion, in this case about one-third (34 per cent users; 35 per cent controls), are more distrustful of others and of events than they need be. We had hypothesized that more users than controls would be overly trusting and naive. That hypothesis was based, in part, upon our prestudy observations of exploitation by some initiators of some LSD initiates. We had imagined that the willingness to be exploited, what the Russells[6] term the core of "idealism," must be reflected in what would superficially appear to be an overly trusting nature. While the trend was in the direction predicted—17 per cent overly trusting among LSD users versus 9 per cent among controls—the differences are hardly worthy of mention. What is striking is the frequency of distrust in a sample of an American elite—persons favored by background, health, intellectual endowment, and actual rewards and achievements. By distrust we meant a set to disbelieve anything or anybody, a fundamental doubt about the intentions of others vis-à-vis oneself regardless of the evidence at hand. It would be, in the Russells' terms, a correlate of cynicism.

One can appreciate the bitterness which must have been generated in these people, presumably as they have experienced exploitation and responded by adopting the ways of the aggressor or vowing eternal wariness. No wonder that such persons might wish to flee the jungle which they perceive themselves to be in, to abandon the strife-ridden external world, and to enjoy an experience, pharmacological and social, where they feel themselves more loving, closer to others, and safe within the confines of the LSD group. But again it is our inference that how they feel and what they are (or how they act) may be discrepant; in spite of their pleasure over the LSD response, as many of the users remain basically distrustful as do the controls.

Other Ratings

Other ratings were made for dependency, dominance, and gross psychological adjustment. We had expected the LSD users to be more dependent and less interpersonally dominant than controls. We also expected more gross disorder among the user sample. None of these expectations are supported by the rating results. Some maladaptive dependency was judged to exist in one-fifth of both groups; the remainder were judged as not maladaptively dependent. Dominance was the same in both groups; about half being judged as showing some interpersonal dominance and about half as not demonstrating any efforts to dominate, at least not in the situations where judgments were made. As for gross adjustment, the majority of persons in both samples were rated as free of any significant disorder. About one-third were described as showing mild disturbance; only a few (one-tenth) in each group were rated as moderately disturbed. One of these, an LSD user, was a former psychotic. He had been free of psychosis prior to taking LSD. Severe disturbance (psychosis) was judged to be present in only one person, an LSD user reported by his acquaintances to have been nonpsychotic before LSD.

These ratings, insofar as they are accurate, demonstrate no difference in gross psychological disorder between the users and controls. Only in the users do we find evidence, however, of a very recent or continuing psychosis. We do not have information on psychotic episodes in the past history of persons in either group. The lack of support for the hypothesis of dependency is important, since some observers of drug use contend that it is a form of dependency reaction. This possibility is not ruled out, but such dependency must be defined in something other than interpersonal terms. Similarly, it is well to emphasize in this context the relative absence of ego undercontrol in either group. Some theories stress the impulsivity of drug-taking persons. Again this may be true for the drug "regulars," but a specific impulsivity would have to be indicated.

Interviewer-Interviewee Interaction

Two ratings characterized the response of interviewer and interviewee. One rated the interviewee on his warmth toward the interviewer; the second required the interviewer to indicate whether he liked, disliked, or was neutral toward the interviewee. The majority of persons interviewed responded with warmth. Seventy-one per cent of those in the user sample and 79 per cent of those in the control sample were described as friendly. A few were ambivalent, and a few in each group cold and unfriendly. This rating excludes those persons who refused to be interviewed. Among those approached directly by one of the four persons on the interview team, no control refused to be interviewed. Among the LSD users, there were thirteen refusals, many of them personnel of the religious-medical center. We must conclude that the outright rejection of the inquisitive nonuser is more likely to happen at the hands of LSD-institution personnel than at the hands of other LSD accepters. We also conclude that the rejection of nonusers by LSD users occurs more often than does rejection of nonusers by controls.

What about the reaction of the interviewer to the interviewee? This, of course, is a personal matter, and the four interviewers differed

114   RICHARD BLUM, EVA BLUM, AND MARY LOU FUNKHOUSER

in their own interests, personalities, and orientations toward drug use. Two interviewers were male, and two were female; the age range spanned nearly two decades. No doubt, these factors influenced interviewer responses. Nevertheless, as we present the results, they are rather surprising. One half of the LSD accepters were personally liked by the interviewer; only one-quarter of the controls were liked. To one-third of the users, the interviewer responded neutrally; to three-fourths of the controls, the response was neutral. Interviewers personally disliked nine (16 per cent) of the users but only two (4 per cent) of the controls.

Obviously the users evoked more emotional response in us, both positive and negative, than did the controls. That occurred in spite of the fact that about three-fourths of both samples were rated as having responded warmly to us. That rating may have been, of course, merely conceit. Obviously, it was not the interviewer's judgment of the warmth of his reception which accounted for his response; other factors must have played a role. Perhaps these include the relaxation and "loving-ness" claimed by some users, viewed as a lack of competitiveness by controls. Perhaps their "striving for understanding," or earnest desire for "fulfillment" evokes a sympathetic response. Or perhaps the rating is sheer accident, based upon chance assignment of particular interviewers to one or another interviewee.

The values, the interest, and the behavior associated with a decision to take LSD, especially with the decision to use it for personal benefit, do evoke emotional responses in the observer, especially those who have rejected the use of LSD. The claims made for the effects of LSD also evoke intense reactions, whether these be based on hope, admiration, envy, or skepticism in the listener. The ideology of the drug movement and all of the cultural currents which it stirs cannot help but arouse the interest of the investigator-citizen. It is that stimulation which we think is reflected in the response of interviewers to the subjects of the study.

SUMMARY

Forty-seven persons who had the opportunity to take LSD but failed to take the drug were compared with seventy-one persons in the same circumstances who had taken it. LSD accepters were more often younger, religiously active, male, and single. The majority of persons in both groups were highly educated, white, Anglo-Saxon, married, and Protestant.

No patients were in the control group. All psychiatric patients, when instructed by their doctor to take LSD, did so. All medical or psychiatric patients instructed by their doctor not to take LSD followed that advice. Thus the nature of medical advice is a controlling factor for LSD use among persons in psychotherapy.

Husbands are also "gatekeepers" for LSD. If an LSD-taking husband asked his wife to take LSD, she did so. Among the control women who refused, divorce followed in each case. Institutional superiors are also powerful influences; when an employer or teacher influences a subordinate or student, it is likely the role inferior will acquiesce. LSD rejectors were less often subject to such influencing efforts by superiors.

The kind of information one has and the corresponding expectations about LSD depend upon the year in which it was offered and one's occupation and social contacts. Persons offered LSD before the drug movement got under way, during the period when LSD was primarily considered a psychotomimetic, more often rejected the drug. Ones influenced by the movement and believing the drug to be of personal, social, or artistic benefit were more likely to accept it. Those expecting unpleasant LSD results were much less likely to take the drug than those expecting pleasant results.

Persons who view LSD as posing a threat to desired self-control or as posing special physical or mental dangers did not take it, nor did persons who lacked interest in changing themselves through drugs or having a drug "adventure." Accepters were not concerned with dangers or loss of control, and often sought an uncertain adventure or self-change. Differences in distrust, curiosity, life and self-satisfaction, desire for change, and awareness of danger differentiate the groups.

Persons accepting the drug are more often dissatisfied with themselves and their lives than those rejecting it. A few accepters (not alcoholics) have already found their only life satisfaction in a drug, alcohol. No control was in that position. Accepters tended to be distressed with themselves; rejectors who had an equal number of sources of unhappiness perceived these to be outside themselves. The inside-outside orientation to what is important, to where troubles come from, and to where change must be made is an important one for drug use. The difference is consistent with the movement's emphasis on "internal freedom." There is no difference, however, either in mental-health occupations or in past psychotherapy experience between the two groups; the inside-outside orientation is not taken to be a function of psychological orientation.

The use of other mind-altering drugs is much more common

among accepters than rejectors; a few of the latter and the majority of the former have taken such substances as mescaline, marijuana, psilocybin, peyote, and methedrine. It is clear, however, that LSD rejectors can have taken other drugs and still not be interested in LSD. A very few LSD rejectors are regular users of one or another drug, in contrast to a minimum one-third of the accepters who are regular users of one or another mind-altering drug. Readiness to take addictive substances for a good reason and under control also is greater among the accepters than the rejectors. The dividing line between accepters and rejectors is, nevertheless, not rigid; during the course of the study, several controls became LSD users.

Although both accepters and rejectors see their lives as having improved over the years since the first LSD opportunity, the accepters report broader and greater changes for the good and fewer changes for the bad. Their emphasis is on self-change or goal reduction; rejectors more often emphasize outside changes and new goals and report changes for the worse as well as the better. Rejectors report more occupational changes for the better, weight gain, and comparatively less reduction in tension and alcohol use. Their orientation remains in and of the world; accepters are in, but less of the world, and enjoy the benefits of reduced striving, more attention to inner life, and, as interpreted here, some euphoria. Dramatic differences characterize the two groups on their appraisal of the long-term results of LSD use among their acquaintances. Rejectors describe the drug as producing undesirable changes or none at all; accepters observe that it is highly beneficial.

In setting up a typology of persons taking and persons rejecting LSD, the accepters take a strong view which is critical of rejectors. The accepters are more often neutral in their descriptions and are only sometimes critical of acceptance. Consciousness of difference taking an emotional and judgmental form is more characteristic of accepters than rejectors. Curiously, the controls are more critical of police attitudes toward illicit drug use than are users. A negative view of police attitudes and information is obviously more a function of general class-occupational factors than of drug use per se.

On ratings, the accepter group was more often characterized as ethnocentric, free from anxiety, and free from fear of loss of self-mastery. No important differences in ego control, trust, or gross personality disorder were observed. However, the only person in the sample with current psychosis was an LSD accepter.[7]

NOTES

1. C. Savage, Ethel Savage, J. Fadiman, and W. Harmon, "LSD: Therapeutic Effects of the Psychedelic Experience," *Psychological Reports,* XIV (1964), 111–120.
2. The time span for controls is slightly longer, since more of them had an early opportunity to take LSD during 1950–1959.
3. The reader is referred to the study of Ditman *et al.* (K. S. Ditman, M. Hayman, and J. R. B. Whittlesey, "Nature and Frequency of Claims Following LSD," *Journal of Nervous and Mental Diseases,* CXXXIV [1962], 346–352) which concludes, "Perhaps LSD is unique in that it prompts so many claims, not only from subjects and patients, but from investigators themselves."
4. Overcontrollers were defined as persons who delay gratification longer than necessary. Overly organized, when overcontrol is extreme, they are rigid, constricted, or emotionally impoverished. See Jack Block, "An Experimental Investigation of the Construct of Ego Control" (Ph.D. dissertation, Stanford University, 1950).
5. Jerome Oremland, "A Critical Review of LSD as a Psychotherapeutic Agent," paper presented before a symposium on LSD sponsored by the San Francisco Psychological Assn., 1963.
6. Claire Russell and W. M. S. Russell, *Human Behavior* (Boston: Little, Brown, 1961).
7. In view of the interest in estimating the risk of psychosis presented by taking LSD, it is well to present other information gathered during the course of the study. There were three groups of LSD accepters, each taking LSD under some institutional auspices (two were LSD institutions per se), where the approximate size of the total recipient population was known. The total number in these three groups was about three hundred. In the course of interviews with psychiatrists in the study samples and in the regions where the institutions were located, there were discussions of the number of cases seen by them and diagnosed as having a psychotic reaction to LSD. This "case-finding" method would miss cases but would not overreport. There were a total of six cases of diagnosed psychotic responses to LSD, all of them hospitalized for short or long periods, reported by psychiatrists. The rate per thousand would then be twenty to one thousand, which may be taken as the minimum risk for anticipating LSD reactions. If one accepts the diagnosis (in this instance, unreliable diagnoses, for there *is* disagreement) by clinical psychologists of psychotic reactions and does not require hospitalization as part of the definition of a case, then, using the same population of three hundred, a total of ten cases of post-LSD psychosis are identified —a rate of thirty-three to one thousand. On the basis of cases known to us, it is our impression that the mere presence of prior personality pathology does not predict LSD psychoses.

PSYCHOPHARMACOLOGICAL CONSIDERATIONS

[VI]

Keith Killam

We are living in an age of chemotherapy of behavioral disorders. Once familiarity with the psychotropic drugs is gained, the next step is to find uses for the drugs beyond the limitation of use in an institution. Can these drugs be used for prophylaxis of mental disease? Who is to make the decision to extend the most advanced and experimental therapeutic measures into widespread use in the community? Further, are the criteria for early warning signs of psychological problems well enough defined to be worth the risk of robbing the individual of freedom by means of medicinal subjugation? Another aspect to be considered is that we live in a time of social and intellectual revolution when very powerful drugs that can affect behavior are available. There are already intellectual habitual drug users who prophesy that drugs will play a role in enhancing performance, making realistic social changes, and shaping the intellectual man of the future. It is with this background and an awareness of my social responsibilities as a scientist who has helped give impetus to the search for drugs that will alter behavior that I welcome the opportunity to comment on Dr. Blum's study of the epidemiology of LSD use.

SIMILARITIES BETWEEN NARCOTIC AND LSD ABUSE

The most striking impact Dr. Blum's report had on me was the similarity between LSD and opiate abuse. Unquestionably a subject can discriminate between heroin and LSD, but the social mores, special languages, methods of proselytizing, and psychological dependence are so strikingly similar that it causes one to speculate concerning any real differences. There are certainly wide social and educational differences between the heroin addict and the habitual LSD user. Today the former is uneducated, a member of a minority ethnic group, from economically inferior urban neighborhoods, and, because of the poor quality of heroin available, not physically dependent upon the drug. The habitual LSD user has a college education or better, has had every opportunity of freedom from ethnic impediments, and is from modern suburbia. He, too, is not physically dependent upon the drug.

Could it be that there are underlying sociopsychological factors predisposing one to seek facile relief from social pressures that are common but manifested differently according to the social stratum of the individual? Although it is difficult to translate the pressures from one culture to another even in the same society, the common surrogates are obvious. These are even manifest in the choice of rotational drugs—the amphetamines and marijuana—to tide the subject over between exposures. Curiously, both groups fail to recognize that they have surrendered part of their intellectual freedom to the purveyors of drugs. In both cases, the latter are not bound by social amenities and can be potentially as unscrupulous as their own social desires dictate. The most alarming aspect of the LSD movement is that it involves individuals considered to represent the intellectual potential of society.

IMMEDIATE AND LONG-LASTING EFFECTS OF LSD

One of the most striking characteristics of subjects under the effects of LSD is the suggestibility that can be imposed by the environment, including the therapists or associates. Single phrases or trivial changes in the surroundings can produce exaggerated shifts in mood. The direction of such mood changes cannot be predicted even with intensive psychiatric evaluations beforehand. Subjects appear to be easily distracted, as though the ability to order one's environment for the purpose of focusing thought or attention had been surrendered to the chance sequencing of environmental stimuli. In certain circumstances which may or may not be contrived by the therapist, subjects will act either in an antisocial manner or with deportment completely out of character. These observations are corroborated by the findings in Dr. Blum's report.

There are claims that LSD-25 therapy is beneficial either in specific psychiatric disorders or as a routine experience in intellectual maturation. To date there is no compelling evidence which supports these claims. Although there are subjects who have been helped or who have withstood the perceptual distortions induced by the drug, there are many who, as judged by their peers, have had personality changes which alter their performance in society. Curiously enough, in contrast to the opinion of competent observers, the most uniform statement of LSD users is, however, that after the drug experience they are better in every way. It can be argued that these individuals were out of place at the outset. However, the population involved is one in which a good deal of administrative and intellectual responsibility resides. In the absence of secondary cues indicating drug use—for example, an alcoholic is easily recognized by the public at large—irreparable damage may be done to society when performance altered by an LSD experience is not recognized.

IMPLICATIONS FOR CLINICAL PHARMACOLOGY

One of the most astonishing findings in Dr. Blum's report is the high rate of repetition of LSD use among professional medical personnel and observers. In the field of clinical pharmacology, it has long been recognized that volunteers for drug experiments are, as a group, psychologically unstable. However, medical personnel taking part in such experiments were considered to be objective and motivated by scientific understanding rather than hedonism. Further, clinical pharmacologists, who routinely test drugs on themselves before initiating more definitive studies, develop a cavalier attitude regarding the risk of toxicity. In the case of LSD the somatic toxicity—liver damage—is minimal. Any thoughts about psychological toxicity are distorted by man's egotistic view that he himself is able to withstand any and all onslaughts on his mind. His curiosity is thus reinforced rather than tempered by his judgment. In the case of psychological coercion without drugs, I need only to mention the power of propaganda. Let us consider an example. Methadone is an opioid exclusively abused by physicians and medical personnel. It has relatively little toxicity and has been purported to be nonaddictive. To their own detriment, many physicians have found otherwise too late.

It seems strange to me that the competent clinical investigator, who carefully constructs population-drug sensitivity curves and who considers 1–2 per cent somatic toxicity to be unacceptable, should fail to apply these standards to psychologically active drugs. Instead, he dismisses such population sensitivity levels as a matter of predisposition; he would never accept liver damage on such grounds.

Psychological dependency upon LSD, although not unequivocally demonstrated, is a distinct occupational hazard for the medical profession. Further, the fostering of a sense of indestructibility through legitimate drug experimentation can be regarded as a predisposing factor which may lead to dependence on LSD or any mind-altering drug.

COMMENTS ON THE POPULATION SEEKING LSD

Perusing Dr. Blum's elaboration of occupational categories involved in LSD use, one is struck by the emergence of the specter of the organization man or of the "golden age syndrome." Could this, coupled with the generalized lack of respect for the possible toxicity of drugs, be a major predisposing factor in our society toward the abuse of pharmacological agents? Although the concept is not original, the concentration of LSD abuse in the intellectual stratum of society focuses concern on these aspects of society's structure. Picture the bright, creative engineer at the age of forty who has done so well for his organization that he is now a group leader. He must now praise the bright young men rather than be praised. His staff and peers treat him with respect, not awe. His physical attractiveness, either frank or vicarious, has lost the edge in a society where physical attractiveness is actively sought. He implements rather than creates major achievements. Yet, in the society of which he is a product, he is a most valuable commodity, an experienced and creative individual. Unfortunately, society does not provide the support for further maturation or transition to the position of creative administration. He must seek his own compromises and substitutions in a position in which, if anything, the competition gets tougher as the pyramid is ascended and the rules of past operation are no longer valid. In addition, in his younger years part of his success could be attributed to absolute devotion to the achievement of his creative goals to the exclusion of all other intellectual development. It seems unnecessary to recount the suicide rate, incidence of alcoholism, and so on which characterize forms of solutions for this state. Is it possible that drug abuse, specifically LSD abuse, will now be added to the list of solutions? Certainly this is an area where research and data are desperately needed.

PHENOMENOLOGY AND SOCIAL CONSEQUENCES

There are at this time a host of drugs which will cause perceptual distortions. Further, there are a number of conditions—for example, sensory deprivation—under which perceptual distortions or hallucinations can be induced. In all cases the effects can be modified and even counteracted by active suppression on the part of the subject. Thus, for the full effects to develop, there must be cooperation by the subject. Predisposition or preconceptions can, therefore, be a major factor in an individual experience and/or in subsequent experiences. Tolerance for the effects can develop, and cross-tolerance—for example, from LSD to peyote—has been demonstrated. This implicates a common mechanism of action. Further, the most receptive psychological substratum is the prepared subject. It can be seen, then, how difficult is the problem of evaluating any therapeutic or beneficial value to the subject.

The social dangers of overtranquilization have often been elaborated. The nation with its creative aggression blunted surrenders itself to an oligarchy who controls the mechanism of tranquilization. Those who advocate LSD use claim more insight into their own problems and to those of others. They equate this with increased tolerance and judgment. These are admirable aspirations, but the evidence for LSD as a solution is not in hand. Further, LSD users are ethnocentric and respond to objective criticism by ignoring criticism and by active proselytizing. In their proselytizing they use the provocative and searching writings of the late Aldous Huxley. However, as is the case where propaganda overrules active intellectual persuasion, the advocates of LSD omit objective appraisals. Huxley provided such an appraisal in *Brave New World Revisited*.[1]

In summary, LSD is a very powerful drug whose properties and propensities for therapy or for social dissolution have yet to be substantiated. As a parallel example, the practice of medicine without benefit of use of morphine would be severely handicapped, although the social use of morphine has no place in a free society. However, the difficulties attendant on ascertaining the benefits and liabilities of LSD pose the most challenging problems in medicine today. Every effort should be made to put the use of this drug into its proper perspective. It is my opinion that this is most efficiently done in a university medical center or its affiliates, where objective yet imaginative evaluations of the drug can be undertaken. Further, the information and methodologies employed can be used to evaluate future agents which affect the mind.

NOTE

1. "Chemical Persuasion," *Brave New World Revisited* (New York: Harper & Bros., 1958).

THE INSTITUTIONALIZATION OF LSD
[VII]

Richard Blum, with Eva Blum
and Mary Lou Funkhouser

During the course of our study, we observed the institutionalization of the use of LSD. By this we mean the development of organizations dedicated to giving the drug and having no institutional purposes
apart from the drug or the goals which the drug is believed to achieve.
One must discriminate between these special LSD institutions and ordinary organizations which may, in the course of varied activities, give
LSD. Among the former are several centers and establishments to be
discussed in this and the following chapter. Among the latter are ordinary university laboratories or hospitals in which LSD studies may be
conducted.

There were four institutions structured about LSD use which came
to our attention and some of whose personnel one of us was able to
meet. One institution was the Mexican LSD community at Zihuatanejo.
Chapter VIII provides a description of its values and operations. Another establishment was a church recently set up in a major metropolitan area, the third was a center for the medically supervised
administration of LSD, and the fourth was a mountain retreat centered
about creative-expressive interests.

In considering the purposes for which LSD is institutionalized, we find three major themes as to what it is believed LSD will do. One theme states that LSD will lead to psychological growth, unfolding, or expanded being. Sometimes, but not necessarily, it is also said to lead, through insight and understanding, to the resolution of psychological problems. The psychological benefits attributed to LSD are said to accrue to mentally healthy persons as well as to mentally distressed ones. The second theme which becomes an institutional purpose is that LSD leads to religious experiences. Its use is recommended to bring man closer to God or the universe, to help him sense his powers in relationship to greater powers, to give him visions of oneness, or to enable him to have a religious feeling and a sense of spiritual well-being. Sometimes it is said that during LSD one dies, so that death is mastered and thereby understood. The third theme is that LSD facilitates art. It is believed to expand one's capacities to appreciate beauty and to understand the significance of works of art and of aesthetics in nature. The visions it brings are also beautiful in themselves and innately admirable. LSD releases creative potentials which enable a person to be an artist, free of the inhibitions or failures in sensitivity which had prevented the release of creative capacities presumed to be innate in everyone.

No institution which is devoted to LSD use and the bringing together of people who have values associated with that use limits itself to just one of these three themes. Nevertheless, each institution emphasizes one theme, and the primary interests of its members are grouped about it. The Mexican community stressed psychological development and expanded being; it had less interest in religion and aesthetics. The urban church centered on the religious experience and had only secondary interests, as expressed in its formal position, in psychology and aesthetics. The center which we describe, like the Mexican community, emphasized the psychological benefits of LSD; although, as one interviewed participants, it was quite clear that religious values were also important and that, for some of the officials at least, they superseded any psychological interests. The mountain retreat had a history of interest in the thoughtful, expressive, and creative. Those of its personnel who were interested in LSD stressed the aesthetic, but not without awareness of the other presumed potentials.

The Mexican community, urban church, and medically supervised center were established within the past few years by people who had been using LSD and who, in company with other LSD users, banded together to formalize and promote their association and drug interests. The mountain retreat was different in that it had been established before LSD use had been widely known. It was only after a number of its guests and participants had taken LSD in other settings that the retreat began to shift its orientation toward the drug. That shift is by no means complete, for the retreat is torn by factionalism. One group, the old guard, rejects LSD use and adheres to the traditional values and actions of the retreat; the other group, which is now physically as well as ideologically separated, has adopted LSD.

In the case of the mountain retreat, one finds not only an illustration of conflict arising with the introduction of LSD—a rather general phenomenon—but also an illustration of how some people with artistic, ecstatic, and self-altering interests are predisposed to LSD experimentation. This experimentation, following exposure to information about the effects of LSD, spread rapidly through the group, the LSD being received from informal professionals who were prior acquaintances.

It is necessary to stress that there can be varied individual motives and interests which underlie the activities of those who are instrumental in establishing LSD institutions. We have observed motives as diverse as altruism, professional service, religious dedication, finding oneself through participating in an accepting group, enhancement of a sense of personal purpose and importance through undertaking missionary work compatible with cultural values, acting out of neurotic conflicts or restructuring of painful psychic problems through conversion to a religious system and thereafter proselytizing, economic exploitation by means of the sale of drugs and one's own services in giving the drugs, passive and parasitic attachment to a group which provides ego support and income in return for loyalty and dependency, psychopathic exploitation by giving LSD to the initiate for the gratification of essentially paranoid delusions centering about power and homosexual seduction, and male exploitation of females through giving LSD and establishing a continuing dependency which provides sexual and power gratifications to the initiator.

It is unlikely that the motives underlying individual efforts to build an LSD-giving and -taking institution differ from those which lead to the establishment of some other structures in our society. Nor is it surprising to find persons whose motives are quite different joining together to form such establishments. What can happen in the intermingling is that the naive and well-intentioned organizers are exploited by the psychopathic and cunning ones, just as the latter can go on to exploit patients, clients, parishioners, or anyone else. Again the pattern is one found daily in politics, industry, business and university communities. Insofar as external controls—either through law, carefully defined roles, respected traditions, or publicity—operate to confine group operations, we may presume that the gratification of exploitative interests is reduced, or, at least, concealed with effort. Insofar as any institution operates peripherally, successfully maintains secrecy, and is not subject to some form of public monitoring, the abuse of human beings can occur. We do not wish to imply that this abuse necessarily occurs in association with LSD institutions; indeed, there are establishments which we feel to be as free from exploitation as any in our society. On the other hand, we do have reports from participants and observers which suggest that some individuals in some LSD establishments have achieved improper personal gain. For example—with reference to another group—it has been reported to us that one LSD promoter, a person with false credentials and a reported background of association with undesirable elements, has demanded and received a fee of $10,000 for giving LSD. Another person, observed by three psychiatrists, has been diagnosed as a paranoid personality. When being observed giving LSD, this person was judged to be getting pathological pleasure from the experience—the judgment "pathological" being derived in part from the psychoses which ensued in the taker and which, presented to attending physicians, suggested the intensity of the interpersonal psychodynamics invested by both the giver and the taker.

What is very clear is that individual motivations intertwine with institutionally derived roles and the cultural values associated with drug use to produce a complex fabric. Because of the newness of LSD institutions, one has an opportunity to observe these processes in sharp outline. What is observed allows no simple conclusion as to *the* reason that institutions which focus on drug use are set up; it does allow recognition of the wide variety of forces which come into play.

THE CENTER

The center has been in operation several years. Its organization was preceded by the association of several people who had taken LSD informally. One of these people, a (non-mental-health) professional person, was reportedly a very competent and successful person. For some time after his introduction to LSD, he had centered many of his interests about the drug and had tried to interest individual psychiatrists and psychiatric institutions in its application in psychotherapy. These medical professionals had not been encouraging to him; many apparently expressed doubts either about the drug itself or about the qualifications of a nonmedical person to recommend it. The outcome of these rejections appears to have been a decision to establish an independent center. Prior to the opening of physical facilities, the professional is said to have initiated many of his own colleagues and subordinates into LSD use. Some became enthusiastic supporters and are still using the drug; they are what we elsewhere call the informal professional group. A few of the early initiates were reported to have very bad reactions to LSD.

In any event, the rather serious psychological problems that at least one of his initiated subordinates experienced did not deter the professional from his enthusiastic efforts to set up a physical center. Sometime during this period or perhaps even prior to it, he was introduced to an energetic and widely traveled LSD proselytizer—one with access to a supply of LSD and connections with establishments already focusing on drug use.

At this time, the energetic proselytizer was introduced to a group of serious-minded persons engaged in a regular religious study and discussion group. To some of the members of this group, as they tried LSD, it seemed that the drug facilitated some of the religious experiences in which they were interested. A centering about LSD soon took place. However, a split in allegiance, associated with a struggle for leadership, developed. One leader wished to continue the discussion group as it was; LSD, if it was to be used, would be used simply as a facilitator of existing religious directions. The leader of the other faction apparently believed that, while the religious purpose of the group was paramount, LSD use would have to be medically supervised, not because his faction had medical treatment or research in mind, but because a medical cover was seen as necessary for legitimate and proper use of a drug even in a religious framework. As one of the observers of this faction observed:

> In America today religion is secondary to medicine, and the priest is the social inferior to the doctor. For them to use LSD, they realized they would have to go along with the existing value hierarchy and to bring LSD use into the fold of medicine. They sought a medical front to cover their sincere religious motives in the use of LSD.

Another observer said:

> The religious group was the right context for LSD, but they were getting too much opposition from medicine so they saw that the way to make it work was to establish it as a psychotherapeutic method. After that they could move into the fields of religion and education. They had to join the psychiatrists, going all out for LSD under medical auspices.

They had to divorce themselves from the religious group; there was friction, and besides it had a bad name in medical circles, and those were just the circles they didn't want to antagonize. They wanted to be straightforward [religious], but events forced them to be devious.

The factions split. One faction joined forces with others interested in LSD, apparently through the tie of the intermediary organizer-proselytizer. The other continued as a discussion group without a physical facility and apparently abandoned LSD use. So joined, the former sought out a physician who would work responsibly with them. After several rather short alliances, stable ties were set up with a physician who looked after the medical responsibility for LSD use. The group expanded, attracting several students of psychology, other physicians, and the like. Persons joining the staff were required, we were told, to take LSD as a condition of employment. After employment various roles in the organization were elaborated; some individuals engaged in interviewing and testing prospective initiates, others in speaking and propagandizing for the establishment, others in being present at one or another stage of LSD administration. As organizational complexity appeared, so, too, did factionalism in the center. Conflicts within the medical staff and between it and some other staffs appeared. Some nurses, psychologists (not Ph.D.'s), and nonpsychiatric physicians were reported to have lost the battle, thus perhaps repeating in the drug center both the conflict and outcome which have occurred elsewhere in mental-health settings. During the growth of the center, there were said to be some remarkable conversions among the opposition. One steadfast community opponent was persuaded to take LSD and within two weeks abandoned his LSD-is-dangerous point of view and changed from a vociferous critic to a center official. But there were also reversals. Other officials or involved persons, moving in their own directions and taking their followers with them, also formed factions, so that dissension occurred among the leaders. Resignations and terminations followed.

Other medical professionals in the community who were sympathetic to controlled LSD experimentation found themselves opposed to the religious emphasis of the center and troubled by reports of incomplete medical examinations and the failure of physicians to be on hand when LSD was administered or to follow up cases. Several blow-ups, including psychotic reactions to LSD and unfavorable publicity, led to further medical doubts. The result was that few outside psychiatrists interested in LSD viewed the center kindly, some saying that, in spite of its medical cover, it was actually a lay-directed organization that was not engaged in medical activities. The problem here can be viewed as one of medical scope and standards, the questions being: What constitutes a proper psychiatric concern? Does it extend to include religious and nontherapeutic but desirable self-expanding experiences? A dispute is also involved in the definition of what constitutes adequate medical screening and supervision for the administration of LSD. Beyond such disputes was the fear, voiced by several physicians, that the methods of the center would arouse public apprehension and would lead to further restrictions on LSD use, thus putting their own work in jeopardy. It is interesting that the same fear was expressed by people associated with the center when they commented on the way local psychiatrists were using LSD and when they commented on the LSD activities publicized in Zihuatanejo.

We conclude, reviewing data from the several establishments, that the drug movement has been fragmented by disagreements over ideology and technique. Major factions (and now we borrow from Dr. Downing's chapter) include the psychologists, who emphasize personality growth; the psychiatrists, who emphasize the same thing but insist on medical auspices; and the religionists. The last may be seen as having two interest subgroups, one primarily Christian mysticism, the other Eastern (Zen, Vedanta, Tibetan) mysticism. There is overlap among these groups and within individuals. Nevertheless, in the history of institutions as we have been able to observe them, we believe that these differing professions and value positions do constitute one basis for factionalism.

We also conclude that each organization faces struggles for power within itself and that, as in any other revolutionary movement, the absence of traditional structure and the lack of the test of time to decide which approach is best lead to shifts in emphasis on ideology and techniques. One factor contributing to distress and intensifying emotional byplay within or between institutions is the worry among participants. Worry derives from the realistic recognition that the participants face considerable opposition from other elements in society and that it is important to move socially without jeopardizing their ability to continue to use LSD in legitimate ways. The drug revolution is just beginning and faces, so to speak, strong counterrevolutionary forces. It is necessary to move with caution so that during the period of weakness one will not be eliminated by the strong—in this instance, by the traditional and conservative forces which are suspicious of the LSD movement. Among these forces the drug "revolutionaries" count among their actual or potential enemies the police, the uninformed public, physicians resentful of nonmedical dispensing of any drug, and orthodox religious leaders jealous of their own prerogatives and establishments.

Given the awareness of the opposition, each LSD institution which we have information about may be said to have taken steps to defend its own security while advancing its interests and, sometimes incidentally, the drug movement. Each has been worried lest the actions and attendant notoriety of other institutions bring down the LSD-suppressing wrath of society upon them all. Spurred by ideological conviction, jealousy, and fear, charges and countercharges have been generated, factions have become splinter groups, and some of the energies of the drug movement have been spent in internecine warfare.

Recognition of the splits should not lead us to overlook integrating forces. These exist, too. Until recently there were two primary vehicles for the promotion of LSD use—an organization based in New England which has sought to organize local chapters among all initiates regardless of their institutional affiliation and a newly organized national publication. In addition, more active institutional officials travel and meet one another; there is considerable correspondence, and occasional seminars and other public gatherings provide opportunity for friendships to be established and points of view exchanged. Viewed in this way, one sees both cohesive and disruptive forces in the drug movement— forces not at all unlike those which influence the growth of other groups whose members are committed to a cause for reasons of value and emotion as well as intellect.

The drug movement is by no means a monolithic organization. It is an abstraction which has as referents the shared convictions, interests, enthusiasms, and aims of people and institutions which vary considerably. As with any goal-oriented interpersonal effort, the movement has two interests: internal and external operations. Internally, it is a very complicated business of organizing; satisfying individual and institutional needs; establishing hierarchies, rewards, procedures, duties, and the like; and providing some meaning for the daily life of the persons involved. Externally, the movement has a much simpler goal: to reach other people and to convert them.

Outsiders are the targets for the efforts of the movement. These targets may be classified in three groups: (1) potential converts, (2) useful people, and (3) enemies. With the potential converts the job is to communicate, present a compelling argument, and convert through an LSD initiation. Useful people are those who can do some of the work of the movement in reaching the first or derailing the third. They are journalists, writers, researchers, public officials, important professionals, and opinion leaders—people with the power to communicate or the power to act. Useful people are to be cultivated, ideally by giving them LSD. If that cannot be done, they are to be provided with special attention and all necessary help and guidance. The enemies are either present or potential. They lie within the unmovable orthodoxy of medicine, religion, psychology, law enforcement, or other committed sectors whose interest areas merge with those of the movement but whose views about how things should be done differ sharply. The unmovable orthodoxy is seen as holding these views because of vested economic, power, or prestige interests or because of stultification and a general fear of change. Any movement must overcome its enemies. The methods are standard and include deception, division, undercutting, counterbalancing through power alliances, buying off, threatening, replacing, direct confrontation, elimination, and so forth. The weaker the movement and the stronger the enemy, the more the need for indirection, quiet marshaling of forces, and playing for time while the major conversion efforts speed ahead.

There has not been opportunity during the course of the present study to observe the work of the drug movement with many of the enemy. On the basis of observation, it would appear that such efforts are restricted primarily to LSD institutions—which are more visible, more militant, and have more at stake—rather than individual LSD enthusiasts. It has been clear that, whatever the pharmacological effects of LSD and whatever the likelihood of mystical contemplative components emerging in personality, the movement has among its leaders, and, indeed, may select them in this way, people quite capable of taking sensible political action toward useful people and against enemies.

Sometimes the requirements for political action force the leaders to abandon the tenets of the movement although, like any able politicians, they maintain the appearance of conformity. For example, the leader of one LSD group pretended to be taking the drug and to be enjoying not only the equanimity it provided, but also the ability of effectively dealing with some visiting officials at the same time. For the followers and observers there was proof that the guru had mastered the drug while enjoying its benefits; his astuteness and calm were much marveled at, for the drug ordinarily incapacitates one for quick-footed social maneuvering. He had known of the coming visits and, presumably, wanted all of his in- and out-of-the-world facilities at his command. By pretending to take the drug and not doing so, he had met the expectations of the followers for proper behavior while enabling himself to deal with the political realities which he, as a leader, had to face.

At this point it is well to repeat that those who run LSD institutions and those who are its clients, affiliates, and followers differ greatly in the degree to which the institution is seen as important and in the effort invested in the politics and propaganda of the drug movement. It is our impression that the majority of LSD initiates who have had their LSD administered in an LSD institute are supporters of that institute, but their lives need not reflect any formal commitment. Many of them informally play an important role in furthering the drug movement by vocal support and proselytizing. For the present these informal person-to-person efforts are, we believe, more important in bringing in converts than are institutional ones. Most LSD initiates who have any in-group feeling and who are active proselytizers have taken and given LSD in informal noninstitutional settings. However, their very interests have led, as we have seen, to a formalization of their association and to the establishment of facilities where, in some cases, there is full-time dedication to LSD diffusion. Thus we may anticipate, barring unforeseen restrictions, that these institutions will gradually overtake homes and gardens as the place where newcomers are initiated, and, in consequence, we anticipate that the drug movement will be characterized by increasingly formal relationships and ritualized proceedings. Insofar as this does occur, it will follow a well-worn road down which religious movements and schools of psychotherapy have traveled. This institutionalization will not occur, except in very limited and artificial ways (as, for example, in highly controlled hospitals), should the use of LSD and other hallucinogens be prohibited by new laws. The development, then, must necessarily be toward black-market use—that is, the direction which marijuana use has taken in the United States. Such use necessarily becomes informal, private, and defensively in-groupish as long as prosecution results from open employment and as long as public opprobrium leads individuals to assuage their guilt and apartness by association with fellow law-breaking enthusiasts. As we have seen, there is already a relationship between informal LSD use and illicit use of other drugs. For those initiated in formal LSD institutions, this relationship is less marked.

We do not intend to use this prediction as an argument for or against LSD use or for or against the institutionalization of LSD use. We shall refrain from taking a position and ask the reader to evaluate the evidence, ours and others, on his own. What we anticipate is that, if the nonmedical use of LSD is outlawed, it will by no means cease, but, as with the use of marijuana, methedrine, peyote, and other illicit drugs, it will become an underground activity maintained informally and discreetly, operating at some cost to society in terms of law enforcement and the public maintenance of those incarcerated for law violation. If it were suppressed, one would anticipate that many persons who might risk taking LSD would not have the opportunities to do so, nor would supplies be easily obtainable. Thus the gross number of illicit LSD users would remain relatively small. On the other hand, should LSD use be sanctioned by law, even if medical supervision is required, more institutions will open. One can predict relatively infrequent use of illicit drugs in association with LSD and, as a result, less expense to society for law enforcement and incarceration. Concomitantly, one must expect considerably more persons to be initiated into LSD use, and the drug movement will expand to larger sectors of our society. Participants in the drug movement see this as a highly desirable goal. The traditionalists, many of those concerned with the pharmacological effects of LSD and the changes it causes in life values and activities, would hold this expansion undesirable. Aside from the pharmacological problem, there are crucial value differences raised by this dispute.

PROSELYTISM

Proselytism is one of the most important activities of the LSD movement. It has been the primary device through which the movement has reached the potential converts. Although increased institutionalization of LSD may mean a reduction in the importance of individual persuasive efforts, as long as drug use is the focus of conflicting social values and, necessarily, of conflicting internal feelings, proselytism will remain important to individual drug users. What is suggested is that proselytism has individual psychological as well as necessary institutional and collective functions for those interested in the drug movement.

Proselytism for personal motives or for the movement means more than persuading another to take LSD. It requires persuasion to have the kind of experience which the persuader is convinced should occur. That persuasion is communicated through relating one's own experiences, providing testimonals about what has happened to others, suggesting books and pamphlets to read, and introducing the potential initiate into a social setting where a whole group prepares him for what should be felt. Then, as the drug is given, there can be further suggestions. Questions are asked, concepts offered, observations made; all this provides an interpretive structure for a powerful but nonverbal event. Afterward there is more group activity—questioning and approval for the "right" answers, the teaching of the drug language, and so on. Continued association confirms original interpretations, and then, as one takes over the job of proselytizing, the conviction becomes complete. Such a view of persuasion is not meant to discount pharmacological effects; these are powerful and apparently specific enough in nature to provide a limiting framework for any verbal interpretations. Nor is this view meant to discount the sincerity and honesty of LSD users who are members of believing groups.

Summary of Proselytism

As an institutional device of the movement, it has been the primary means for bringing new converts into the fold. By giving journalists, writers, and other useful people the drug, new communication media have been opened to the movement.

In using a controversial substance about which many people are dubious or opposed, any admitted user faces hostility and deprecation (if not worse, as in the case of criminal offenses) from his acquaintances. Insofar as he converts these potential critics into users, he nullifies their opposition. Since drug users are likely to suffer damage to their self-esteem in their arguments with others, proselytizing serves to preserve esteem by ensuring that one's friends favor drug use. Conversion also helps maintain a stable social fabric; if one's friends and intimates did not come around to a favorable view, one might very well have to drop them.

If the drug does, or is believed to, produce desirable changes in others, it is a Utopian tool. Elsewhere one can see drugs used to mold behavior: sedatives are given by physicians in hospitals to produce passivity in patients who are "crocks" and "cranks"; mothers give tranquilizers to children to make them docile. LSD can be used as a device for social engineering, a "Utopiate" to construct more pleasing surroundings and to mold people to one's desire.

The first experience with hallucinogens is considered to be a gateway, a door to insight, a great event. Implied here is that the initiator gives a gift which is ultimate and, in so doing, obligates the receiver for the rest of his life. Intense emotional ties develop among those sharing experiences or among those brought together during critical maturational periods. Presuming that the introduction to drugs is such an experience, the leader binds himself in a special relationship to the receiver, one which, in fantasy at least, could continue for the rest of the recipient's life.

By offering LSD to others and having them accept it, one repeats what happened to oneself and receives, each time, the confirmation that what one did is acceptable. Successful proselytizing is a form of reassurance. One can then say, "Everybody does it; I'm not really different."

The "contact high" phenomenon, whereby a user watches another and catches the latter's ecstatic state without taking the drug, may have a role in proselytizing (contagion, communication of affect, identification, and telepathy have been offered as possible reasons). If it is true that the first drug experience has special significance, then, by watching someone else take the drug for the first time, one may relive one's own experience. The vicarious aspect is important.

Direct power and control, seduction and dominance, can be implied. One gives, and the other takes. One establishes dominance by being the feeder or giver, by controlling the supply and setting the conditions of the gift. The other, in accepting, becomes subordinate. Sometimes the sexual overtones are clear, as when actual seduction follows.

Insofar as the drug is valued and the experience is good, the giver can believe himself to be doing a kind act, thus furthering his idea of himself as a generous person.

Because we are social animals, shared experiences are important. Internal experiences become more real by being discussed; they take on an external reality. The external structure presumably adds to the intensity of an experience and the ease of recollecting it. The whole is more than the sum of parts and social experience potentiates drug effects.

The Russells postulate that, rather than seek and be denied (which he fears), a person liable to addiction reverses the process, becoming the tempter and rejector.[1] Addiction as the Russells use it is psychological, not pharmacological. Evidence for such thinking is found among some observed drug users who proselytize very actively but maintain only shallow or exploitative relationships thereafter. The initiate, expecting acceptance, may be subsequently rejected, disdained, manipulated, or deprived. What is sought, of course, is not a drug, but a kind of human relationship; the drug seduction is only a weapon in the neurotic process.

To understand some of the special conditions necessary for successful proselytism, the observations of Redl are of considerable interest.[2] Describing social contagion, the spread of effects in groups, Redl suggests that determining variables include the group status of the initiator, the relevance of the new behavior to group values, and the likelihood of the new behavior's allowing expression of suppressed needs among the largest number of group members with high status. The more fluid (informal) a group and less the substructure in it, the greater the contagion. In larger groups ritualistic behavior spreads more easily. Redl points out that both group and individual factors influence efforts and response. Important intrapsychic factors to be considered are the existence of acute conflict areas, the strength of impulse and ego or superego, the degree of liability in the area concerned, and the potential attraction of a shared acting out which frees from guilt or fear. Of importance for the understanding of intensely negative responses to proselytizers are Redl's conceptions about scapegoating and shock effects.

PERSUASION: A SPECIAL TECHNIQUE

Proselytism may be engaged in by sincere and by insincere persons; it can take place spontaneously and informally, or it may become systematic. The methods employed by LSD institutions for the creation of particular kinds of LSD experience would be expected, as in any bureaucratic structure, to become less personal and more systematic and prescribed. On the basis of lengthy interviews with persons not members of the samples elsewhere described in this volume, interviews taking place over a period of weeks or months as initiates have gone through the LSD experience at one institution, it is possible to present a composite picture of some of the special techniques that can be used.

The institution may prepare people for LSD by first giving them a series of sessions in which CO_2 is administered. Before receiving the CO_2, the subject is reassured that he will receive more than enough oxygen. He is not told that CO_2 can be dangerous, nor that its inspiration is, in itself, a respiratory stimulant, nor that abnormal amounts of CO_2 in inspired air lead to distress. Physiological studies show that 2 or 3 per cent of CO_2 produces increased respiration and discomfort. Most persons report distress at 5 per cent, and 10 per cent of CO_2 in inspired air produces effects described as unbearable and which are, in fact, quite dangerous as respiratory depression sets in. At the institution subjects receive 30 per cent CO_2 and 70 per cent oxygen.

As the institution official holds the mask over the subject's face, the subject does, of course, go into respiratory distress. He is told that he should "let go," and any anxiety he feels is discussed in terms of the important people or events which he has been asked to think about or call to mind. When he says he is suffocating, a normal physiological response, he may be told that he has feelings inside himself which are suffocating him—feelings which must come out. The emphasis continues to be on relaxing and letting go. Should the subject remain anxious or constrained, he is told, "You must trust yourself." Failing to trust or to let go, staying "anxious," are problems which, he may be advised, must be overcome so that the most can be made of the later LSD experience.

Reassurance is continually given. As an introduction the subject watches the "therapist" take CO_2 (which he does for twenty seconds), and then the subject is given the mask to hold for himself. During self-administration of CO_2, some subjects grow more confident and enjoy the sensations. What was at first a nightmare becomes pleasurable. Others do not find it so and refuse further CO_2 sessions. Those who do come to enjoy it say that it is "delicious," "tingling," or "like an orgasm." In this regard it is to be noted that orgiastic sensations may be facilitated by increasing the CO_2 level.[3] In any event, some of the subjects do report pleasure and continue to self-administer CO_2 until they pass out. Fainting is to be expected, since 30 per cent of CO_2 is an anesthetic dose. Forty per cent can be fatal.[4] As the subject progresses through these CO_2 experiences, coming to enjoy them, he may be told, "We saw you struggling with your problems and winning; you're coming along well."

It is, of course, quite likely that genuine anxiety emerges during these sessions. Some subjects do panic at the notion of loss of control, a few at the dependency relationship which they are required to enter. Some have fears of LSD effects, and they ask about the likelihood of psychosis or suicide. We are told that all such distress is handled with gentle encouragement and reassurance. Those who are worried about becoming psychotic are told that LSD has no such effect, except on those who were previously psychotic. Since the subject is likely to be assured he is not psychotic, there is nothing for him to worry about, or so they say.

During these intense preliminary episodes, in which fear as well as uncertainty is aroused, one would expect the subject to become quite dependent on the "therapist" for safety and support, starting an intense relationship such as can arise between a dependent and a strong person in any emotionally critical period. Such relationships do seem to occur, and subjects report that they learn to trust and be grateful to the drug administrators, "They really know what they're doing, and you're awfully glad they do," and "They're really wonderful—so understanding and accepting of you." The administrators are not unaware of this relationship and appear to try to enhance it. Somewhere during the series they also give the subject tasks—writing an autobiography which is to be discussed and giving them methedrine to take at home, apparently as homework.

During the preliminary period the subject may also receive suggestions that he might have religious revelations during LSD—suggestions which speak of God and Christ and the capacity to see them. Various religious symbols are in the room, and these stage properties presumably have some effect. Prior expectations, if not in line with institutional beliefs, may be contradicted while the self-probing and mystical emphasis is transmitted. The subject comes to expect, having been so told, that darker recesses of his being exist and will emerge; resistance against finding these buried continents is interpreted as incompatible with the transcendental experience. One is told he *must* let go in order to come to terms with the administrator's point of view; otherwise he will not be ready for the vision of the promised internal land.

After some weeks one is judged ready for the journey. Librium and methedrine may be given and then, thirty minutes later, LSD and mescaline. There is a wait, and then a dark cloth is placed over the subject's face. He is told to lie down and to let impressions come, not to struggle against them. Physiological changes—coldness in the extremities, for example—are interpreted as resistance. Nausea, too, is not a pharmacological product; it is an "illusion" produced by the resisting mind of the subject. After several hours objects—paintings, pictures, flowers, and so on—may be brought in, and the mask is taken off. The sudden sunlight after the blindfold can be shocking; some subjects are told that the brightness they see at that moment is God himself. The rest of the day may be spent in listening to music, talking, looking at photographs the subject has brought, and so on.

In talking to subjects from the weeks before to the weeks after their experience, it is interesting to see the changes that have been wrought. Subjects at first interested in novelty, "kicks," or the solution to particular problems are gradually brought around. They begin to speak of love, at first skeptically, but later with increasing intensity. Similarly, irreligious subjects, however much they spoof at first, later talk of their mystical experiences. They do not always become theists, but some religious spirit in them has been evoked. Similarly, their interest in self increases and inner focusing occurs, so that those who might not have wanted an introspective experience—certainly people who had never conceived of the current theories of self-enhancement—begin to think of their own unfolding and look forward to it. During the preparatory sessions, during the LSD itself, and afterward in the company of others initiated at the institution, there is ample opportunity to consolidate what has been learned, primarily through discussion and the happy experience of sharing, being accepted, and getting social and psychological support for the new person one is trying to form. One must not overlook the supportive role which the new groups formed among the initiates can play. God, love, and self, a rather powerful triumvirate, have been invoked and, once manifest, are cherished by the group. There are individual variations, of course. Some persons emphasize one aspect more than another. Some respond antagonistically to what they call "brain-washing" or to "those people playing with their chemistry sets on me"; some have unhappy personal reactions to a staff member; a few reportedly become psychotic.

Institution staff and many of their clients would contend that the responses to LSD which emerge there are internally generated, released only by LSD, but reflecting the inner existence of fundamental truths. It may be that these responses *are* in the nature of man and the universe; certainly many contemporary students of mind, matter, and religion would hold this to be so. It is also possible that these are only notions intellectually created by the mind and then imposed, as concepts, on the raw processes of brain. There are many scholars who would hold that. Others, good committeemen and eclectics, would plead compromise and accept either internal generation or external impositions to account for these institutionally induced LSD reflections of a world which may or may not be.

SUMMARY

Observations were made on three institutions which developed about the use of LSD and a fourth in which one faction centered on its use. Each institution emphasized a major theme—psychological growth, religious experience, or artistic-expressive endeavor.

Existing institutions devoted to any one of these themes can be torn by factionalism when some persons adopt LSD use as the primary means for achieving pre-existing ends, while others adhere to traditional approaches. Individuals who become active in the establishment of LSD-centered institutions may do so for differing motives, some covert. These range from humanitarian and professional dedication to economic and psychological exploitation.

Some of the conflicts in LSD institutions leading to factionalism represent extensions of power struggles found elsewhere—physicians versus psychiatrists, psychologists versus psychiatrists, psychiatrists versus religionists, and so on. Institutions forming about LSD cannot escape the strains and competition inherent in the professional roles and outlooks of those who constitute their membership.

Proselytism is one of the most important tools of the drug movement, of its institutions, and of "convinced" LSD users. Its functions are varied, but its effects provide lifeblood for the expansion of the movement. Special techniques of persuasion may be systematically employed by LSD institutions in order to convey to the initiate the experience the institution intends. Manipulation of physiological reactions and interpersonal relations can be parts of such techniques.

It is predicted that repressive legislation cannot eliminate the use of the hallucinogens but will restrict the spread of the movement. Present lawful practices, it is predicted, will result in increasing institutionalization, formalization, and expansion of LSD use.

NOTES

1. Claire Russell and W. M. S. Russell, *Human Behavior* (Boston: Little, Brown, 1961).
2. Fritz Redl, "Contagion and 'Shock Effect,'" in *Searchlights on Deliquency*, ed. Kurt Eissler (New York: International Universities Press, 1949), pp. 315–328.
3. The enhancement of orgasm by increasing the CO_2 level helps account for the elaborate efforts of certain fetishists who bind themselves and put scarves or ropes around their necks. When their mechanical devices for achieving partial suffocation work too well, these people—usually men—end up hanging themselves. The same relationship between increased CO_2 concentration in the brain and the facilitation of orgasm may account for the tight holding of breath by some people during intercourse.
4. The danger in the use of CO_2 must not be ignored. Persons suffering from certain abnormal metabolic states, metabolic acidosis, for example, ones not easily detected even by complex laboratory studies, can experience a fatal response to heightened CO_2 inhalation. It can also be fatal to people with certain respiratory disorders.

ZIHUATANEJO: AN EXPERIMENT IN TRANSPERSONATIVE LIVING

[VIII]

Joseph J. Downing

Unique claims have been made for the value of the group use of psychedelic[1] (hallucinogenic) drugs. Increased perceptivity, reduced defensiveness, heightened insight, enhanced interpersonal sensitivity, and acceptance have been reported. These effects, as alleged interactional phenomena, have been termed "transpersonative," a word coined by Alan Watts.

As far as is known, there are no previous reports on the group psychedelic experience. Research workers and therapists have employed the drugs in group settings, but their reports have been limited in scope. With the establishment in 1963 of the International Federation for Internal Freedom (IFIF) Psychedelic Training Center in Zihuatanejo, Mexico, there was an opportunity to observe individual behavior and social interaction concurrent with the use of psychedelic materials, primarily LSD.

I asked Timothy Leary, the leader of the center, whether a psychiatrist who was not a member of IFIF would be permitted to make observations there. Dr. Leary agreed without hesitation, for which I wish to express my appreciation. The report presented here has been reviewed by the IFIF staff. Their comments and point of view will be found in Chapter IX.

PHYSICAL SETTING AND POPULATION

The physical and social setting was important in determining the nature of the interaction possible at the center. Zihuatanejo is a tropical village about one hundred eighty miles north of Acapulco at the end of an unsurfaced road, open except during the rainy season. It is a village of fishermen and woodcutters, on a large and beautiful surf-fringed bay. The attractive, dignified people of the village are poor, but there is an abundance of fish and coconuts, and tourists provide employment. Zihuatanejo is a resort of middle-class families who tend to avoid the high prices and fashionable international set at Acapulco. Relative isolation is enforced by the three-times-a-week airline service and the once-a-day bus service from Acapulco. At the same time, the ease of access (fourteen hours by air from Los Angeles or New York) encouraged newswriters and photographers, invited by IFIF, to visit.

The largest local hotel, the Catalina, was leased for the exclusive use of IFIF guests. Located about one and one-half miles from the village, over a rutted, abrupt, hillside-clinging road, the hotel's green bungalows straggled down a steep hillside covered with palms, mangoes, and flame trees, looking across the blue bay waters to the Pacific. Above and below a central open-air bar and dining room, the six bungalows, each with four double rooms, were sufficiently scattered to ensure free interaction but considerable open-air privacy. String hammocks on the verandas gave a view of the hills and bay, accented by an occasional flight of parrots.

The beach was cut off from the village by a high rocky point. On the other end of the beach, there was a coconut plantation. Morning and evening a colorful, friendly stream of woodcutters, burro drivers, hunters, and peasants passed, machete or gun in hand, from the town back to their palm-leaf huts at the far end of the bay. During the day an occasional tourist from the plaza walked along the sand.

Small groups tended to form among members of a given cottage; however, most of the IFIF activity took place either on the beach just below the foot of the lowest cottage or in the dining hall. Another central focus for activity was the sessions room, used for the drug sessions. It was an end room in the lowermost cottage, partially screened from view. Its mattresses and walls were covered with colorful Indian prints.

Psychedelic sessions were not limited to the sessions room but might involve walking up and down on the mile-long beach, swimming, going to the dining room, or resting. The setting was such that reasonable safety did not require physical limitation or confinement during the psychedelic experience.[2]

The rooms were simple, attractive, and well cared for. There was frequent interruption of the water supply, most commonly because the water tank had run dry. Generators provided electricity from shortly after sundown to midnight. Most of the men gave up the unequal struggle with water and electrons and let their beards grow.

New arrivals from large cities felt the peace and beauty of the place as a tangible feature of the atmosphere. Both servants and hotel guests seemed to live according to a slower and graceful rhythm, yet, beneath this surface indolence and leisure, many IFIF guests were intensely preoccupied with efforts to change or grow and with their involvement in group interaction.

Demographic Characteristics

Between May 1 and June 16, 1963, thirty-five persons were resident at Zihuatanejo for the purpose of studying the transpersonative effects of group interaction with the concurrent use of LSD-25 (lysergic acid diethylamide). Twenty-nine were actually observed between June 1 and June 16. The large majority were mature business and professional people; all were white, and most were Protestant. The great majority came from four United States metropolitan areas—Boston, New York, Los Angeles, and the San Francisco Bay area. Most were successful in their work. None were below twenty (omitting the three non-drug-using children of one couple), and none were over sixty.

The largest profession was clinical psychologist (six), followed by businessman (five), physicist-engineer (three), teacher (three), artist (three), student (three), rabbi or minister (two), and one psychopharmacologist, research assistant, editor, and architect. The remaining four persons were either of unknown profession or had no specific skills.

Approximately 60 per cent were men and 40 per cent women. Marital instability characterized many, for 50 per cent had been separated or divorced. Nine were single and unmarried, seven married, and the status of two was unknown.

Previous drug experience had been largely with LSD, for 50 per cent of the guests had had LSD before coming to Zihuatanejo. Approximately 30 per cent had had psychotherapy of some type. Two said they had had psychiatric treatment limited to CO_2 inhalation. None reported the use of narcotics. Eight persons (20 per cent) reported one experience with marijuana but denied repeated use of that drug.

Staff members had used LSD, psilocybin, DMT, and mescaline in past experiments. The use of marijuana or other drugs was prohibited at the IFIF center, so that the sole drugs available at the center were LSD and methedrine (used to potentiate the LSD effect). Only invited guests were permitted to use these. About a dozen marijuana users who arrived without reservation or invitation were asked to leave by the next public transportation.

The guests, or student group (these terms were used interchangeably), were intellectual, sophisticated, and well acquainted with psychological thinking. Most had had the psychedelic experience at least once before arrival. On arrival, 70 per cent (twenty-seven) had a positive attitude toward the drug; 18 per cent (seven) were undecided or ambivalent; one was negative. Persons who were ambivalent tended to be younger, not to have had the psychedelic experience before (two persons), and to be impressed and frightened by the intensity of the emotions and percepts induced by the drug. The one negative person was older, had not had the drug before, and distrusted its purported release of emotions.

Population Change

The center was closed down by action of the Mexican authorities at the end of the second week in June, but thirteen people had left before the expulsion of the entire group from Mexico.

Of the guests leaving for personal reasons, the most common was the end of vacation (ten). Other reasons included refusal of a spouse to join one at the center (one); a feeling that a more active life in business was preferable to the quiet Zihuatanejo one (one); and a desire to escape from the IFIF group (one). The last person had struggled to attain group control but had failed. Psychologically threatened and socially defeated, this person left to visit the "magic mushroom" *cuanderos* of Oaxaca. All of these people who left before the expulsion departed with positive feelings about their experience.

Reasons for Coming

The goal for the Zihuatanejo center given in IFIF literature was that it was to be a center for study of the transpersonative relationships and for training leaders in the use of LSD for this purpose. These leaders would be expected to head similar groups at other places. As far as is known, no standards for these leaders were established, nor did the guests there view themselves as potential leaders. It was expected that anyone coming to the center would be known to a member of the staff and would be leadership material.

Dr. Leary stated that, of five thousand applications, only five hundred were accepted. How this screening was done is not known. It is possible that the screening was only in terms of order of application, since there was a natural limit of fifty persons at a time in the center. Limiting the remarks made here to the twenty-nine persons actually seen by this observer, the expressed and presumptive reasons given for coming to the center can be classified under six headings.[3]

The IFIF goals of establishing a center for demonstrating the value of the psychedelic drugs and for training others. Four persons, all on the staff, gave this as their primary reason; five other people expressed it as a secondary reason for coming. It is also inferred from the amount of publicity and from the fact that a public-relations agent was hired by IFIF in Los Angeles that one of the other goals of the IFIF staff was to utilize the center as a promotional device. Writers from national periodicals and television were invited to witness the center in action. (*Time, Life, Newsweek, Saturday Evening Post,* and C.B.S. television were scheduled to observe and report on the center during the summer of 1963, according to staff members.)

For specific treatment and help with personal problems. Thirteen persons had treatment for such problems as alcoholism, severe difficulty with interpersonal relations, neurotic symptoms, and marital maladjustment as a primary objective, and one had it as a secondary objective. Of some interest is that 80 per cent (ten) of the persons stating this objective reported that they had received worthwhile assistance even though the majority had to leave prematurely, when expelled.

The search for self-knowledge and insight. Eight persons reported their primary objective to be self-knowledge, and twenty persons gave this as their secondary goal. Such interests are consistent with the high percentage of psychotherapeutic experience prior to coming (slightly over one-third of those attending) and the high percentage sensitive to interpersonal discord in their lives.

Of particular interest were four people who offered as a primary objective their search for religious faith and enlightenment. Six others mentioned this as a secondary reason. It is the writer's impression that these people were searching for a personal faith. Several indicated they wanted to realize the basic unity of all mankind and the universe in a transcendental experience.

Research. Seven people came to the center with research as a secondary goal. Research on the effects of the psychedelic drug on group process, on perception of interpersonal relations, and on extrasensory phenomena was to be a principal activity of the center.

Curiosity or a thrill. Three persons appeared to have curiosity or thrills as a primary reason for being present; four appeared to have this as a secondary reason.

Narcotic-chemical substitute for reality. No person, as might a morphine or heroin addict, sought a substitute for reality as a reason for coming. None said that LSD was essential to their maintaining a tolerable existence. Nevertheless, it is possible that for three persons such a dependence on the drug might have developed. Of these, two were refused LSD by the staff; the third person was given the drug and had a prolonged depersonalized reaction to it.

Since LSD was freely and frequently used at Zihuatanejo, the question of continued dependency should be raised. In regard to the habit-forming or addicting qualities of the drug, it seems to be fairly definitely established that the drug is not physiologically addicting. As with other drugs, psychic dependency may probably be established. Of the twenty-eight persons who took the drug at Zihuatanejo, half said they wanted to take more in the future; the other half said they did not want to take it again. However, among the latter only three were strongly of the opinion that they did not want the drug at any subsequent date. Among the former, only five were strongly of the opinion that they would want the drug. Twenty, or about 75 per cent, did not express themselves strongly.[4]

GROUP ACTIVITIES

Specific activities were those of a quiet, family-type, informal resort in a warm climate. People arose about ten o'clock. After a swim and a leisurely breakfast, about half of the group engaged in some disciplined activity such as sketching, yoga exercises, or rhythmic calisthenics. Surfing and swimming followed, then lunch was served at three o'clock, after which there was usually a siesta, although some persons might go into the village for sight-seeing or shopping. Before ten o'clock dinner, people usually gathered at the bar for one or two drinks; after dinner there were usually a number of small informal group discussions, followed by bedtime around two o'clock. Some persons would go swimming. About once a week there would be a fiesta and dancing, with a band coming from the village.

The prominent and central interest was the psychedelic experience produced by LSD. A great deal of time was spent in discussing the effect of the drug, of the insights gained by the drug, and of the "game-no-game" concept outlined later in this chapter.

A small library dealing with transcendental and humanistic psychology and enlightenment (particularly the works of Aldous Huxley and Alan Watts) and containing the works of the Zen theologians and modern Judaeo-Christian theologians such as Buber and Tillich was at hand. Of particular interest to many was a draft translation of the *Tibetan Book of the Dead,* which formed the basis for a sessions manual prepared by the staff. This draft was eagerly circulated and discussed.[5]

There were no purely diversionary activities, such as card-playing. All activities were shared by the community. Other than the staff, no stable, distinct groups were observed. There appeared to be no clique activities; newcomer groups quickly disappeared after the first two or three days. Stable two-person companion groups were uncommon except for married couples. The only solitary activity was that of walking on the beach or swimming, which usually occurred when an individual was undergoing a psychedelic experience.

Boredom and monotony were not a problem; the general feeling was one of leisurely but continual activity, with a considerable degree of pleasure found in being with other members of the group. The majority seemed to feel that time was passing too rapidly.

In general, it was a goal-oriented, introspective group with little interest in diversion and recreation. Considerable time was spent in contemplation, reviewing the material and emotions evoked by the psychedelic experience, and pondering the interpersonal relations of the group interaction. In a mutually supportive, pleasant, intensely introspective atmosphere the participants appeared superficially relaxed, yet highly charged intrapsychic conflicts were being exposed and dealt with.

The pattern of LSD use at the center was that established by the IFIF staff.[6] Guests averaged about two sessions a week. There was no evidence of any sales by village citizens of marijuana to the center guests although, according to report, marijuana was used to a limited degree by the villagers. Such use is not seen as a social problem there. Alcoholism, on the other hand, did appear to be a serious social problem in the village.

Alcohol consumption by center guests was moderate. Based on examination of bar records, which were billed to the guests rather than paid directly, alcohol consumption was somewhat less than the equivalent of two ounces of eighty-proof alcohol per guest per day. According to the bartender, this was about half what a similar vacationing group usually consumed.

GROUP ATTITUDES AND VALUES

The reigning group values were those evolved in Boston by Leary and Richard Alpert and transferred by the Boston staff to the Mexican center. The values, methods, and goals set down by Aldous Huxley in his essay-novel, *The Island,* were referred to as the basic premises of the Mexican center.[7] No clearly articulated and organized psychological theory was ever expressly enunciated to the Zihuatanejo students by IFIF spokesmen or literature. Instead, the IFIF staff emphasized the nonobjective, religious-aesthetic implications of the drug experience. Nevertheless, even these hazily defined concepts appeared to present interesting parallels to certain contemporary notions about behavior and personality development. Based on observation and a minimum of explicit comments from the staff, the following points can perhaps be taken as a fair appraisal of the IFIF basic theoretical assumptions and values.

The "normal" pattern of individual personality development and socialization produces necessary but seriously limiting effects, known as illusions, on the individual personality potentiality.[8] These limits, or illusions, result in anxiety and inhibition of potential function, an inhibition which can be reduced or removed through the psychedelic experience. The person then experiences liberation, a loss of anxiety and increased creativity, and sees the world in the clear light of reality. The IFIF assumption is that the individual human personality has been limited and to some degree warped by the inevitable process of socialization. Through the transcendental, or transpersonative, effect of the drug, the individual can be liberated from these limits and become aware of the illusory nature of most life experience and sensations. Confusion arises from the interchangeable use of terms derived from traditional Buddhist theological writings and from modern Western personality theory. The term "illusion," derived from Buddhist writings, is never explicitly defined. Translated into the terms of conventional psychology, illusion would seem to mean "selective misperception and misinterpretation of present observed behavior and cues based on remembered past experience." In some ways, illusory behavior is equivalent to neurotic behavior.

Through awareness of illusion, the individual is able to understand the full complexity of his relationship to himself, his past, others, and the entirety of the universe; he gains a nonverbal insight into his life. The result is greater serenity and lessened anxiety. The effect on the transpersonative relationship is that the individual who is freed from illusion tends to approach people in a one-to-one, direct, here-and-now, personal way. Rather than viewing his fellow man as a projection of his own unresolved past conflicts and traumas or illusions, through liberation he knows emotionally that the other person is an equally unique self, not an object to be used as a source of satisfaction for personal needs. In neurophysiological terms, established learned, or imprinted, neural patterns are unlearned, or erased, permitting new learning based on present, accurate perceptions rather than on past, irrelevant memories.

Theologically speaking, the I-thou relationship of Martin Buber is attained, for one moves away from the conventionality, mechanical adjustments, and social artificiality that insulate one human being from close personal contact with another. One attains instead a reciprocal, loving, personal set of relationships and treats people as human beings rather than objects.

This psychedelic experience can be gained by a variety of measures, including long study of philosophical works, long meditation, instruction in such Eastern disciplines as yoga and Zen Buddhism, ecstatic religious experience, or the disciplined use of such drugs as LSD. The result of the psychedelic experience is to produce improvement in relations with the self and with others by placing the individual life into a truer perspective in the universe; reducing anxiety; and increasing conscious awareness and control of personality defenses, both in the individual himself and in his awareness of the defenses of others.

Stereotyped learned patterns, or "games," created by familial and social pressures during personality development are considered to inhibit direct person-to-person contact because relations are in terms of neurotic needs and social role-playing, rather than direct, currently perceived, reality relationships. An implicit group aim was to increase the individual's awareness of his own game, that is, to help him become consciously aware of his own stereotyped interpersonal and social role behavior. Examples of game-playing might include acting in a professional role in all interpersonal contacts, whatever the degree of intimacy; need for group dominance; a need to be cared for as a weak, passive individual; and emphasizing sexual attributes rather than the total self. Game-playing was considered neither good nor bad; as a necessary social mechanism, the aim was to make it conscious and voluntary.

The IFIF way to highlight individual game-playing was to initially emphasize that there was a minimum of group rules—a very simple IFIF game which could be understood without difficulty. This minimum included only an absolute prohibition on the use of consciousness-influencing drugs other than LSD, prohibition against leaving the hotel grounds while under the influence of LSD, and specific rules governing the sessions.

Behavioral change, including temporary abandonment of status and security-seeking activities through accentuation of role relationships, can be observed in other groups characterized by isolation from customary surroundings, acceptance of new forms of conduct, and dominance by respected leaders. From this standpoint, the game-no-game structure served to minimize the customary role attributes of predominantly professional middle-class people and to maximize the dominance of the IFIF staff members, who were the only people with defined status and authority.

Group Behavior in a No-Game Setting

At Zihuatanejo the no-game emphasis appeared to have observable effects. The newcomer's first impression was of the openness of group members. The ritual greetings and inquiries and the customary politeness through which people maintain a rigidly predetermined social and personal distance from each other were largely absent. The visitor, whatever his purpose, was approached directly and personally. The group member appeared to be concerned with the visitor's desires rather than with his institutional or other socially assigned role.

Prior to the group's expulsion, the presence at the center of newspaper reporters and Mexican government immigration officials put this trait in high relief. Despite the knowledge that the presence of these people was a major threat to the community, the reporters and inspectors were warmly accepted into the group insofar as their predilections or defenses would permit. Even after the dissolution of the community had been decreed by government order, this was so. At the Zihuatanejo airport at the time of leaving, the combination of traditional Latin American courtesy and the group's openness produced an ironic scene in which the group members and deporting officials said good-by as though they were old friends.

Another example of openness and acceptance was seen in the group behavior toward a disturbed, hostile woman who appeared to be suffering from a schizophrenic psychosis. This woman arrived without invitation; she resembled, to a startling degree, the lank-haired vampire mistress of cartoonist Charles Addams' haunted Victorian house.

In the painfully testing fashion of many insecure people, she was insulting, tried to start a physical fight with several women guests, and publicly showed embarrassing and disrupting abnormal behavior. Refused LSD by the staff because of her mental condition, she demanded marijuana or other drugs, which were also refused. On one occasion she skillfully painted herself with red and blue ink in a grotesque, artistic parody of the crucified Christ and appeared before a group of visiting Mexican government officials who had come to investigate the center. Despite such behavior, both staff members and group members sought her out and persisted in involving her in interpersonal relationships at her own level, that is, without expecting her to function at a usual, rational level, to show normal social restraint, or to desist from her bizarre behavior.

Following the usual courteous policy toward uninvited visitors, the IFIF staff gave her lodging until the next plane to Mexico City. It is difficult to know what effect the knowledge that she had to leave in three days had on her behavior. There was some evidence from her statements that she viewed this as the rejection of her presence that it was. Nevertheless, from the second day of her arrival, she showed a remarkable diminution of abnormal, psychotic behavior, began functioning with restraint, showed little openly grotesque or abnormal thought or speech, and to all intents seemed to be a brittle, hysterical, highly sensitive, nonschizophrenic woman. The evening before she left, the woman appeared richly dressed in Hindu costume and showed appropriate thought, feeling, and behavior throughout dinner. The following day she left without protest in the company of Dr. Leary. In all, this was a remarkable demonstration of group concern and acceptance of a highly disturbed individual whose initial behavior was that of hostility and demandingness. The group as a whole functioned with more perceptiveness and helpful acceptingness than I did. Based on my work with similar schizophrenics, I had initially stepped out of my research-observer role to recommend that the woman be returned to a Mexico City hospital. This advice was not accepted; to my surprise and edification the ill woman's behavior showed a remarkable degree of improvement in short order. The low level of anxiety, the high level of understanding, and the generally low level of individual counter-aggression and hostility seem to be illustrated by this episode.

Confronted by an unfamiliar social situation that required a maximum of role restructuring, newcomers ordinarily reacted with uneasiness and sought to restore equilibrium by imposing the customary structure. For example, within three days after a new group arrived, there would be recurrent requests by the newcomers for scheduled lectures, seminar discussion, and activity groups. The staff accepted these insistent requests without insisting on adhering to the no-game rule, for it would propose a reasonably active group schedule and put it on the bulletin board. Inevitably, the schedule was entirely ignored by the group, including those newcomers who had urged it.

Another group characteristic somewhat startling to Anglo-Saxons was the fact that the group functioned more as a Latin American family group than as an Anglo-Saxon family group as far as the touching taboo was concerned. Although in fraternal groups direct contact between men, such as putting arms around the shoulders or backslapping, is acceptable to a limited degree, the Anglo-Saxon culture generally disapproves of friendly, nonerotic contact. At the center, however, touching and friendly embraces were accepted and common. These served the purpose of nonverbal communication of interest and concern.

Biological Effects

Food intake was at usual levels. No members mentioned weight gain or loss.

Sleeping was reported as initially greater than usual, then somewhat less than customary. Reliability of this self-observation is questionable in view of the siesta custom.

Men reported lessened erotic drive with the repeated use of LSD, amounting to erectile impotence in two instances. Women reported no change in erotic drive, except one who spoke of a lessening of inhibitory shame. Sexual activity was seemingly less frequent than might be expected from vacationers. Homosexual contacts were absent as far as could be learned. These observations were confirmed by the inquiries made to the ever observant hotel employees.

Hostility and Anxiety

In general, members appeared to be serene and happy; there was frequent smiling but infrequent laughter. Even under apparent provocation, such as the presence of inquiring reporters, the examination of documents by government immigration inspectors, or the open hostility from uninvited mentally sick guests, there was no expression of resentment by the guests, either directly or to one another. Although not personally concerned or responsible, I several times found myself reacting with resentment or hostility to such provocations, but this did not appear to occur among the IFIF guests. Such behavior was not a matter of indifference or lack of concern, as there was considerable open discussion and expression of concern as they considered the steps to be taken to meet the very real social problems. Even the immigration officials who carried out the government edict to close down the center were treated with consideration. One immigration inspector and three reporters were so impressed that they wanted to take LSD themselves. The harassed staff was able to arrange it for one reporter but not for the others.

Themes and Myths

The prevailing theme was the game-no-game concept. The leaders apparently were well acquainted with the meaning of this concept but did not attempt to be specific about it with the transient group members.[9] As a result, each member made his own interpretation, most coming to the conclusion that patterned interpersonal and social behavior was necessary but that the goal of the group experience was to become consciously aware of such patterns in order to consciously minimize inappropriate or unnecessary patterns and maximize appropriate or useful patterns.

The emerging emphasis on individual responsibility for behavior, the stress on providing an unstructured situation in which the individual becomes spontaneously self-aware of behavior determinants, and the making conscious of previously preconscious or unconscious behavior are all popular contemporary ideas. Most particularly, the triad of ideas is consistent with traditional psychotherapeutic goals, including those of orthodox psychoanalysis.

The intellectual content of the IFIF group is still evolving. At the present the basic world and theological view are a mixture of modern psychology, New England intellectual mysticism, and modified Mahayana Buddhism. The urbane and skillful writings of Aldous Huxley and Alan Watts, the Tibetan Buddhist emphasis on mystic preparation for the death-rebirth experience, and the stern, no-nonsense pragmatism of Chinese and Japanese Zen Buddhist philosophy with its emphasis on *satori* (transcendental enlightenment) have been adapted to order and rationalize the other-worldly experience which this school of thought attributes to the psychedelic drugs. Specifically, from the English translation of the traditional Tibetan sacred writing called the *Tibetan Book of the Dead* or the *Tibetan Bardo*, a guide to the drug experience has been evolved. From the *Bardo*, *The Tibetan Manual* was adapted by the IFIF staff, to be read by the participants before using the drug, then to be read aloud by the individual present as a companion at the time of drug use.

The manual describes and interprets the psychedelic experience in its several stages. The aim of the drug experience, it is claimed, is to transcend reality if at all possible, to know both the inner (self) world and the outer (material) world in their true form of illusion. If this is not possible, then the manifold visions and sensations produced by the drug should be recognized as being illusory and unreal, the product of past individual problems and conflicts. The individual seeks to escape and work through these problems so that he will not continue to be perplexed by them in present interpersonal relationships.

My impression is that the teaching implied that, if the individual were able to gain the transcendental experience and avoid involvement in the lower stages of drug-induced visions and sensations, all lower-order (developmentally generated) anxieties and conflicts would be understood and treated as illusion and thus no longer be operative in producing behavior effects in the individual. If that impression is correct, IFIF doctrine is consistent with the Zen Buddhist concept that true peace and serenity follow from the intuitive (nonverbal) grasp of the simultaneous, identical nature of self and of the universe. There need be no requirement for disengagement from worldly concerns by the person who has thus gained enlightenment.

There does not appear to be an organized IFIF world view in the sense of an integrated and cohesive explicit philosophical system. There is an implied rejection of the philosophical assumption labeled "naive realism"—that the world does exist apart from the perceiver and that our perceptions do correctly inform us as to the nature of that objective reality. Insofar as IFIF doctrine does challenge the philosophical basis for modern science, it may be interpreted as an antirational, antimaterial reaction. That reaction is found far beyond the IFIF boundaries. It may be seen in the popularity of Eastern mysticism in America today, which reflects, one may surmise, a growing dissatisfaction with life in a reality-oriented technological society. The link with Zen Buddhism serves as a ready-made, prestigious theological point of departure.

The Educational-Theologic versus the Medical-Psychotherapeutic Position

The IFIF position is one pole of an active debate on the proper place of the psychedelic experience in contemporary United States society. The division is between the medical-psychotherapeutic and the educational-theologic point of view. The medical-psychotherapeutic group contends that the greatest value of the drugs is the relief of symptoms and that the drugs should be used solely in a clinical setting

supervised by a medical doctor. The consciousness-expanding and transpersonative effects are viewed as intriguing side effects incidental to the
primarily therapeutic goal. A close, conservative limitation of drug
access, similar to present laws for dangerous drugs, is advocated.

The medical-psychotherapeutic position regards the psychedelic
drugs as powerful forces, potentially damaging. Preliminary preparation
through medical review and indoctrination plus close supervision during the actual drug experience are emphasized. The physician therapist
may not be psychiatrically trained but in any case takes the authorita-
tive, supportive, directive doctor role, while the drug-taking individual
is cast in the traditional passive role of the medical patient.

The educational-theological approach represented by IFIF sees the
psychedelic drugs as benign agents having "door-opening" effects on
the psyche. The individual must have preliminary education and instruction to go through the door once it is opened. He must be guided
during a follow-up so that he integrates the experience afterward. Such
preparation is considered teaching in the mentor-disciple sense, the
mentor being called the guru. Reporting a low incidence of complications and of physical effects with the psychedelic drugs, the IFIF leaders deny the need for medical supervision.[10] (Dr. Leary reported that
IFIF had no serious complications in over four thousand drug experiences in selected individuals.) The IFIF group takes the position that
the psychedelic experience is not a medical procedure and does not
require medical supervision or the presence of a medical doctor.

According to IFIF, personality growth is the primary value of the
psychedelic experience, with relief of personal distress and symptoms
as a worthwhile but incidental side effect. Neurotic symptoms and other
distressing feelings are viewed as the results of unsuccessful and un-
healthful personality growth, symptoms which will clear up through
reliving the past and ceasing game-playing. Personality growth and the
discovery of inherent strength and potentialities will cause symptoms to
vanish. General availability of the psychedelic drugs, perhaps under
legal controls similar to those for alcohol, is advocated. (Interestingly,
the respected British medical journal, *The Lancet,* recently advocated
the availability of one nonnarcotic drug related to the psychedelic
drugs, marijuana, noting that its effects were less deleterious than those
of alcohol.)[11]

The educational-theological group recognizes that the drug-induced experience causes shifts in personality defenses, that periods of
heightened anxiety may result, and that the person may feel himself
in a painful, psychological impasse. They say, for example, the individual may become anxious because of awareness of an existing but un-

recognized personality pattern which is no longer ego-syntonic but which one finds himself unable to change. That difficulty is called being "hung up." The staff takes responsibility for being with the "hung up" person, encouraging him to verbalize, meditate, and, at an appropriate later date, take the drug again. In extreme cases of anxiety verging on panic, the medical-psychotherapeutic approach would tend to give an anxiety-relieving drug, such as chlorpromazine; the educational-theological approach would avoid medication, emphasizing continuous close interpersonal contact aimed at working through the anxiety-laden area.

These two viewpoints have become sufficiently clear and divergent that Dr. Leary of IFIF, who represents the educational-theological viewpoint and was formerly on the advisory board of the paramedically oriented LSD group in Menlo Park, California, the International Foundation for Advanced Study, has been asked to resign. The Menlo Park foundation reportedly has forbidden its adherents to participate in the activities of the educational-theological IFIF group represented by Dr. Leary.

Publicly, the Menlo Park foundation has adopted the traditional medical viewpoint on the necessity for close medical supervision and control of any drug, limiting the psychedelic drugs to those defined as patients despite the fact that the primary direction and support of the foundation is nonmedical. The IFIF educational-theological position that the drug should be generally available is viewed as reckless. To advocate wide distribution of a poorly understood personality-modifying drug without socially condoned controls will, it is feared by medically oriented advocates, invite hostile attacks on the use of psychedelic agents in any form. The recent spate of negative, critical, anti-LSD, and anti-IFIF articles probably confirmed this viewpoint.[12]

The educational-theological faction sees the medical position as monopolistic and unnecessarily restrictive, limiting potent agents of tremendous social benefit to a small and secondary field of application and perpetuating an unnecessary traditional medical monopoly on all agencies for mental change.

> It is vitally important . . . that research institutions not be panicked by unfounded rumors and fears which always seem to spring up around the word "drug"; and that, in view of the importance of setting (physical, social and cultural surroundings) on experience in this area . . . research not become the monopoly of a single school of thought on the ultimate significance of the substances in question.[13]

From this standpoint there has been extended to psychedelic drugs the struggle between medical and nonmedical therapists about who has the right to try to change behavior through manipulation of interpersonal relations (psychotherapy).

An important new element in this long-standing struggle between medical and nonmedical persons for control of the agents of mind change has appeared. The educational-theological group has been joined by intellectual leaders of considerable reputation, including Aldous Huxley and Alan Watts. Possibly intellectuals, particularly those with highly developed skills in communication, including writing and television, might find the nonverbal aesthetic experience of the psychedelic drugs appealing since it is a means for direct, private experiencing of the highly valued self. The exotic yet essentially simple nondeistic Buddhist doctrine which evades the Christian doctrine of forgiveness, sin, guilt, faith, redemption, and salvation could also appeal to an agnostic aesthetic based on intellectualism, pragmatism, and rationalism.

Changes in Common Beliefs

The disagreement between the educational-theological and the medical-psychotherapeutic factions has crystallized. It has occurred as the drug movement has gained prestige and adherents. The cleavage is between the group identified with organized medicine and the group identified with or at least led by certain clinical psychologists. The medical-nonmedical cleavage can be illustrated by the role assigned by the staff (psychologists) of the Zihuatanejo center to this observer (a psychiatrist) during certain events three days before the center was closed. (As an observer without any assigned responsibility, my physician-psychiatrist role had been almost entirely de-emphasized).

Confusion and uncertainty attended the closing of the center by the Mexican government. As a result two events took place which probably would not have occurred had normal conditions prevailed. Three men eager to take the drug arrived and were permitted to do so. One, however, became alarmed at the presence of the government agents and left. The other two did not have time to become integrated into the group as had previous arrivals. One individual had an obvious personality aberration, and this had created some doubts as to his suitability as an LSD candidate. Nevertheless, because of his insistence, he was permitted to take the drug, which produced in him a state of confusion, indecisiveness, and immobility. The leaders interpreted that response as his being "hung up" on a particular problem, to be resolved through intensive and prolonged contact. Group members endeavored, in psychoanalytic terms, to "help him work through" this problem. When there was no apparent improvement after several days, I stepped out of my observer role and suggested that appropriate medication be given. The offer was not accepted. Only when a serious behavior problem result after the group was forced to move to Mexico City and the man refused to return to his home in the United States was medical assistance sought. By then it had become necessary to hospitalize the man. Under normal conditions, the usual screening done by the center might have ruled out the drug for such a borderline personality or, afterward, might have achieved a "cure" through support without medical intervention. However, once what appeared to be a pathological condition occurred, it seemed that doctrinaire considerations prevented use of treatment that appeared appropriate to the medical observer.[14]

A second case occurred the night before the group was taken to Mexico City by special plane for deportation. Another man, with previous drug experience, wanted a "big" experience with a heavy dose. He took five hundred gamma and became panicky, out of contact, and injured himself painfully. After medical treatment, he was able to return home to the United States where further surgery was necessary, but no psychiatric care was needed. Ten months later, this man believed that the entire episode, although painful and frightening, was of definite value in working out some deep personality problems. He also believes that the staff was ill-advised to permit him to take the drug in the unsettled and insecure period just before leaving.

Accepted Values and Covert Values

The IFIF staff and students were observed under well-controlled although rapidly developing conditions and under a condition of social threat, ending with actual dissolution of the group. In both normal and stress conditions, the IFIF staff values of individual self-determination, acceptance of individual behavior, and group responsibility for the welfare of the individual were not seen to change. The staff was under continual pressure from hostile reporters and the Mexican immigration service, and its assistance was required for the usual drug routine of the students. On only one occasion, when a staff member was under persistent and inappropriate verbal attack by an angry student, was there any irritation shown. Irritation was short-lived and did not harm the effective relationship with the student. The consistency of this calm, helpful attitude among the staff members was particularly noteworthy.

POWER AND PRESTIGE

The IFIF leaders were the group associated with Leary and Alpert in Boston, most of whom are psychologists or their wives. As the organizers and directors of the center, they were the sole source of psychedelic drugs. They showed a remarkable equanimity and serenity, talked less than the students, and made the decision about drug use. The students sought to emulate them.

Four sources of specific student prestige were observed. The greatest prestige was to be under the drug influence. Such a person was viewed with respect and given special consideration, as if possessed by a power or magic. The ability of the center staff to carry out normal routine when "high" was remarked and respected. Next in prestige was to have a special relationship with the leaders, that is, with Dr. Leary or his assistants. Such a relationship was primarily having one of these persons as companion for a drug experience, secondarily as a nondrug companion. A third prestigious experience was to attain without LSD a state of *satori*, or transcendental experience. This is also spoken of as the first stage of the illusion experience as given in the *Tibetan Book of the Dead*. A fourth was to be chosen as guru, or companion, to another or to a group having the drug experience. Role away from the center gave no added status.

No basis for rejection could be found in the brief period of observation except for the exclusion of unstable, addicted, marijuana-seeking, or uninvited guests. There is the possibility that, if an individual persisted in valuing the drug experience differently than the group did, it would make him an outsider; however, this was not observed. There was some suggestion that the psychiatrist-observer, representing the medical rather than the educational viewpoint, was suspect in terms of loyalty to the group. (This is courteously denied by the IFIF staff.)

IN-GROUPS AND OUT-GROUPS

The only designated antagonists were university medical administrative advisers who were viewed as unavoidably reactionary and fated to play a losing opposition role.[15] This view of the academic antagonist had been developed in the United States but was transferred to Mexico, where certain academic psychiatrists of considerable experience in the use of psychedelic drugs were seen by the IFIF group as intolerant, self-serving pseudo-experts who, out of professional prejudice, refused to give a favorable report to the Mexican Department of Health and

Sanitation. Only in this regard did the calm good will and acceptance of the IFIF leaders falter.

There was no resentment expressed toward the Mexican government. In fact, there was appreciation for the difficult position in which it found itself—that is, forced to act in response to advice from medical experts felt to be reactionary in a highly publicized episode.

Allies seemed to be chosen from well-known writers and persons in the communications media, including mass periodicals, newspapers, and television.

The villagers were perceived as unique individuals, not as incomprehensible and curious aliens. There was a consistent attempt to maintain the friendship with the villagers and their officials through doing hotel purchasing locally, inviting the villagers to the Saturday night fiesta, and by maintaining a generally close relationship.

The expulsion of the group was considered by the IFIF staff to be a top-level governmental decision not shared by subordinates. The openness and friendliness of the center people to Mexicans seemed to work to advantage in relationship with them, who were accustomed to having Anglo-Saxons seem distant and unfriendly.

Hotel staff members several times spontaneously said that the IFIF group was the friendliest, most pleasant, and least complaining group that had been served at the hotel. How much this reflected true feelings and how much was native politeness is unknown.

There was no involvement with the local police, although local inspectors did arrive on several occasions and were received cordially. Local politicians, including the mayor of the village and the governor of the state of Guerrero, had previously been invited to the center, where the aims and procedures were explained. A pleasant but good relationship had been established, but it could not stand up against the sensationalism of the press, the innate Mexican resentment against United States citizens, and the *Realpolitik* of the forthcoming national elections.

FACTORS IN EXPULSION

The IFIF group was expelled from Mexico on specious grounds —that, as self-designated researchers or students, the Americans should not have been on tourist visas.[16] The reasons that the group became a sufficient embarrassment to the Mexican government, customarily quite tolerant of tourist idiosyncrasies, are varied and curious.

Narcotic- and marijuana-using United States citizens are a recurrent problem in Mexico not so much because of their addictions, but because of their conspicuously antisocial aberrant behavior. Discreet, publicity-free deportation is the usual way of handling such a group. The IFIF group was not antisocial, addicted, or misbehaving, but this narrow distinction was not made by the story-seeking Mexico City newspapers.

The IFIF staff had sought notice through holding press conferences in both the United States and Mexico City. They were not seeking anonymity and hence were fair game for negative as well as positive news stories.

Some dismayed advocates of IFIF have seen in the onslaught of condemnatory articles evidence that the Establishment seeks to discredit and destroy the IFIF leaders and through them the psychedelic movement. (The Establishment presumably is a power elite which controls or has access to national communications media.) Such an assumption seems unnecessary—indeed, unjustifiable—given the present hypertrophy of the news media, fierce competition for reader-catching stories, and great interest in science, education, and medicine.

The press is constantly perusing the medical literature for newsworthy items and could not fail to note the increasing number of cautionary admonitions issuing from prestigious medical sources.[17] Further, publicity originating at Harvard included both editorials in the student newspaper and news stories in Boston daily papers. The academic expulsion of Leary and Alpert, an act with few precedents in recent generations, blew the flame of journalistic interest, a fire further fed by the Mexican expulsion.

Systematic publicity-seeking by the IFIF leader through influential adherents, press cooperation, news conferences, and hiring a publicity agent (for a Los Angeles speech) also created journalistic awareness. The resultant publicity was sought by the leaders, although the negative content presumably was not desired. Even here one can not be sure, for "The Politics of Consciousness-Expansion" exactly foretold the challenge to constituted academic authority and its vigorous conservative response.

The IFIF group was certainly not on good terms with the academic psychiatric advisers to Mexican health officials. Dr. Leary believed this lack of amity was largely owing to an unfortunate and unavoidable incident in which he seemed discourteous to an important psychiatrist; however, this also fits into the break with Harvard academicians which occurred at about the same time.

Most exotic is the role attributed by one informer to two upperclass women in Oaxaca, the center of the "magic mushroom" or "God's flesh" practices among the *cuanderos,* or native witch doctors. Reportedly, these two women were influential among the governing classes. They were also protective of the native religious customs which have been gradually eroded by money payments for the mushroom rites. Fearing that the overflow from the IFIF center would journey to Oaxaca and thus accelerate the commercialization of the *cuanderos,* they used their considerable influence to get the IFIF group expelled. Since, as noted, one person did leave Zihuatanejo for Oaxaca, they were probably right.

The specific trigger that activated these latent tensions was, ironically, the quite proper refusal by the IFIF staff to give LSD to an uninvited and unstable American visitor. Acting presumably in revenge, the visitor wrote to a reporter for a prominent Mexico City newspaper an inaccurate letter, full of falsehoods; it was published as factual news. With an impending national election and the constant affronts by American tourists to Mexican pride, the government could not afford to ignore the IFIF group even after investigation showed the newspaper stories to be false. Therefore, acting entirely within its rights and responsibilities, the government decreed expulsion but acted with courtesy and consideration in doing so.

GOALS AND RITUALS

In a forthcoming book on the psychedelic drugs by Leary and Alpert, a foreword by Aldous Huxley discusses the social significance of the psychedelic drugs in terms similar to the game-playing concepts of Leary and Alpert. An incomplete statement of this foreword would be that the necessary process of socialization so severely limits the individual's mental capacity that he is crippled in his understanding of himself, his relations with others, and his perception of the total meaning of existence. With the aid of psychedelic drugs, the individual can retain his necessary social controls and at the same time regain the spontaneity and emotional freedom which are lost in earlier socialization. In addition, the individual can gain an ineffable, greatly satisfying understanding of his identity with other people and his identity with the whole of the created universe.

The movement considers that, under reasonable conditions of social preparation and control, this unique and powerful experience should be available to all citizens.

Some accept prevailing institutions as God-given and inviolable. Others see them as conventions which can block freedom, stifle creativity, and stunt lives as readily as they can support these and make them possible. One need think only of current patterns of racial discrimination and prejudice against the mentally ill, for examples. Insofar as our prevailing institutions and attitudes do inhibit the full release of man's potentials, the added awareness that indole substances engender is likely to make this fact more evident. Concern to reform the debilitating institutions should naturally follow, as should attempts to develop new ones.

New social institutions are indicated. In particular, it may be important that experimental communities based on new perspectives which indole substances produce be established both to provide support for these perspectives and to test their validity.[18]

One technique recommended for achieving this goal was the formation of small groups which would set up putative research projects around the United States and for which IFIF would be able to obtain licenses and distribute LSD. It is stated that group support and direction would be sufficient to maintain realistic security for the individual taking the drugs.

Rituals and Reaction

The predominant ritual was that of the tower. A ten-foot tower with a six-foot platform was built on the beach in front of the hotel. This tower was known as the "soul" of the group. The intent was to have one person under the influence of LSD in the tower at all times, day and night. At sunrise and sunset a new person would ascend the tower, take a self-chosen amount of LSD, and remain until the next arrival. Visitors were permitted, the name of the tower occupant was passed around, and inquiries as to his progress were frequent. Over-all, there was high awareness of his presence. The ambiance was that of a dedicated ceremony. To be permitted to take the drug in the tower was much sought after and was granted by the leaders.

The seriousness and power attached to the tower are illustrated by the following anecdote which became part of its lore. Leary had ascended the tower to take the drug and replace another staff member who had been on the tower. The staff member, a young woman, had forgotten to get a set of keys from Leary, so she ran down the hillside steps to the beach where the tower was located. As she reached the bottom of the steps and started toward the tower, she began to feel the characteristic tingling that accompanies the first stage of the LSD drug reaction. By the time she had climbed the steps to the tower, she felt so "high" that she thought she was going to go into the characteristic second stage, sensory change. She asked for the keys and left hurriedly, the characteristic LSD-induced sensation vanishing as she withdrew from the vicinity of the tower.

The Mexican Center as a Utopian Concept

As a Utopian society, the Mexican center barely got started. It was unable to gain acceptance from the larger society for its particular use of psychedelic drugs. The lack of acceptance seems, in retrospect, inevitable because of the publicity sought by IFIF, publicity designed to convince important segments of that society that LSD was desirable. Had the group been willing to be discreet, avoiding publicity, the notoriety which led to its expulsion could have been avoided. There is no reason to believe that the latter, superficially easier route would be chosen if it were to be done again, since the Mexican center was a means to an end rather than an end in itself.

The group had no self-supporting or productive responsibilities; it had only to exist. It could not accomplish this. Nevertheless, the stated IFIF goals of closer empathic relations, self-knowledge, and transpersonative experience seemed to be on the way to attainment when the group was broken up. What were the relative contributions of the beautiful, isolated, tropical setting; the opportunity to meet like-thinking intellectuals; and the particular LSD-induced mental state cannot be separated. Presumably, the IFIF planners would not attempt to separate these elements, having consciously planned a total program to achieve the desired effects.

DRUG EFFECT AND SOCIAL CONSEQUENCES

In an article in *The Reporter,* Noah Gordon quotes from a memo by David C. McClelland, chairman of the Center for Research in Personality, headed "Some Social Reactions to the Psilocybin Research Project." The memo states:

> Among effects of the drug are (1) disassociation and detachment ("initiates begin to show a certain blandness or superiority, or feeling of being above and beyond the normal world of social reality"), (2) interpersonal insensitivity ("inability to predict in advance what the social reaction to a 'psilocybin party' would be"), (3) omniscience, religious

and philosophical naivete ("many reports are given of deep mystical experiences but their chief characteristic is the wonder at one's own profundity rather than a genuine concern to probe deeper into the experience of the human race in these matters"), (4) impulsivity ("one of the most difficult parts of the research has been to introduce any order into who takes psilocybin under what conditions. Any controls have either been rejected as interfering with the warmth necessary to have a valuable experience or accepted as desirable but then not applied because somehow an occasion arises when it seems 'right' to have a psilocybin session").[19]

The effects observed are a consistent though usually transient consequence of the psychedelic experience. With frequent, continued use they become semipermanent (presumably) personality features, comprising what Jack Shelton has named the "holy man syndrome."

The impression has been gained, but not documented, that positive changes in life patterns frequently occur after the LSD-induced transcendental experience. The question of drug-induced instability has been raised as a possible harmful side effect. In considering this matter, the fact that the individual chooses to have the LSD experience indicates that a review of life is occurring and that a desire for change is present, at least latently. The drug experience may be either incidental or additive. If there is a failure to prepare the individual for the changes in his perception and awareness that may follow—the psychedelic experience that will be particularly acute for four to eight weeks and require unfamiliar conscious control of impulses rather than the previously automatic game-playing—he may make sudden ill-considered decisions. For example, because of the usual post-LSD euphoria, one young woman resigned her well-paying but unpleasant job within a week after taking the drug in a medical-psychotherapeutic setting. She later regretted this hasty decision but could not remedy it.

The euphoria and detachment that so commonly follow frequent use of the drug seem to be habit to people who take the drug every week or two. The person who shows this euphoria as a result of repeated use of the drug may intellectually anticipate future problems but not be sufficiently concerned about them to act on the information. To the observer it seems that the drug experience sufficiently reduces general anxiety and customary learned unconscious defense mechanisms to require conscious defense. It is as if the drug dissolves both realistic and neurotic fear and anxiety of life. The subject considers this general effect valuable because the majority of life's anticipated dangers and perplexities never materialize. He consequently feels safe and much more free from anxiety; indeed, he may feel actually euphoric. Unfortunately, when real trouble comes along, he may be too detached to act in what an outside observer would see as his best interests.

One may hypothesize that during childhood one learns to anticipate problems. Such learning includes warnings—that is, anxiety, which is associated with stressful events. A given stimulus associated with past pain reactivates anxiety, which quickly clears when the new stimulus turns out to be a false alarm. As the individual becomes older, the continuing effect of learning through experiencing new problems is to trigger more preparatory warnings and, consequently, a higher general level of anxiety. The clearing of anxiety is, possibly, lesser and slower, owing to physiological aging. Under the influence of the psychedelic drugs, the individual is able, to some degree, to unlearn; that is, he no longer reacts with the same frequency to preparatory stimuli. The individual must then substitute conscious mechanisms in the place of previous unconscious ones or run the risk of getting into trouble.

Group Effects

When several persons use LSD simultaneously, their actions toward one another show considerable empathy and mutual understanding. It appears as if there were less rigid boundaries between the self and others.

The members of the Zihuatanejo community were certainly not mutually withdrawn or indifferent; in fact, they may be described as having a group ego, the usual process of group identification having been carried to a point where the individual member extended the boundaries of his own self-concern to include the individual intrapersonal concerns of the other group members. There was little or no direct pointing out of behavior or defense patterns as there is in group psychotherapy. Under the influence of the repression-releasing LSD effects and the unstructured no-game social environment, individuals would rapidly become consciously aware of personally unacceptable traits and defenses. Periods of anxiety, depression, preoccupation, and acting out of distress would follow. Seeing this, other group members would spontaneously go out of their way to take heed of the distress, to talk, or to provide whatever support seemed appropriate. No organization for group process existed or seemed indicated. Whatever was necessary seemed to occur spontaneously, although the staff was continually monitoring the entire group. To what degree such behavior was a function of the drug rather than of the explicit no-game structure or the fact that this was a leisurely, isolated, vacationing group with no task other than self-study and introspection cannot be said. This group did bear a strong functional resemblance to the therapeutic-community-hospital psychiatric wards which are also oriented toward assisting the individual to become aware of the developmental and social antecedents of behavior and symptomatology and to provide support and assistance in a life setting for joining social awareness to self-understanding and working problems through.

When the expulsion from Mexico was made official and there was the prospect of the group's breaking up, there was some drawing back of interest into the individual or subgroups. This divisive phenomenon had not been previously seen and was not marked up to the time of the actual dissolution of the group. It then became evident. If the integrity of the group had been ensured, the identification with the group would probably have continued even after the individual had left the "mother center."

Observations and reports suggest another socially significant possibility: a decreased ability or greater unwillingness to compartmentalize life activities, isolating less gratifying activities from more gratifying ones. Persons who have had the LSD experience may have more difficulty in compartmentalizing activities into work and leisure. As a result, they tend to seek work which is more ego-syntonic and gives gratification in terms of an over-all life goal. Some persons who have known several people who have had the LSD-induced experience suggest that there seems to be a tendency to gravitate into teaching, whatever the original field.

REVIEW AND REFLECTIONS

The Zihuatanejo Center for Transpersonative Living seemed to fulfill most of the claims its founders made for it. It also confirmed some of the skepticism and alarm directed against LSD in general and IFIF in particular.

The over-all impression was that both staff and guests were mature, serious, intelligent people who intended to use the group relationship and the insights provided by the psychedelic experience to deepen their religious faith, remove their personal symptoms, promote such positive personality characteristics as greater acceptance of others and greater understanding and sympathy, and reduce such negative feelings as anger, resentment, and envy.

The no-game structuring, the LSD-induced introspection, and the isolated residential setting produced seeming self-awareness, interpersonal insights, and behavior change with a rapidity and strength that was startling to this observer, who is more accustomed to the tedious and leisurely process of psychotherapy. It was not possible to separate and weigh the effect of each factor in producing this change. The permanence of this change has not been followed. Nevertheless, the overall effect seemed beneficial, and the persons observed did not seem socially indifferent or irresponsible either then or later.

One highly successful upper-class American businessman for whom LSD had been advised visited and observed the Zihuatanejo group for four days prior to making a decision. Asked his opinion of the group, he replied, "I don't see anybody drunk, I don't see anybody fighting, I don't see anybody chasing somebody else's wife. Everybody is quiet and going about their own business. I think I'll have this experience."

Despite this favorable impression, three serious counts might be made against the use of LSD and against the IFIF transpersonative mode of using it. First, frequent use of the drug produces the heedlessness of social realities described by McClelland, the case in point being the loss by Leary and Alpert of their academic positions at Harvard and the expulsion of IFIF from Mexico. Second, IFIF permissiveness and loose supervision of the psychedelic experience resulted in serious psychological and physical injury to several people and possible danger to many more. Third, IFIF methods were neither scientific nor suitable to serious inquiry.

The first charge is difficult to evaluate, for motive and goal, as well as judgment, must be examined. Individual data on the personalities involved were not obtained, so motive can only be inferred from the behavior and public statements of the IFIF leaders. Leary and Alpert were undoubtedly perceptive in predicting that power centers of the medical and academic professions would react vigorously to the IFIF manifesto.[20] This may have been a self-fulfilling prophecy. However, as far as is publicly known, they did not seek or desire to break with Harvard University, which seemingly did its best for some time to conform to the tradition of academic freedom and professional tenure by accepting their investigatory methods. Alpert was finally charged with violating a commitment to avoid giving drugs to undergraduates and released from the faculty. Professional notoriety, even institutionally embarrassing behavior, is usually tolerated in academic circles. Was the critical difference here one of morals, imminent danger to psychic health, discretion, or drug use? Possibly both men had become such a serious institutional liability that the most expeditious method had to be used to be rid of them. There have been some reports that undergraduates' parents' complaints were a major factor.[21]

At Zihuatanejo, in a quite different culture, one immigration official could not believe that IFIF was legitimate and as represented, even after observing the group for a week. He confided, "Señor Leary must be either crooked or crazy; he could get $1,000 a month for this, and he charges only $200!" Similar comments have been heard regarding a medically directed center for LSD research and treatment. Nearly every researcher using these materials encounters similar skepticism and thinly disguised hostility concurrent with eager interest and clearly magical expectations; a portion of Leary and Alpert's experience can probably be attributed to the mere fact of psychedelic drug usage and consequent social fear.

It is neither sufficient nor proper for the researcher to dismiss such individual and institutional reactions on the basis of lack of knowledge or unfounded prejudice. Such feelings indicate a widespread suspicion that the drug researcher, benevolent though he appears and beneficial though his ministrations are, has an unexpressed motive, a desire all the more dangerous and fearful because of disguise and denial. There is evidence that this feared yet tempting motive attributed to the researcher is related both to unconscious temptations to regressive gratification of all types and to fear of passivity and control.

Gill and Brenman discuss a closely related state, hypnosis:

> Usually implied, though sometimes explicitly stated, is the "promise" to the subject that if he will permit the hypnotist to bring about the deprivations and losses of power . . . he will be rewarded with a new kind of experience . . . a new world will be opened to him. . . . The appeal is to that universal infantile core which longs for such wholesale abdication.[22]

Pardell suggests that

> . . . the hypnotist is a person who is willing, and perhaps desires, to accept the position of the controlling and omnipotent parent figure and who at the same time is willing, and perhaps desires, to allow the patient to satisfy the regressive longing that is characteristic in hypnosis.[23]

Deep fear and fascination are ordinarily directed toward the hypnotist, who is seen (unconsciously) as motivated by desire for dominance and who is feared (unconsciously) as employing seductive techniques to attain socially forbidden gratification at the expense of the subject. The general interest in the psychedelic experience, coupled with fear and various defenses against fear, is probably similar. It is possible that suspicion of the IFIF group was based on both (unconscious) desire for abdication of responsibility and (unconscious) perception of their aim to become a controlling and omnipotent parent figure.

The conflict between IFIF leaders and older, more powerful and traditional parent figures—the physicians and the university—appears more understandable in this light. Harvard's specific charge was that undergraduates, toward whom the university traditionally stands *in loco parentis,* were given drugs—that is, seduced into allegiance to other surrogate parents. Presumably graduate students were not included in this assumption of responsibility, yet, if the issue were solely one of psychic health, the university could not approve administering the harmful materials to anyone. Imminent danger to psychic health was secondary to worry about a shift in the students' choice of ego ideal. The university presumably understood that the parents had sent their boys to school to become Harvard men, not IFIF ecstasy engineers. In Mexico and at Harvard, the new religion of LSD was a threat to traditional social stability, with responsibility and dominance by physicians and university officials. IFIF was trying to break up a well-established game by introducing new house rules. They were thrown out.

No valid comparison between the experience of the Harvard undergraduate group and the heterogeneous Zihuatanejo group can be made. Judging from the Mexican observations, the IFIF staff was friendly, professional in attitude, and concerned about the individual well-being and progress of each student. There was no reason to feel they were receiving any direct gratification beyond that of helping the students attain their own goals; as parent-surrogates their power strivings appeared as well sublimated as those of any competent ethical therapist.

The Zihuatanejo center experience appeared to be valuable to the majority of persons present. Staff judgment seemed adequate, if not perfect, in this. All but one of the difficult episodes previously cited could have been avoided but can possibly be discounted because of the unavoidable lack of experience in developing the limits of a new method in a new setting. Still, from these observations there is basis for social concern over the consequences of the widespread use of LSD and other psychedelics other than in a structured, professionally supervised setting with adequate psychiatric consultation. At Harvard, as at Zihuatanejo, powerful social forces were aroused by the manner in which serious psychological areas were approached. Both in the drug research and in the representation of society, an initially negative social reaction could have been expected in any case; the IFIF leaders did not appear to take this into sufficient account.

The IFIF leaders did not seem concerned that frequent continued use of psychedelic drugs may produce an unrealistic detachment and euphoria. Their own effectiveness in attaining their own announced goals in both the sheltered academic setting or in the more ruthless general society seemed to be sharply reduced. IFIF has splintered and dissolved. IFIF's original Messianic purpose—to change society as a whole by formation of a nationwide drug-centered federation of like-minded people centered on the ideology developed by the IFIF leaders and receiving LSD from headquarters—has now changed to a small group with seclusive sectarian characteristics. The leaders of the former IFIF, however, should not be dismissed as either scientists or agents for social change because of their expulsion from Harvard and Mexico or their widespread condemnation in national publications. They are recognized from past work as competent psychologists. A hegira is often the necessary preliminary to review, restructuring, and conquest. Consciousness-expansion as a life experience and as a magic solution to individual problems is now known to the educated public as it was not known before.

Advance and retreat—expansion-contraction, in IFIF terms—are the common fate of ideological movements. In age, character, and native ability, the former IFIF leaders are well prepared to work and wait for the next period of expansion. Their estimate of the academic situation, of the readiness of younger faculty members and students to seek psychedelic consciousness-expansion, may be quite correct. It does seem supported by reports of LSD synthesis in university chemistry laboratories and subsequent group use à la IFIF. In this case, they can become the spiritual and intellectual leaders of significant intellectual forces because no other group is as systematically considering the intellectual, interpersonal, and psychic significance of the psychedelic experience.

The second charge was that of unwise, dangerous, and overpermissive use of LSD in the emergencies connected with leaving Zihuatanejo. I am inclined to view the untoward results as following from the disintegrating social structure and not proving major staff culpability. Presumably, the staff had not realized the extent to which previous treatment settings had provided essential ego support, support that was lost in the crisis of the dissolving Zihuatanejo-IFIF culture. If the leaders have learned from this experience, future difficulties could probably be avoided. The selection of students seemed sound; management of the psychedelic experience was not on the medical model, yet was safe and satisfactory in several hundred drug administrations. The error was in tenaciously adhering to a nonmedical doctrinaire position at a point where greater safety and responsibility to the drug taker dictated emergency medical intervention.

Leary and Alpert have been challenged as unscientific, and as yet no acceptable experimental control study on the scientific model has been issued under their name. In itself, this does not brand them as unacceptable researchers, for, viewed as a problem for systematic study, the psychedelic experience per se, being subjective, presents problems in data collection similar to the psychoanalytic process. Indeed, the psychoanalytic process, being interpersonal, is more readily studied through direct observation and verbal recordings of the analyst-analysand interchange. Nevertheless, even in psychoanalysis, intrapsychic change can be studied only secondhand through reports by the analysand and observations of his behavior. To study the intrapsychic experience induced by the psychedelic drugs, self-reporting by a number of self-experimenters must be relied on for data. Behavior change induced by the experience can be studied interpersonally and by observation subject to the considerations of sophisticated control of variables.

In view of the tendency toward euphoria and subjective changes of perception resulting from repeated LSD use, it seems necessary that in addition to close, continual self-reporting, a trained, non-drug-using, neutral observer be involved. Possibly the observer's role would not be that of a psychoanalyst or therapist but rather the guru, or teacher.

The occurrence of the "holy man syndrome" in drug-using persons must be reckoned with. Individuals who have had repeated large doses might be described, in Riesman's term, as "inner-directed" although the nature and source of the "inner-director" would be rather different than the "introjected superego figure" originally conceptualized by Riesman.[24] Such effects are not in themselves necessarily total contradictions of repeated use; it might be that certain capable persons would wish to induce these specific mental effects for the purpose of understanding the nature of their own mental function for either scholarly report or individual purposes. Society, in the person of its legal and medical arbitrators of what is right, would have to decide whether such interested persons could be permitted to pursue mysticism through drugs.

Except for a few small and scattered contemplative religious orders, general approbation seems unlikely in our present materially oriented culture which is discomfitted by individuals who fail to conform, however personally stable or unobtrusive they appear to be. Whether IFIF will be tolerated remains to be seen.

CONCLUSION

If clear regulatory controls over LSD use are not introduced soon, the psychedelic experience stands in jeopardy of being used and viewed much like the use of marijuana or other illicit drugs. Delay in setting up legislation which defines the proper conditions for psychedelic use can only be disadvantageous to further research and the development of effective LSD employment.

In *The Island,* the late Aldous Huxley depicts a highly structured socially and religiously integrated use of psychedelic materials in a coming-of-age ceremony. Huxley's picture of a potentially constructive social use of the psychedelic experience seems generally supported by the Zihuatanejo experiment despite its conflicts and emergencies. The lawful, controlled, constructive, socially approved use of psychedelics conceived in *The Island* stands in vivid contrast to the present questionably illicit, uncontrolled, socially disapproved use of LSD in the United States.

Medical use of psychedelics for the relief of symptoms appears to be a potentially valuable and socially acceptable employment. Society is generally more open to experiment in order to arrest or cure disease than to gain greater health or contentment. Not impossibly, the occasional psychedelic experience might become integrated into religious experience in church-sponsored retreats for adults. Such an integration, occurring in a religious setting, could possibly be a unique and helpful addition to spiritual life.

From these observations at Zihuatanejo and from other clinical observations of the effects on the individual patients, I feel that much more research of all types, individual and group, in a variety of clinical settings needs to be done before the psychedelic drugs are considered for general release. At the same time, I feel that it would be a mistake to prevent wide experimentation by qualified, responsible investigators.

There is realistic social apprehension about any internal or external agent which even potentially affects the established interpersonal and social equilibrium. Simultaneously, there is a great need in this age of anxiety for assistance to the individual in attaining greater serenity, personal integration, and a realistically lowered level of anxiety. Lacking the Oriental tradition of training from childhood on in detecting and releasing tension, we have turned more and more to continual dosing with a variety of chemical agents that modify the internal-external equilibrium. The infrequent skilled use of the psychedelic materials in selected individuals has been clinically shown to be a means of gaining lessened anxiety and greater serenity without paying the social price of drug-induced euphoria and unrealistic or passive response to the complex challenges of everyday living. In what manner such use could be integrated into our present culture still remains to be demonstrated despite either enthusiastic or hostile statements to the contrary.

William James stated:

> As a result, mystical states merely add a supersensuous meaning to the ordinary, outward data of consciousness. They are excitements like the emotions of love or ambition, gifts to our spirit by means of which facts already objectively before us fall into a new expressiveness, and make a new connection with our active life.
>
> Mystical states indeed wield no authority due simply to their being mystical states. But the higher ones among them point in directions to which the religious sentiments even of non-mystical men incline. . . . The supernaturalism and optimism to which they would persuade us may, interpreted in one way or another, be after all the truest of insights into the meaning of this life.[25]

NOTES

1. "Psychedelic," or "mind-manifesting," the term coined by Dr. Henry Osmond, is more neutral than "transcendental" or "enlightening," other terms in common usage to describe the subjective, perception-modifying drug effect.
2. This is a major advantage over the limitations imposed in the usual confined office or clinic. Many claim that insights are gained by physical activity and direct contact with nature.
3. According to the IFIF staff, the population in May and June, 1963, was rather different from that expected in July and August, the major period of the experimental transpersonative community. May was a trial period, so, in practice, the reasons for being there would have been different for those coming later in the summer. The latter would presumably have less interest in therapy and more in psychedelic training.
4. In a follow-up of twelve persons over the next three months, all had direct access to psychedelic or similar materials, including LSD, peyote, marijuana, and morning glory seeds. Six had used them, four more than once. All six had used such materials previous to Zihuatanejo.
5. It was later published as *The Psychedelic Experience: A Manual Based on the Tibetan Book of the Dead* (New Hyde Park, N.Y.: University Books, 1964).

6. The session rules established by the staff were: (1) a seventy-two-hour waiting period after arrival; (2) a minimum of seventy-two hours between sessions; (3) filling out the presession research outline, including goals in taking the drug and expectations of the experience; (4) selection of group companions if a group experience were intended and obtaining staff approval of the projected experience; (5) a conference with the staff member who agreed to accompany and be responsible for the experience; (6) follow-up conference on the experience; (7) completion of research form reporting the details of the experience.

7. Aldous Huxley, *The Island* (New York: Harper & Row, 1962).

8. The personality theory implied in this statement does not differ remarkably from many other contemporary theories except for its emphasis on the role of LSD as a facilitator of change. The implication of a specific potential toward which growth and expression strive is also to be found in the "becoming" thesis of Gordon W. Allport, in the "enhancement" described by Hadley Cantril, in the "individuation" of Karl Jung, in Carl Rogers, in the "growth" motives of Abraham Maslow, and, to some extent, in the "search for identity" which is of interest to Erik Erikson. Similarly, when the limiting role of the environment is discussed as the force contributing to stultification, one sees a view derived from psychoanalytic theory. The conflict of the growing child—his id impulses—with reality is seen as leading to control and repression as a special form of control. The social environment as oppressor, as is implied in the LSD theory, is quite consistent with traditional analytic views. One may, of course, wish to challenge either the teleology of the expanding-potential theory or the polarized conflict portrayed in the society-as-constrictor position; however, to do so immediately returns one to the conventional debates of general personality theory—a debate which we anticipate the LSD group cannot escape, regardless of the evidence which may eventually be brought to bear on the effects of LSD itself.

9. This lack of communication and specific teaching might have been because of the staff preoccupation with legal issues rather than conscious policy. At the same time, it served the purpose of forcing the student to strive to understand the leadership group, thus placing him more in the traditional disciple or novice role.

10. Sidney Cohen, "Lysergic Acid Diethylamide: Side Effects and Complications," *Journal of Nervous and Mental Disease*, CXXXI, No. 1 (1960).

11. Editorial, "Pop 'Pot,' " *The Lancet*, Nov. 9, 1963.

12. Bob Gaines, "LSD: Hollywood's Status-Symbol Drug," *Cosmopolitan*, Nov., 1963; Noah Gordon, "The Hallucinogenic Drug Cult," *The Reporter*, XXIX, No. 3 (1963); John Kobler, "The Dangerous Magic of LSD," *The Saturday Evening Post*, Nov. 2, 1963; Andrew T. Weil, "The Strange Case of the Harvard Drug Scandal," *Look*, Nov. 5, 1963.

13. Statement of Purpose of the International Federation for Internal Freedom, Jan. 24, 1963.

14. A personal communication from Dr. Leary: "This man . . . recovered spontaneously after return to his United States home. He had full awareness of the situation in Mexico but 'chose' this withdrawn state. He now feels he gained greatly and was not injured psychologically."

This "hung up" view of the drug-induced depersonalization experience would be consistent with viewing some acute psychotic episodes as transitional states occurring during a resolving of problems and a readjustment of personality defenses. As stated by Thomas M. French and Jacob Kasanin, ". . . an acute psychosis may be a transitional episode in the process of emancipation from an old method of adjustment and 'learning a new one.' " *The Psychoanalytic Quarterly,* X, No. 1 (1951), 278.

15. Timothy Leary and Richard Alpert, "The Politics of Consciousness-Expansion," *The Harvard Review,* I, No. 4 (1963), 43–54.
16. On representation of the American Embassy, the order which barred the readmission of these individuals as tourists only was lifted on August 10, 1963.
17. D. L. Farnsworth, "Hallucinogenic Agents," *Journal of the American Medical Association,* CLXXXVII, No. 10 (1963); R. R. Grinker, Sr., "Lysergic Acid Diethylamide," *Archives of General Psychiatry,* VIII (1963), 425; *idem,* "Bootlegged Ecstasy," *Journal of the American Medical Association,* CLXXXVII, No. 11 (1964).
18. Leary and Alpert, *op. cit.,* p. 44.
19. Gordon, *op. cit.,* p. 37.
20. Leary and Alpert, *op. cit.*
21. Weil, *op. cit.*
22. Merton Gill and Margaret Brenman, *Hypnosis and Related States* (New York: International Universities Press, 1961).
23. S. S. Pardell, "Psychology of the Hypnotist," *Psychiatric Quarterly,* XXIV (1950), 483–491.
24. David Riesman, Nathan Glazer, and Reuel Denny, *The Lonely Crowd* (New Haven: Yale University Press, 1950).
25. William James, *The Varieties of Religious Experience* (New York: Doubleday, 1954), pp. 386–387.

RATIONALE OF THE MEXICAN PSYCHEDELIC TRAINING CENTER

[IX]

*Timothy Leary, Richard Alpert,
and Ralph Metzner*

The Psychedelic Training Center at Zihuatanejo was organized and run by the Harvard-IFIF Research Project. During the three years preceding the Mexican experiment, over thirty-five teaching assistants, research assistants, and faculty members from three Boston area colleges had been engaged in a variety of projects studying the effects of psilocybin and other consciousness-expanding substances. This project, probably the largest organization of scholar-scientists ever assembled to research the psychedelic effect, had sponsored over four thousand drug ingestions. The Mexican center was a logical application of the findings and theories of the project.

From the viewpoint of the history of psychology, the Harvard-IFIF project is seen to be highly orthodox. The research was based directly on the theories of Gustav T. Fechner, the founder of experimental psychology, and William James, the most distinguished American psychologist, and revised in the light of the findings of modern neurology and pharmacology.

The basic theoretical assumptions of the research are neurological. The goals of the research are also neurological—the expansion of consciousness so as to utilize more of the capacities of the brain.

The central metaphor is as follows. The human brain contains over ten billion cells. Any single cell can be in interconnection with up to twenty-five thousand other cells. About one billion impulses flood into the cortical computer each second.[1] The potentialities of consciousness at any one second are thus seen to be of the order of

$$(1,000,000,000) \times (10,000,000,000)^{25,000}$$

The educated adult utilizes about five thousand concepts to experience the world within and without. An astonishing filtering and constricting process occurs which reduces the enormous potentials of consciousness to the few cultural modes of experience routinely employed.

Psychedelic drugs are seen as interfering with or counteracting these reductive processes so that the subjects are able to experience immediately, beyond the limits of the learned cultural programs.

The process of going outside, going beyond learned modes of experience (particularly the learned modes of space-time-verbalization-identity), is called *ecstasis*. The ecstatic experience. *Ex-stasis*.

The science of ecstatics is the systematic measurement, description, and production of the ecstatic state—that is, the expansion of consciousness.

This process has been studied by every culture in recorded history under many names—*samhadi, satori, numina, nirvana,* mystic or visionary state, transcendence. Those who are concerned with conformity and adjustment like to call the ecstatic state psychotic. Psychoanalysts use terms such as "primary process" or "regression in the service of the ego."

It has been known for centuries that the ecstatic process can be produced by techniques which alter body chemistry—fasting, contemplative focusing of attention, optical alterations, yoga exercises, sensory deprivation, and the ingestion of foods and drugs. The drug-induced *ecstasis* is now called the psychedelic experience.

Philosophers have for several thousand years speculated despairingly about the impossibility of describing the ecstatic experience in words. The fastest verbal communication operates at a slow, sticky-static rate—about ten phonemes, or three words, a second. The neurological potentials of consciousness are several million times faster than verbalization. Then, too, most words in the English language refer to external game artifacts or social game sequences which have little direct relevance to the flashing mosaics of neurological experience.

The energy sciences have found it necessary to develop specialized models and languages capable of expressing the speed and complexity of energy transformations. A new nonverbal language of experience capable of expressing the speed and complexity of our cortical potentials is necessary. The Harvard-IFIF group has worked out some rudimentary steps toward the development of a nonverbal experiential language, and one of the purposes of the Zihuatanejo center was to train people in the use of this language.

THE PRODUCTION OF THE ECSTATIC EXPERIENCE

The goal of the research sessions run by the Harvard-IFIF group was not to produce and study frightening disturbances of consciousness (which was the goal of most psychiatric investigations of model psychoses), but to produce the ecstatic experience, to expand consciousness, to provide the subject with the most memorable, revelatory, life-changing experience of his life.

The rationale was based on our conception of the almost limitless potential of consciousness, and our actions were guided by the set-setting hypothesis. Most psychologists and behavioral scientists (Jungians excepted) work from a different rationale. This may account for much of the misunderstanding of our activities and aims. Our position is very similar to the post-Einsteinian physicists who labored for decades to release the energy locked in atomic structure. A classic Newtonian physicist would have looked with incredulous dismay at atomic-fission experiments and quantum speculations. Such approaches violating the clockwork symmetry and lacking the control of classic macroscopic experimentation would be denounced as a reckless psychotization of the divinely ordered equilibrium. (See, for example, the controversy between Newton and Whistoh.[2])

Most psychologists have been trained to accept a brain model diagramed like a side of beef, with areas blocked out like fancy cuts—motor, sensory, optical, association, and so on. Our concepts of neurological function supported by psychedelic drug data visualize the brain as an enormous electrochemical network sometimes held in clock-like contracted conceptual game attention but capable of being swept by rapidly changing ecstatic processes.

From the beginning of our research our attention was directed to the engineering of ecstasy, the preparation for, the setting for, the architecture of ecstasy. Like post-Einsteinian physicists we sought to release (harmoniously and peacefully) the neurological energy latent in the cortex. Preparation of the subject. Set and expectancy. Collaboration with the subject in arranging the sort of session he wished. Careful planning of the setting to be supportive, understanding, aesthetic, spiritually meaningful, close to nature, and so on.

After many sessions in urban situations we came to some ironic conclusions about the set and setting of a psychedelic experience. We realized that an ecstatic psychedelic session should be arranged the way a person would arrange his own ideal life situation. He should surround himself with spiritual, relaxed, open, loving, happy people. He should arrange his environment aesthetically. He should approach the occasion with informed trust, intelligent faith, skeptical humor, humility, and, above all, courage. He should direct the experience toward spiritual rather than material goals.

THE IMPORTANCE OF PREPARATION

During the first year of our research, we followed a naturalistic design, scrupulously attempting to avoid imposing our model on the experience. We wanted to see how psychedelic drugs affected a wide range of persons in a wide range of situations with a wide, random range of expectations. We found that, if the setting is supportive, around 70 per cent of volunteer subjects would have pleasant, revelatory experiences.[3] The subsequent interpretation and application of the experience varied. Although over 50 per cent of subjects were reporting changes for the better following their session, follow-up studies suggested that the meaning and value of the experience depended on the subject's over-all situation. There were marked individual differences in the ability of the individual to use his insights. Most people drifted back into the magnetic field of their personal-cultural games. Although it was possible to produce instant *satori,* the illumination tended to be temporary.

We noted that subjects who came to their session after years of intellectual or spiritual preparation tended to get the most from the session. It was obvious that subjects with training in any ecstatic philosophy or discipline could make better use of their experience. Philosophic training (Western or Eastern) was helpful. Professional religious subjects made the best candidates. Subjects with backgrounds in mysticism, Sufi scholars, Hasidic rabbis, monastics, students of Gurdieff, scientists who had spent time speculating about the metagame aspects of the energy sciences—all these possessed a frame of reference in which to fit the psychedelic voyage.

We gradually came to the conclusion that a psychedelic session should be preceded by a long and thorough training in the nature of the metaverbal, metagame phenomena. Exploration of the speed and breadth of the subject's nervous system should be preceded by as much specialized training as soloing in an airplane or use of a high-speed computer.

It was ironic that, starting with behavioral science assumptions, we came closer and closer to the wisdom of the religious mystics. Rigorous training and a courageous commitment to metapersonal ideals was the best training for an LSD session.

It has been widely reported in the popular press that IFIF promotes the unrestrained civilian use of drugs. The truth of the matter is exactly the opposite. IFIF was the only psychedelic research group that urged the need for training guides—ecstaticians, if you will—to provide the experience to others. The Mexican center was set up to be such a training center. The plan was that carefully selected subjects (who had had one or preferably several psychedelic sessions before coming to Mexico) would learn to run sessions for themselves and others.

THE NEED FOR A CONTINUING PROGRAM

The Harvard-IFIF group does not see the psychedelic session as a medical procedure or as a curative intervention. A new term and a new institutional context are needed, but of existing institutions our concepts were closer to aesthetic-educational-religious.

The psychedelic experience is seen as a tool like a telescope or microscope which brings other space/time dimensions into focus. You have to be trained to use the tool, and you use it not once (for "kicks" or cure), but whenever your situation calls for an examination of other dimensions of reality. You don't go to school once, you don't go to church once in your life, you don't take a plane ride just once in your life. You seek out these experiences when necessary and relevant to your spiritual or secular goals.

The psychedelic session is like sex. Anyone who has not had the experience cannot really grasp the meaning. The first experience is entirely a function of set and setting. A bad first experience does not rule out further trials. And the frequency of its repetition is a highly personal matter. Both the sexual and psychedelic experiences are fiercely attacked and controlled by those who do not like it themselves and do not want others to have it. All of the familiar psychological escapes from and distortions of the sexual impulse are seen to operate in relation to the psychedelic experience—fear, hysteria, rationalizations about protection of the young, repression, rumor, puritanical control.

The Mexican center was the first (and of this date the only) attempt to provide a series of guided psychedelic sessions for prepared volunteer subjects. Like any other form of educational or spiritual experience (including the sexual), the psychedelic experience is most productive if it is built into a systematic and planned sequence. Our training strategy involved a few "free flights" followed by a series of systematic, programed sessions in the direction of the subject's goals.

Before the Mexican program of 1963, the research group had experimented with programed sessions. In some of these sessions we employed program charts which allowed the subject to review his set (emotional and cognitive) and plan the sequence of stimuli to which he would be exposed. The chart also had a series of horizontal lines representing the time dimension and making it possible for the subject to plan his session like a symphonic score or like a pilot's flight plan. For example, the subject might plan that at a certain time during the session he would listen to a particular reading (scientific, religious, and so on) or be shown a picture or an object which would be expected to open up a line of associations. After the session the subject would go over his chart and fill in the details, minute by minute, from memory.

The most systematic attempt to program sessions involves the tape recording of eight or ten hours of sound and silence to be played during the session. The tape opens with an introductory statement by the subject about the goals of the session. This is followed by music and silence, occasionally interrupted by the person's own voice giving himself reassurance or instructions. The use of taped programs eliminates almost all need of interruption or action by anyone during the session. The psychedelic state is so sensitive that any action, however innocuous (even changing records), by guides and observers can swirl consciousness off in unplanned-for dimensions.

One of the key training devices planned for the Zihuatanejo program was session programing and session charts. Such techniques can be used only by experienced subjects and are, for the most part, of restricted usefulness in initial sessions.

THE NEED FOR MANUALS

The psychedelic session whirls the subject through eight hours of unimagined experience—to use William James's phrase, the drugs "open a region though they fail to give a map." Although the specific dominant moods and major themes of each session tend to differ, there are certain sequences which occur in many sessions and certain broad types of reaction which reoccur. One of the aims of our research is to obtain more precision in producing, predicting, and describing these reactions. There is no consideration of this problem in the contemporary psychological literature. Consciousness, its expansion, and its control are almost completely ignored by the behavioral sciences and by psychiatry today, though it was, of course, the primary subject of interest for men like Fechner and James.

There is, however, elaborate consideration of states of consciousness in nonpsychological literatures. For instance, the Christian mystics and Eastern philosophers and psychologists have spelled out systems for producing and describing the flow of consciousness from one level to another. Many of our project members and over eighty of our subjects hold theological degrees and contributed to our understanding of nonpsychological attempts to chart the ecstatic process.

It becomes apparent that any system for describing consciousness is metaphorical. To say that the matter is basically neurological is simply to choose the neurological metaphor. It is obvious that manuals— road maps for psychedelic voyages—are badly needed. But which metaphor? Our answer to this question is pluralistic—many maps, many manuals, to fit the linguistic systems of the subjects. Any theoretical system, any cultural or scientific game, provides metaphors which can be applied to the ecstatic process. For every *stasis* there is an *ecstasis*. For every fixed conceptual system there is the metasystem.

Our answer was then translated into the intention of writing manuals which would fit many types of psychedelic experiences. We are writing a manual on the psychotherapeutic psychedelic experience. For the aesthetic. For the interpersonal or group session. We are also "translating" several existing manuals for consciousness-expansion so that they can be applied to psychedelic sessions. The *Divine Comedy* of Dante describes a visionary voyage into three realms of awareness—horrible hellish hallucinations; personal, purgatorial appraisals; celestial lights and radiance. The scenes and details of the *Comedy* are duplicated over and over again in our files of session reports. The *Egyptian Book of the Dead*, the *Tao Te Ching*, *The Secret of the Golden Flower*, *Pilgrim's Progress*, the mythic voyages of Aeneas, Odysseus, Gilgamesh, Christ— all these are accounts of voyages beyond our conceptions of space and time, and all come from someone's cortex.

The visionary sequence which seems to be most ideally suited to the psychedelic session is the *Bardo Thödol* (the *Tibetan Book of the Dead*). This manual was reportedly handed down orally from guru to disciple for centuries and appeared in written form only in the eighth century A.D. and in English only in 1927. The metaphor system happens to be Mahayana Buddhist. The book treats of the intermediate state between life and death, but the esoteric aim of the book was to instruct adepts in changing consciousness. It is a book of the living, a manual for recognizing and utilizing ecstatic states of altered consciousness and applying the ecstatic experience in the postsession life. The *Tibetan Book of the Dead* is an uncanny portrayal of states regularly encountered during psychedelic sessions. It is eminently practical, including detailed instructions for the guide and designed to be read by the subject before his experience.

Because of its precise relevance to psychedelic sessions, our project has "translated" the manuscript from the scholarly style of the Evans-Wentz translation into psychedelic English.[4] This manual has been used for over two years by our project in preparing selected subjects for sessions. It must be emphasized that this manual has been revised so that the Buddhist metaphors and the hallucinatory content appropriate to a pastoral people in earlier millenniums have been changed to the visions, ecstasies, and terrors of our times.

THE ZIHUATANEJO TRAINING CENTER

The training center in Zihuatanejo operated for two summers, 1962 and 1963. The first summer program involved only members of the project and was therefore able to reach a higher level of organization and training much more quickly. Starting in May, 1963, the Hotel Catalina was leased for two years as a research-training site.

The interpretations, appraisals, and observations of Joseph J. Downing (Chapter VIII) are his own and differ from those which we would make. It is natural and proper that Dr. Downing choose his own metaphors to describe the events of that time. A more detailed account of the operation based on our records is being prepared and will be published in the near future.

If everyone who was present were to write his own impressions of the Zihuatanejo program, each one would write something different. Dr. Downing's story is neutral, thorough. If every Utopian attempt to set up a transpersonative community had been lucky enough to have a social-psychiatrist-observer of Dr. Downing's caliber, our empirical knowledge of the mechanics of ecstasy would be the richer.

NOTES

1. R. Campbell, "The Circuits of the Senses," *Life,* LIV, No. 27 (1963), 64–76b.
2. L. C. Stecchini, "The Inconstant Heavens," *The American Behavioral Scientist,* VII, No. 1 (1963).

3. Timothy Leary, George Litwin, and Ralph Metzner, "Reactions to Psilocybin Administered in a Supportive Environment," *Journal of Nervous and Mental Diseases*, CXXXVII, No. 6 (1963), 561–573; The Editors, "The Subjective After-effects of Psychedelic Experiences: a Summary of Four Recent Studies," *The Psychedelic Review*, I, No. 1 (1963), 18–26.
4. Timothy Leary, Ralph Metzner, and Richard Alpert, *The Psychedelic Experience: A Manual Based on the Tibetan Book of the Dead* (New Hyde Park, N.Y.: University Books, 1964).

PSYCHEDELIC EXPERIENCE
AND RELIGIOUS BELIEF

[X]

Joseph J. Downing
and William Wygant, Jr.

Widespread, unsupervised, questionably licit use of LSD-25 may soon be ended by closer control over the raw materials for the drug, harsher penalties for illicit use, and tighter police enforcement.[1] At this point the socially condoned psychedelic experience may be entirely banned or permitted only because it is found socially useful in modifying individual behavior.

Evaluation of the social utility of LSD-25 can be made in four areas: (1) medical-therapeutic use, such as the relief of neurosis or alcoholism; (2) social adaptation, such as changes in social adjustment or criminal behavior; (3) psychophysiological investigation, such as modification of normal brain function; and (4) mystical-religious purposes, such as enhancement or weakening of accepted religious, moral, ethical, and dogmatic attitudes and beliefs.

It was thought proper, as part of this study of psychedelic drugs, to examine their effect on religious belief or experience. Many people taking LSD have reported an experience which appears to be related to the experiences recorded by religious mystics.[2] The mystical-religious experience induced by LSD-25 has been frequently, often eloquently, reported.[3] No detailed examination of the nature and quality of these changes has been published, however, although one study is known to have been undertaken.[4]

THE SAMPLE

Forty-two of the ninety-two persons interviewed in Blum's sample were asked to answer thirteen questions about religious beliefs and changes. There were eight clinic patients, twelve private patients, ten members of the informal professional sample, and twelve members of the religious-medical-center sample. Doses of LSD ranged from 0.87 to 5.0 micrograms per pound of body weight.

The Appendix to Chapter X presents a breakdown of replies to each question. In summary, the basic findings were:

1. Sixty per cent stated their religious feelings were changed:
   a. Thirty per cent experienced a deeper understanding of their previous religious feelings and felt closer to their church.
   b. Thirty per cent experienced a change in their religious thinking in a variety of ways.
2. Sixty per cent trusted God (or life) more; 35 per cent trusted people more.
3. Forty per cent indicated their understanding of the teachings of their own church had changed, largely toward an increased understanding of doctrine.
4. Forty per cent expressed lessened anxiety regarding death, elaborating this in a variety of ways.
5. Thirty per cent felt a greater conviction of the existence of a supreme being.
6. Eighty per cent stated they were more secure people.
7. Fifty per cent indicated they were freer, more tolerant, or less guarded. Sixty per cent felt their personal conduct had changed for the better; 30 per cent believed their moral standards had changed toward increased personal responsibility.
8. Forty per cent felt a different relation between themselves and other people.

ANALYSIS OF FINDINGS

Eighty per cent reported at least one change—greater personal security—whereas 60 per cent feel their religious attitudes are changed. There appear to have been no extreme changes in the subjects' religious beliefs. That is, no agnostic became a believer or vice versa. The greatest confidence in responses was in other questions dealing with basic belief;

the least confidence ("both," "don't know") in more abstract or inter-personal items (see Appendix to Chapter X).

Leary and Clark have similar findings in a sample of four hundred volunteer professionals, graduate students, professors, and creative artists receiving psilocybin to produce the psychedelic effect. "Most subjects claimed to have been helped. . . . 62 per cent stated their lives were changed for the better. . . . Such terms as 'God,' 'divine,' 'deep religious experience,' 'meeting the infinite,' occurred in over half the reports." A subsample of thirty-six maximum-security prison inmates ". . . reported classic mystic, conversion reactions. 'All is one.' 'Thy will be done. . . .' Many . . . reported that their spiritual sensitivities . . . expanded. Biblical passages or religious terms formerly meaningless or pale have suddenly acquired vivid meaning."[5]

The religious or belief changes reported appear to be of a specific nature—that is, a clarification and underlining of positive religious beliefs already held by the subject. Reinforcement of beliefs is accompanied by an increased understanding which results in a broadening, opening, and freeing of pre-existing concepts. The subjects seem to be more tolerant of other religious views.

The underlining of beliefs previously held by the subjects who reported change deserves some attention. First, this points out that no new concepts were evolved in the psychedelic experience but that new attitudes, new understandings, or new aspects of previously held concepts were elaborated. Second, the change seems to be that the subject felt increased ability to accept the truth of such abstract concepts as God, the majesty of God, the evolving life force, the reality of life after death, the universality of religion, and so on. On the basis of the descriptions given, this increased ability seems to rest on increased trust. From the subjects' statements, God, the world, and death were things of which the subjects were now less afraid. This interpretation is supported by the fact that the area of largest change shown in the study was an increase in security (80 per cent) and ability to trust (60 per cent). Third, the area of trust which showed the greatest change, according to this study, was the individual's ability to trust himself. One could therefore create the hypothesis that, because the individual came to be on better terms with his own unconscious, his concept of himself was altered. Because he now saw himself differently, he found it possible to view other people and things in a different, more positive light.

Under the conditions in which these subjects received LSD 25, it appears that only positive religious concepts were reinforced in the psychedelic experience. Possibly negative concepts of the nature one is concerned with are here based on fear associated with lack of trust. If the person can directly encounter the causes of his inner fears and master them, he then can trust himself. If he can trust, he can love— that is, extend the compass of his own newly found integration of "real" self and "unconscious" self to include an other physically or spiritually outside of the self. For example, one can see this principle in the change in concepts of life after death. In considering the consequences of one's own dissolution, it would seem that the element of trust is involved. As Job cried, "Though he slay me, yet will I trust in him." As the subject meets and accepts his own fears, he feels more able to accept others and other things and to be accepted by them. He is less fearful even of physical dissolution. Possibly, because of his sense of self-acceptance, he increasingly sees himself as a part of the whole.

PSYCHEDELIC EXPERIENCE AND RELIGIOUS MEANINGFULNESS

Are these changes truly or really religious? Are they self-deception? We can say only that the elaborations presented by the subjects in answer to our questions appear possibly, not certainly, to be of a religious nature. It is impossible to make dogmatic statements as to what the experience described by the subjects under LSD "really" is because of its subjectivity. One can say that some, not all, of our subjects believed in the religious nature of their experience. Is there any other criterion to use?

As far as we know, the drug effect adds nothing new to the individual unconscious. Whatever is experienced is already present but not in conscious awareness. It would seem that certain psychological filters which are used to help an individual tolerate certain external stresses of sound, sight, and so on and to censor unacceptable or fearful memories partially cease to function. In conjunction with this, perception is either heightened or at least more sensitive to internal stimuli because of the absence of the psychological filters.[6]

Relation of Real Self to Unconscious Self

Heightened perception and lowered internal defenses leave the subject consciously aware of facing his unconscious. For this study, the real self might be conceived as standing in a tightly focused spotlight trying to be "good." The light which closely surrounds real man would be that area of himself which is known to the individual—his "conscious ego," to use Freud's terms. Around real man stretches a shadow, gray at first, but deepening into black—the "preconscious" and "unconscious," in

Freudian terms. It is black not because it is dangerous, dirty, or unpleasant, but simply because there is an absence of light, understanding, of conscious knowing or experiencing. This shadow is, however, fearful for the real individual because, although it involves him more directly than any other thing possibly can, it is the unknown, feared and "bad" part of himself.

The neurotic individual carries in himself a secret concept which may be stated as: "If people knew all there was to know about me (that is, my 'bad unconscious'), they would think that I was a pretty nasty, unpleasant, worthless individual." This concept of the unworthiness of the hidden, evil unconscious is held to a lesser degree by many mentally healthy people. The psychedelic experience permits the real man, if he will only take advantage of his lowered defenses and greatly heightened perception, to turn the light on and see his formerly blacked-out unconscious. Many individuals cannot face the light; their fear of what they will see is too great. Under LSD some actually experience walking into the shadow and finding a great inner light. Freed from that shadow, a person sees his experiences and may relive them through total recall or experience them as symbolic visions. As he looks into the formerly dark corners, he discovers that his inner self is not unacceptable, destructive, chaotic, nasty and altogether unacceptable. He discovers that he is not so bad as he had believed, that good, love, meaning, and value are in him. Real and unconscious self unify into a total, integrated self neither wholly good or bad, but both actively positive and purposive.

The Relation of Self to Other People

The result of this self-unifying experience is that the individual has a new, total view of himself. He sees that he has good in him, that he has value. He finds that he can like himself more, that he can love himself. Such positive changes toward oneself also alter one's view of other people, for one's concept of others is always colored by the way one sees himself. If the individual accepts himself more, trusts himself more, loves himself more, he can also trust others and love others to a greater degree.

The Relation of Unconscious Self to God

We have hypothesized that the beneficial psychedelic experience causes some persons to become more aware of and accepting of their own inner self or unconscious.[7] But becoming aware of and friendly with one's unconscious should not be passed over lightly. Profound religious connotations—connotations based on an ancient idea concerning God and man—accompany this psychological effect. In many religious systems, including the Judaeo-Christian, it has been taught that man first confronts the evidence of God in his own unconscious. Schaer and White have elaborated the view that only through inner experience can the greater totality outside of self be encountered.[8]

RELIGIOUS AND PSYCHOLOGICAL VALIDITY

Is God the unconscious of man? The phrase "the evidence of God" is used here with purpose. God himself is not conceived as being confronted in the unconscious of man because that would tend to limit God to man's unconscious, and this is held to be untrue. Rather, man confronts in himself the good (in the sense of the gift) which God has ordained for all men if they will accept it from Him. In religion the gift is stated as being the gift of life given by the life-giving God.

St. Paul talks about this gift of God. It is impossible to find the full meaning of St. Paul's use of the word "life" without careful study of all the underlying meanings found in the original Greek and a careful analysis of the way Paul uses the work in various situations. To Paul the gift of life is physical animation of the body plus the meaning, value, direction, and purpose experientially revealed by the act of God in Christ. Religion has long accepted that man finds this gift within himself when he searches for it. Meditation and prayer are the traditional paths to the inner voice. The psychedelic drugs are merely another way to look within and temporarily overcome the factors which make the search more difficult.

The Judaeo-Christian religions speak of love and trust. It was Jesus who pointed out that the great Jewish *Shema* was the most important of the laws of the life-giving God: "And thou shalt love the Lord thy God with all thine heart, and with all thy soul, and with all thy might" (Deut. 6:5; ". . . and with all thy mind," Matt. 22:37). Note that these statements taken from both the Old and New Testament point out that the whole man, both the conscious and unconscious, the real and inner selves, is to love God. He also said that the statement of Leviticus was the second basic law: "Thou shalt love thy neighbor as thyself" (Lev. 19:18, Matt. 22:39). Jesus is here talking about relationships—the relationship of oneself with himself, with others, and with the cosmos, the first cause, and God. All these relationships are mediated through love which has, as its basic ingredient, trust. No love relationship, whether to self, others, or God, can exist without trust. It would seem that the subjects in this experiment became more loving and trusting toward their inner unconscious self. They therefore came a little nearer to meeting the demand of life to love oneself, others, and God. In so doing, they found the gift of God of which St. Paul speaks, the "life more abundant," which includes meaning, value, and purposive existence. "Life was no longer haphazard," as one subject expressed it.

A few subjects reported various visual and auditory manifestations which had a religious frame of reference. For example, several spoke with conviction of having seen the Godhead, Christ, Mary, and so on while under the influence of the psychedelic drugs. The religious, supernatural nature of these manifestations cannot be concluded from the results of this experiment. Were they internally (psychologically) generated or external (supernatural) manifestations? If one accepts the hypothesis presented, one must assume the manifestations to be hallucinations, since this whole interpretation is based on the belief that the entire result of the experience comes from the subject's own unconscious, not from an external, supernatural source. This experience could come to have religious value if the subject is able to realize what the hallucination represents to him and thus moves closer to the free nature of the real God existing outside his own unconscious. If the subject remains convinced of the external, supernatural origin, it likely will reinforce pre-existing religious belief.

A few subjects in the experiment gave elaborations which might be interpreted as a negative change in religious thinking or concepts. One subject felt more negative toward organized religion and stated that "fewer remnants of Christianity hung on to him." According to the religious hypothesis outlined in this study, such a statement could come from an individual who had a misconception of what organized religion was saying and doing. The psychedelic experience may have made it possible for him to grasp for the first time what basic, personal, feeling, and experiencing religion has always tried to say. A strong tradition in Western religions has always held that basic religion is, and always has been, talking about the emotional life and its relationships.

Another subject stated that the sacrifice symbol taught in Christianity was in error because he now saw that one person cannot save another person pain. He seemed more inclined to reject Christianity because of his experience with LSD. If so, he is suffering from a misconception, since Christianity does not teach that one person can save another pain. It teaches that Jesus Christ died on a cross so that man might have the gift of God (value and purpose in life), which, says

St. Paul, God intends for us through Christ. This gift, which can be man's through an inner relationship with Christ and God in this life, also extends to the afterlife.

The concept of doing away with pain in life is not the purpose of Christ. Pain is an essential aspect of life which we evade at our own loss. Christ offers us a closer relationship with God through which we can receive the gift of God. This gift is completeness, wholeness, and integrated being through oneness with God, called "salvation" in Christianity. Thus, pain still comes in life, but for an integrated being it can be borne and in itself have meaning. If the subject is referring to the pain of Hell (which, as used here, is the absence of God and hence the absence of His gift), the result of salvation is not the permanent removal of the pain and suffering of Hell, but the wholeness and integration resulting from receiving God's gift.

Religion has always struggled with the problem of helping people find their way to basic love (with its root of trust) of themselves, others, and God. The churches teach that, to be really known, all effective religion must be an inner experience. This is held to be correct; only when religion begins at the emotional level of man's existence can it be known to the full. Some people are able to find this emotional knowledge, but many others are able to attain only an intellectual acceptance of external rules, while the ideal of a union of emotion and knowledge and the external rule is completely missed. Such people miss much in religion and need help with this.

Man asks, "What am I really like? What is my real inner nature or self?" Much traditional Christian theology holds that man is innately evil, originally sinful. Some interpretation of Freudian psychology has reinforced this belief through the concept of the id and unconscious as disorganized, chaotic, raw instinctual impulses driving blindly toward unreasoning expression. The atheistic psychoanalytic patient can be just as convinced of his basic destructiveness and lack of worth as the most fundamentalist Pentecostal Christian. When he looks into his unconscious and finds, often to his surprise, value and good there, he therefore loves (trusts) himself to a greater degree. Through positive action he tends to test his findings against his external world of people close to him. When he is loved, accepted, and trusted in return, his feelings concerning himself are reinforced. He feels himself good, to have some value despite the continuance of certain negative feelings. Further, because of this view of himself, he concludes that others have value and meaning and that the world is made with purpose and value.

Alienation, the strange feeling of being separate from and not a part of oneself, other people, and life in general, is a frequent complaint today even among churchgoers. People complain they feel different from other people, that the world seems incongruous, detached, or distant. They may speak of being estranged from themselves, from others, and from any meaning in being alive. This is not to say that alienation is new; cries of inner pain and estrangement are as old as recorded man. Nonetheless, in the mid-twentieth century, the Freudian revolution, unprecedented social and technological changes, great geographical mobility, and general cultural and familial breakup seem to have resulted in more extreme and severe feelings of alienation affecting more people.

In a more stable, less diverse and technological society, religion provided the general organizing focus for all of life's activities; in a society concerned with television, radio, moving pictures, and recreation, religion becomes but one of many intellectual and perceptual attractions which must compete for time and attention. The church affects far less of the available free time; in attractiveness it is hard put to compete with grosser, blatantly seductive, although much shallower, organized commercial activities. In the past, the church also met the sensuous needs of the people through ritual, music, color, sermons, and ceremony. Through sight, sound, scent and harmonious social organization, drab everyday lives had a satisfying sensory as well as unifying spiritual experience. Today commercial attractions now equal or excel the church in most of these areas.

The general level of external sensory stimulation and information input is higher today than ever before primarily because of mechanical and electronic advances; nonetheless, people frequently complain of monotony, the rat race, and lack of gratification and satisfaction from living. Modern urban life and technology have brought a great deal of comfort and security, alleviation and softening of pain and suffering, considerable passing distraction, and a marked loss of direct experience and ecstasy. The increasing general preoccupation with "thrill" sports, with more and more activity for its own sake, with diverse erotic and other sensual gratifications, partners, and techniques can be interpreted as blind attempts to achieve a more satisfying emotional—that is, ecstatic—experience. Pain, grief, childbirth, and death are generally blurred today by painkillers and tranquilizers. Strong positive emotional experiences are also modulated to the point of extinction by middle-class social disapproval of any but the most discreet display of joy, happiness, or overwhelming emotion. Only through warfare—both direct and substitute—are general strong emotions of group feeling, both constructive and destructive, released with social approval.

Again, in other cultures, organized religion provides for annual periods of unrestrained, orgiastic release through festivals and carnivals ("flesh days") such as the pre-Lenten celebrations or the Oktoberfest of contemporary Bavaria. In the past, the salvation and revival sects of the United States included even the presently staid middle-class Methodists and Baptists. One observer of the great nineteenth-century Methodist camp-meeting revivals observed drily, "It was hard to know whether more souls were saved or conceived." The Foursquare Gospel Church founded by Aimee Semple McPherson, many Negro churches, and the Pentecostal sects still provide ecstatic religious group experiences of a largely nonerotic type.

• We therefore hypothesize that, in the absence of opportunities for recurring strong emotional experience, either painful or pleasant to the point of overwhelming grief or ecstasy, individuals will tend to develop generalized feelings of alienation and estrangement. Their relations to self, others, and God will be affected.

Such intense emotional experience occurs far more commonly in contemporary nontechnological societies and our own nontechnological past. Birth and death took place at home without anodynes, violence was more common at all social levels, and restraint of feeling and expression was not the social norm. Where does the middle class have direct, deep, emotional experience today? Institutionalized religion is pallid, ecstatic religion is viewed as lower class and hence unacceptable, and salvation, formerly a normal stage in personality maturation, is almost unheard of. Religion has turned to psychiatry and psychology for meaning, possibly because the psychiatrist is still socially licensed to deal with people in directly expressed emotional terms.

The ministry of salvation has given way to the ministry of adjustment. Psychology and psychiatry have gained increasingly more power in religious counsels because the ministry is looking for new content to fill the old ministerial role. The church tends to divert the churchgoer from direct experience and to join the general social conspiracy to evade, cover over, and distract from direct experience. The emphasis in the home, in business, in school, and in the church is on minimizing strong feelings, covering over differences, compromising, being a good team member, and going along.

There was a time when through the religious experience the churchgoer expected to feel passion, grief, joy, and sorrow of ecstatic proportions and to share the passion of Christ. Today any such behavior might well be indication of a need for psychiatric consultation or at least a recommendation to ask the medical doctor for tranquilizers.

Organized religion cannot be exclusively blamed for sharing in a general social movement toward suppression of all emotion except tooth-gleaming affability and coffee-cup socialization. Every year hundreds of tons of chemical restraints in the form of tranquilizers and alcohol are self-administered or prescribed by physicians to maintain individual internal equilibrium in the face of this increasing social constraint. Thus there is a religious loss. Fewer people are able, through Christ, to attain the gift of God that St. Paul described as bringing life more abundantly. Not surprising, then, is the number of sensitive intellectuals who are turning to the psychedelic experience to gain direct deep emotion and release, ecstatic heightening of perception, and consequent re-experiencing of the usually alienated inner self. Through the psychedelic experience, this release and resynthesis is often, although not invariably, attained.

SUMMARY

This paper has offered the findings that a significant proportion of people report that LSD has helped them take a first step toward trusting themselves. It consequently appears that they were able to take further steps toward trust of others and God, usually without LSD. It has done so in no weird, inexplicable way, but by what appears to be understandable steps which may be subjected to proof and then be accepted as demonstrable knowledge. If the hypothesis presented here is true, it would seem that religionists would find it wise to study carefully these effects so that their value might be further determined. In general, this experience seems to justify such careful study through use by competent personnel with carefully chosen subjects. Judging from the reported psychedelic experience of these subjects, who were not selected for their religious inclinations or outlook, organized religion might well investigate this chemical mode of reuniting the would-be believer to himself, his religious brother, and God.

NOTES

1. George Larrick, commissioner of the United States Food and Drug Administration, quoted in *Chemical Week*, August 16, 1963.
2. Willis W. Harman, "The Issue of the Consciousness Expanding Drugs," *Main Currents in Modern Thought*, XX, No. 1 (1963).
3. For example, see Charles Savage, James Terrill, and Don D. Jackson, "LSD, Transcendence, and the New Beginning," *Journal of Nervous and Mental Diseases*, CXXXV (1962), 425–439.
4. Max Rinkel, C. W. Atwell, Alberto DiMascio, and J. R. Brown, "Experimental Psychiatry, V: Psilocybin, a New Psychotogenic Drug," *New England Journal of Medicine*, CCLXII (1960), 295–299.

5. Timothy Leary and W. H. Clark, "Religious Implications of Consciousness-Expanding Drugs," *Religious Education,* May-June, 1963.
6. Joseph J. Downing, "On the Mind-Altering Function of LSD-25," San Mateo County Mental Health Services, 1964 (mimeographed).
7. Certain psychedelic experiences occurring in unselected, unprepared people are definitely not beneficial.
8. Hans Schaer, *Religion and the Cure of Souls in Jung's Psychology* (New York: Pantheon, 1950); Victor White, *God and the Unconscious* (Chicago: Regnery, 1953).

APPENDIX TO CHAPTER X:
QUESTIONNAIRE RESPONSES

The subjects came from a variety of religious backgrounds and experiences. There were nine people who described themselves as having no religion or being agnostic in their religious attitude. There were seven who stated that they were not practicing the religion in which they had been raised; of these, three had been reared as Jews, two as Roman Catholics, one as a Presbyterian, and one as a Methodist. Six indicated their religious view merely as Protestant; eight stated relationship with the Episcopal Church, and three stated relationship with the Unitarian Church. Two subjects indicated membership in the United Church of Christ of the United States of America (a recent merger of the Congregational-Christian and Evangelical and Reformed denominations). The Presbyterian Church was represented by one subject. The Jewish religion was represented by three people. Three described themselves as "mystics," "universalists," and having "a belief in a supreme being." No practicing Roman Catholic was included in this or any other sample studied. The questions and responses were as follows:

1. What is your religion?
    The responses to this question are recorded above.

2. Have your feelings on religion and what it means changed any as a result of your LSD experience? If yes, in what way? No: 18 (40%) ; yes: 24 (60%).

Elaborations of the affirmative answers fell into two main groups. In the first of these, twelve subjects felt that they had experienced an emotional change, a deepening of understanding of religious concepts, such as those concerning God, which were already held by the individual. They therefore felt closer to the church because of this understanding. The individual felt that he now *knew* that God was truly uncanny and awesome, as he had been taught that He is.

The second group experienced a change in their religious thinking in that they were not so dogmatic, authoritarian, or ritualistic as before. More tolerant of organized churches, as well as other religions, this group now saw all other religions to be basically the same, different paths to oneness with God. "Religion is a state of being or relationship, not mere acceptance of a doctrine or code." Two people now could understand and accept the religious experiences spoken of by religionists as being a singular oneness or experience of unity.

One individual stated he felt more negative toward organized religion and Christianity.

3. Have your feelings about the existence of a supreme being changed as a result of your LSD experience? If yes, in what way? No: 29 (70%) ; yes: 13 (30%).

An intensified knowing, more conviction of His existence, was expressed as the "evolving life force," a "deepening of faith," a "part of His being," "this is the force within."

One individual stated that the loving aspect of God was brought to the fore by the LSD experience, indicating that a previous doubt or distrust of the loving aspect of God was now swept away.

4. Have your feelings about life after death changed any? If yes, in what way? No: 24 (60%) ; yes: 18 (40%).

Again, the largest number who answered this question in the affirmative (twelve) indicated an intensification of concepts previously held. Some now felt convinced that there is no death, that life is really continuous despite physical change. Death to them now seemed simply continuation toward the mystical goal of oneness with God.

Associated were lessened anxiety, greater acceptance of death, lesser necessity of factual knowledge concerning the afterlife, and more pleasure in living because of lessened anxiety about death.

5. Has your understanding of religious doctrine (i.e., the teachings of your own church) changed? If yes, in what way? No: 23 (60%) ; yes: 19 (40%).

Once more, the greatest change was toward increased understanding of doctrine already accepted or believed. Some described their understanding of the universal nature of religion as being heightened, an increase in understanding of "the thread that runs through all religions." This included such concepts as "all religions being based on universal precepts such as love for one's fellow men" and "the unity of the universe." Others also described increased, clarified understanding of some more general concepts, such as the concept that religion is, at bottom, trust. Views of religious concepts were liberalized—such as the willingness to now understand and accept mystics; some individuals' concept of prayer was changed so that for the first time it seemed real and significant for them. Another claimed an increased conviction of a subjective reality and the truth of the unity of all things. This was described as helping to confirm religious truths. In connection with this increased understanding, one individual stated that he had done more religious exploration since the LSD experience.

One individual stated that he now saw that the sacrifice symbol of religion is a ". . . mistake, since one person cannot save another pain." Another claimed a complete change of religious attitude, stating that ministers do not have the foggiest idea what religion is.

6. When talking to other people about religion, do you approach them differently? If yes, how? No: 30 (70%); yes: 12 (30%).

The majority of affirmative responses to this question involved more understanding of, tolerance of, and openness toward others. The largest group of responses falling in this category indicated more tolerance, acceptance, and understanding of others' views on religion. The responses reflected more openness to different views and less antagonism. One subject said that he now felt a oneness with others that he had not felt before. Another individual stated that he now saw that religion was basically trust and that he now understood why others must be able to trust him and he them.

7. Do you trust people more than you did? How? No (same as before, no change): 25 (60%); yes: 14 (35%); don't know: 3 (5%).

This question is of interest, since 35 per cent of all ninety-two users were rated by the interviewer as significantly distrustful and 17 per cent as overly trustful. Fifty per cent did not show the degree of trust considered normal by the interviewer. Interviewer trust ratings were not available for this subsample of forty-two.

Thirty-five per cent saw themselves as more trustful, 60 per cent as unchanged. The majority indicated they now trusted themselves more and as a result could trust others. Elaborations included being able to "entrust more of themselves," "more giving," "more open," "increased ability to express personal feelings," "more willing to take a chance on being disappointed." One "saw more depth in others" because ". . . [his own] defenses had been lowered"; another stated that he was "more discriminating of people's motives" but wanted to "do" for others; a third now realized "other people are also human," that they thought and felt as he did.

8. Do you trust God (or life) more than you did? How? No: 18 (40%); yes: 24 (60%).

The majority of the affirmative answers stated an increased ability to accept the inevitable and/or a feeling that life was not so vindictive or negative as it was once viewed as being. Some indicated this by saying that they now felt more able to give in to the "wisdom within," to "the way of God," or to "the Tao." They now saw that "God is in all things that happen." Others stated that they felt more convinced of the complete order and wonder of life and they could now see a definite plan of or rhythm to things. Also, some in this category felt that they now knew "there is an Answer. Even if specific answers are still unknown, . . . this is now enough." A single person said he no longer viewed life as a nasty or prankish thing. Others said that they were more interested in experiencing life because of newly increased trust. Another stated that he was no longer planning to commit suicide. Some stated that they felt they had more self-control than previously and that this gave a greater sense of inner security and a general sense of well-being.

9. Would you say you are a more secure person? How? No: 7 (15%); yes: 33 (80%); perhaps: 2 (5%).

The greatest number of affirmative answers listed psychological changes for the better in relation to self—a greater feeling of confidence and ability to trust oneself, a greater freedom in making choices, increased optimism and self-reliance, and a deepened understanding of oneself and others. There was also a general sense of being less anxious.

The next largest group of the affirmative answers to this question stated a change in teleological knowledge in such words as "I know where I am going," "I know what it's all about," "nothing seems haphazard." The statements of this group are related to those given in the preceding paragraph but are reported as a separate category because they describe changes of feeling in relation to the external world.

Others stated they felt more dependency on the "God within," not so dependent on outside sources for a sense of security or a "feeling of belonging."

10. Has your personal code of conduct changed? If so, how? No: 15 (35%); yes: 21 (50%); don't know: 8 (15%).

The largest number of affirmative responses to this question indicated change in the area of one's attitude toward himself and others in the sense that the individual felt able to be more honest with himself and more free and open, to be himself, to have better control of hostile feelings, or to be more conservative in dress and manners.

Other responses reflected a positive change in the individual's actions; he was more discerning, able to refrain from drinking, "not as guarded or defensive," more tolerant toward shortcomings, and had an increased ability to be honest with others.

11. Do you feel you are a more or less moral person than before? If changed, how? Unchanged: 26 (65%); less: 2 (5%); more: 7 (15%); both: 4 (5%); don't know: 3 (5%).

The majority of the responses that indicated change stressed the idea that the subjects felt that they were now both more and less moral. They believed themselves to be less moral according to society's view (or what they termed "false standards") but more moral toward themselves. They now felt they could see "larger issues" and could be more honest about themselves.

Another group saw change in themselves regarding guilt and morals. These subjects stated that they now have more guilt feeling regarding promiscuity and "their search for closeness" in the sense that they felt more nagged by their conscience.

A third group indicated an increase in their concept of morals in relation to others. These subjects claimed that they now try to "keep from lousing others up," that they "felt more loving toward others," or that they felt an increase in the feeling of "oneness" toward others.

One subject claimed that he now did less moralizing about others.

12. Do other people look at you differently? If yes, how? No: 18 (45%); yes: 16 (35%); don't know: 8 (10%).

The largest number of subjects who elaborated on this question said that others saw them as more relaxed and less defensive; hence others were more willing to relate to the subject, and the subject was also more willing to relate to others. In some cases the subject stated that others appeared to be less hostile to the subject because of this change.

The second largest group of subjects felt that others had more faith in them or a new respect or liking for them.

One other subject said that others have said that they noted a change in the subject's personality, but that he himself is not sure that the change is all because of LSD. He based this on the fact that other factors, such as previous therapy and the fact that he had just been married, were involved. He did feel, however, that his LSD experience must be given a large part of the credit for his personality change.

13. Are you less or more concerned with other people? If changed, how? Unchanged: 13 (30%); less: 4 (10%); more: 18 (45%); both: 6 (10%); don't know: 1.

The largest group of descriptions showing change indicated that the subjects now felt more conscious of others' feelings. Some also indicated that they "worried" about others more or felt "worry"; it is therefore difficult to say from the results whether this points to a negative result of the psychedelic experience.

The second largest group of subjects felt that the change they noticed involved "balance"; they felt more concern for others but less concern about what others think about them. They felt they were now more concerned with seeking self-approval than external approval.

The next largest group of subjects felt that they could more openly show their concern for others in the sense that they now wanted to do more things for others and were more willing, cooperative, and "better blenders." Only two stated a desire "to help free others" or "help others through difficulties"; two others were more concerned for those close to them but less concerned for more distant relationships.

SOCIAL AND LEGAL RESPONSE TO PLEASURE-GIVING DRUGS

[XI]

Joel Fort

It should be our earnest intention to insure that drugs not be employed to debase mankind, but to serve it.

John F. Kennedy

That humanity at large will ever be able to dispense with artificial paradises seems very unlikely.

Aldous Huxley

All laws which can be violated without doing any one any injury are laughed at. Nay, so far are they from doing anything to control the desires and passions of men that, on the contrary, they direct and incite men's thoughts the more toward those very objects; for we always strive toward what is forbidden and desire the things we are not allowed to have. And men of leisure are never deficient in the ingenuity needed to enable them to outwit laws framed to regulate things which cannot be entirely forbidden. . . . He who tries to determine everything by law will foment crime rather than lessen it.

Baruch Spinoza

Despite the recent attention given to drugs of the LSD type in the public press and, to a lesser degree, in professional journals, a clearly articulated social and legal attitude toward these substances has yet to

be arrived at. When such attitudes or responses and their associated
policies or laws are developed in the next few years, mainly by the
common representatives of the common man—legislators and the communications media: newspapers, radio, and television—they are likely
to follow the pattern of past and present policies toward the use of
other pleasure-giving drugs, such as cannabis (marijuana), and narcotics. To a much lesser degree there will be a similarity (as well as
major discrepancies) with policies toward alcohol use and abuse. A
review of the scientific, social, and legal attitudes and responses toward
these other drugs will therefore be profitable both in itself and in understanding and predicting future policies toward the LSD-type drugs.

As a first step toward understanding, however, we must carefully
examine our terminology and conceptualizations since most of it currently dooms us to erroneous conclusions and generalizations. Even the
word "drug" often carries unfavorable connotations in this context.
Among the terms which have been used for such drugs as LSD are
hallucinogen, psychotomimetic, psychedelic, and consciousness-expanding. All of them have an inherently biased connotation, the first two
stressing the experimental or dangerous aspect and the latter two the
positive or beneficial aspects. I hereby suggest that the simplest, most
meaningful, most specific, and most scientific term would be "LSD-type
drug." Not only would this preclude biased terminology, but, in speci-
fying LSD (lysergic acid diethylamide), psilocybin, mescaline, and so
on as members of the class, it would help to prevent the presently mis-
taken inclusion of almost totally different families of drugs, such as
cannabis, simply because in rare instances an individual may experience
hallucinations or illusions.

The next distinction needed is between use of, abuse of, and addiction to what I am calling the "pleasure-giving drugs." I urge adoption
of this term rather than such vague, meaningless, and negative terms
as "narcotic," "dangerous drug," "addiction-producing drug," and so
on. Alcohol, cannabis (marijuana), opiates (opium, heroin, morphine),
stimulants (caffeine, amphetamine, cocaine), sedatives (barbiturates
and the like), tranquilizers, and so forth are all drugs which I would
categorize in their voluntary nonmedical use (particularly in the United
States) as being sought after and continued primarily for their social
and psychological pleasure-giving effects (even though they do not
provide pleasure for all who use them). The new term is also appropriate since it is the pleasure-giving capacity of the drugs which brings
forth most of the condemnation from prisoners of the Judaeo-Christian
ethic. All of these drugs are, and have been, widely used in most areas
of our planet and in most eras of human existence. With each of them,

some (not all, and usually only a minority) become abusers, and some of these become habituated or addicted. Common usage, based upon distorted and incomplete information, has led to calling all users of these drugs (except for alcohol) addicts and all the drugs, when misused, narcotics. Thus the public has developed a stereotype of a socially unacceptable criminal every time a marijuana (or other illicit drug) user is arrested.

The most commonly accepted and used scientific definitions of drug addiction and drug habituation are those promulgated by the Expert Committee on Addiction-Producing Drugs of the World Health Organization in 1957. It defined drug addiction as a state of periodic or chronic intoxication produced by the repeated consumption of a drug (natural or synthetic). Its characteristics include (1) an overpowering desire or need (compulsion) to continue taking the drug and to obtain it by any means, (2) a tendency to increase the dose, (3) a psychic (psychological) and, generally, a physical dependence on the effects of the drug, (4) a detrimental effect on the individual and on society. Drug habituation is defined as a habit or condition resulting from the repeated consumption of a drug. Its characteristics include (1) a desire but not a compulsion to continue taking the drug for the sense of improved well-being which it engenders, (2) little or no tendency to increase the dose, (3) some degree of psychic dependence on the effect of the drug but absence of physical dependence and hence of an abstinence syndrome, (4) detrimental effects, if any, primarily on the individual.

Just this year, however, the World Health Organization committee has recommended adoption of a new term, "drug dependence," to replace both drug addiction and drug habituation because of continued misuse and confusion associated with the old terms. Drug dependence is defined as a state arising from repeated administration of a drug on a periodic or continual basis. Its characteristics will vary with the agent involved, and this must be made clear by designating drug dependence of a particular type in each specific case—that is, drug dependence of morphine type, of cannabis type, of barbiturate type. As an example, drug dependence of cannabis type is described as a state arising from repeated administration, in some areas almost exclusively periodic, in others more continual. Its characteristics include (1) a desire or need for repetition of the drug for its subjective effects and the feeling of enhancement of one's capabilities which it effects, (2) little or no tendency to increase the dose since there is little or no tolerance development, (3) a psychic dependence on the effects of the drug related to subjective and individual appreciation of those effects, (4) absence of physical dependence so that there is no definite and characteristic abstinence syndrome when the drug is discontinued. The description of types of drug dependency are confined to medical aspects only, but the committee stresses the importance of considering the risk of public health and socioeconomic factors in determining the appropriateness of particular controls. Unfortunately the Expert Committee has excluded alcohol from its studies and recommendations, thus apparently reflecting the unscientific biases discussed below. Among the many myths dear to the public about narcotic addicts (a concept including marijuana and sometimes other drugs, such as the LSD type, considered bad) are the ideas that the drugs stimulate sexuality, lead to violent crime, and destroy one's health. In fact, none of these or similar myths occur, but they do emphasize the importance of stressing that none of the pleasure-giving drugs produce a uniform and consistent effect based on their pharmacological properties. The effect of these drugs, including alcohol, on an individual user depends on a complex interaction between the pharmacology of the drug itself, the personality of the individual taking the drug, and the social setting in which the drug is taken.

Other parameters or dimensions to be considered in evaluating or objectively determining the effects of the pleasure-giving drugs would include such concepts as harmless (in the case of alcohol) beverage or cigarette versus harmful drug; small doses versus large ones; regular use versus intermittent use; viewing with alarm (dangers) versus pointing with pride (benefits); overconformity versus negative rebellion; lower class (with its greater contact with and prosecution by law and its scapegoat function) versus upper class; the purity or potency of the drug (opium versus heroin); the mode of administration (speed and intensity of effect from drinking, smoking, eating, injecting); opinion and propaganda versus science and fact; normality versus illness versus crime; and generalizing from some to all.

The attention we are giving and have already given to the LSD-type drugs is both less than is often believed or implied and, paradoxically, far more than is justified on an absolute scale. Why are some segments of the press and public so interested, and why are medical and social scientists devoting their energies to this rather than to the many great social and health problems confronting our country and the world? Rarely has so much been said by so many about so little.

ALCOHOL

Known and presumably used by man during the Old Stone Age, one million years ago, alcohol is the most widely used and abused pleasure-giving drug in the Western world. It is also a growing problem in Asia and Africa. In sharp and ironic contrast to the social and legal response to the other related drugs, alcohol is essentially uncontrolled, freely, albeit expensively, available to all, and considered a harmless beverage rather than a dangerous drug. Its use is strongly encouraged in most occupations and all social classes as an intrinsic part of commercial and social life. In the United States alone, some eight hundred million gallons of wine and distilled spirits and one hundred million barrels of beer are produced legally each year with a per-capita consumption of more than seventeen gallons yearly from forty thousand liquor stores and thousands of additional grocery and drug stores. The alcoholic beverage industry in the United States grosses $12,000,000,000 a year with expenditures of nearly $200,000,000 a year for advertisement (exceeded only by expenditures for auto and food advertisement) to associate the consumption of alcohol with youthfulness, health, beauty, acceptance, sex, and success.

Despite being thus far excluded from consideration by the Addiction-Producing Drug Section of the World Health Organization, alcoholism in the old terminology is both habituating and addicting and in the new terminology would definitely be a form of drug dependence similar to the barbiturate type. Probably the best definition of alcoholism, particularly in its emphasis on its social effects, is a chronic personality disorder manifested by repeated episodes of excessive drinking to the point that it interferes with the individual's social or vocational adjustment and/or health. It is an illness affecting all social classes and occupational groups, with less than 5 per cent of alcoholics on skid row. As a drug alcohol in small to moderate doses is self-administered orally to produce relaxation and euphoria and to conform to contemporary mores. These doses concomitantly produce some impairment of judgment, coordination, and vision, as they exert a pharmacologically depressant action on the frontal areas of the brain. With larger doses consumed regularly and daily over a period of weeks, addiction develops, with its severe withdrawal symptoms (delirium tremens) of convulsions and/or toxic psychosis when the drug is sharply decreased or discontinued. Over a period of years of consumption of large amounts either regularly or intermittently, irreversible damage to the brain (atrophy), peripheral nervous system (neuritis), liver (cirrhosis) develops, all of these consequences being much more serious than the long-term physical effects of the other pleasure-giving drugs.

From the standpoint of public health and socioeconomic consequences, alcoholism is also a serious problem. Out of some eighty million consumers, there are, perhaps, six million people in America alone and more than twenty-five million in the world with drug dependency on alcohol. Around fifteen thousand deaths and two hundred thousand injuries associated with drunken driving occur yearly in the United States. Alcoholic cirrhosis of the liver is one of the major causes of death; vast absenteeism, accidents, and job loss in business and industry occur, with an annual estimated loss of $500,000,000; many, if not most, divorces and broken homes occur in connection with excessive drinking; one-third to one-half of all traffic arrests are for drunkenness, far outnumbering any other category of arrest; 60 per cent of all arrests are for offenses directly related to use of alcoholic beverages, and 50 per cent of those in prison committed their crimes after alcohol consumption; and an unknown but significant amount of decreased productivity, welfare costs, and so on must be considered.

Despite this massive evidence of harmfulness, except for the fourteen years of the unenforceable, extreme, corruption-breeding Volstead Act and the Eighteenth Amendment, alcohol has always been available over the counter without prescription and without specific legal controls. Present controls in the United States and most other countries are at best weak and ineffectual tokens, consisting of taxation, licensing and minimally regulating sales outlets, weak laws against drunken driving, and poorly enforced prohibitions against drinking under certain ages (eighteen to twenty-one). This is amazing even if not surprising, particularly in contrast to the present and proposed controls on the other pleasure-giving drugs. Alcohol's status as a major source of revenue to state and national governments and the rich and powerful lobby of the alcoholic beverage industry naturally impede adoption of significant or meaningful controls. Also the failure of total prohibition is usually illogically cited as proving the lack of merit in attempting to bring about temperance or moderation through law.

SEDATIVES AND TRANQUILIZERS

Sedatives and tranquilizers are easily available at moderate expense from drugstores by physician's prescription or, to a lesser extent, by black-market routes. Their availability is controlled only by laws requiring a physician's prescription, which is refillable. These drugs are being extensively used and abused by probably more than one million people in the United States alone. The federal Food and Drug Laws require labeling most of them "habit-forming," and possession of them except by prescription is illegal under the dangerous-drugs sections of the criminal codes; in a few states driving under the influence of these drugs is unlawful. The drugs are available mainly in pill and capsule form for oral consumption, but also in liquid oral and injectable forms, being widely used for medical (and self-) treatment of insomnia, anxiety, tension, and emotional disturbance. The prototype and most commonly used family of these drugs are the barbiturates which came into use after 1912 with about fifty types being marketed under many trade names. In each of the past ten years more than seven hundred thousand pounds of barbiturates have been produced in the United States, enough for more than thirty doses per year for each adult and child in the country. Other commonly used sedatives include chloral hydrate, paraldehyde, meprobamate, and chlordiazepoxide. The latter two are falsely advertised as tranquilizers, but, like the other sedatives, their use has been shown to lead in some cases to habituation, addiction (in the case of the fast-acting barbiturates, in doses over six hundred milligrams a day), and dependency, with the severe withdrawal symptoms of convulsions and/or toxic psychosis, but not the irreversible physical damage of chronic alcoholism. Except for alcohol the oldest sedative drug is the group of bromides, which can produce habituation in the form of psychological dependency and toxic psychosis from excessive amounts, but no physical addiction. The true tranquilizers are mainly drugs of the phenothiazine family and are used mainly for the treatment of psychoses. They have little immediate pleasurable effect, are not addicting, and can ordinarily be consumed in very large amounts without serious harm. Like alcohol, sedatives even in small to moderate doses adversely affect reaction time, vision, and judgment. Between 15 to 20 per cent of all physicians' prescriptions are for the more than three hundred sedative and tranquilizing preparations available in the *United States Pharmacopoeia.* There are about one hundred and fifty "sleeping aids" available without prescription for over-the-counter sale since they do not contain "habit-forming drugs" (usually having as ingredients antihistaminics, aspirin, and belladonna or scopolamine). Although comprehensive scientific data are not available, the above figures and the incomes of pharmaceutical companies would indicate that there are several million regular users of these drugs in the United States; arrest figures in several states, including California, show a rise for arrests for dangerous drug offenses (barbiturates and amphetamines), particularly among young adults and teen-agers. Several thousand suicides each year utilize these drugs, and thousands of other people accidentally or deliberately take an acute overdose of the drugs without dying. Used mostly by the middle and upper class and widely advertised as safe, nonaddictive, and happiness-producing, these drugs are sought after for euphoria and thrills analogous to the use of alcohol or illicit narcotics. Both the World Health Organization Expert Committee and the United Nations Commission on Narcotic Drugs have stated that barbiturates pose a danger to social and public health and have recommended that governments place the production, distribution, and use of barbiturates under strict control. Recent legislation by the American Congress controlling drugs in general failed to include sufficiently strong controls on the sedative or stimulant drugs because of the opposition of the pharmaceutical industry and the American Medical Association.

STIMULANTS

The most widely used stimulant drug is caffeine, almost universally available over the counter in coffee, tea, and cola drinks without any legal or social controls. Although habituation and some physiological tolerance to the drug occur, there is no addiction or toxic effects except with very large doses. Another almost universally available stimulant drug is nicotine, used mainly in the form of tobacco cigarettes and chiefly of interest today because there is far more evidence to justify the banning of tobacco cigarettes than the banning of marijuana. Cocaine, still widely used in several South American countries and to a slight extent in the United States, produces habituation, toxic effects, and drug dependency, but no physical addiction. Its manufacture and distribution are carefully controlled in the United States, and medical prescriptions are required for purchasing it. Other stimulant drugs are also available by medical prescription, but the most prominent and widely used family is the amphetamines such as Dexedrine and Benzedrine, which have been in use since 1933 and are available in oral capsules and liquid injectable forms. The amphetamines produce habituation, physiological tolerance, toxic effects, and drug dependency, but not physical addiction. They, like the barbiturates, are extensively and increasingly used both by the upper classes and by delinquent teenagers and young adults for euphoria, alertness, relief of fatigue, suppression of appetite, or "kicks." In small or moderate doses their main side effects are insomnia, weight loss, and restlessnes, but, in larger quantities taken for several weeks, a severe toxic (paranoid) psychosis and, sometimes, convulsions occur.

CANNABIS (MARIJUANA)

Just as the social and legal responses to alcohol use show great inconsistency, so do the responses to cannabis use (all use in the United States is now erroneously thought of as abuse or addiction) although in the direction of excessive control. Known to be used by men for nearly five thousand years; widely grown throughout the world; used illicitly and sometimes licitly in America, Mexico, the West Indies, India, Egypt, and the rest of Africa, this pleasure-giving drug comes from the dried leaves, tops, or resin of the female hemp plant. It is consumed by smoking or eating, is known by many names, and unlike alcohol does not produce, even with prolonged or excessive use, addiction or irreversible physical damage to the body, although dependency or habituation and toxic effects can occur. In the countries where it is widely used, there is no scientific proof of over-all harm or danger either to the individual or to society. Marijuana might well be more beneficial to mankind than alcohol, but any reform of present laws in terms of increasing the availability and use of cannabis would probably be opposed by the alcoholic beverage industry and certainly by poorly informed legislators and representatives of law enforcement. Except for India and Morocco, where various forms of the drug are legally used by many hundreds of thousands of people, its use is currently banned under national and local laws and international treaties. It is not medically prescribed even where technically permitted. In nineteenth-century America many hemp preparations were available without restrictions; after 1900 its use spread through the country in the form of marijuana and was used by people in all social classes. As a result of hysterical propaganda campaigns led by law-enforcement officials and the sensational press, numerous states banned its use, and in 1937 under the pretext of passing a revenue act Congress passed the Marijuana Tax Act under the urging of the United States Treasury Department and the commissioner of narcotics. In his testimony the comissioner stated that there was rapidly increasing use of this drug and associated marijuana with assassination, danger, high-school children, addiction, violent crimes, irresponsibility, insanity, and sexual degeneration. (Surprisingly, in view of statements in later years, he indicated there was no association with heroin use.) Among the statements made by witnesses urging this legislation was: "Marijuana is a curse eating away at the very vitals of the nation." Of course, unlike the situation with alcohol, there was no organized lobby of users or manufacturers to proclaim the benefits of the drug. No scientific evidence was presented or even asked for, and the only opposition and only rational statement on the drug came from a representative of the American Medical Association, who recommended leaving the handling of the problem to the states and pointed out the lack of foundation for many of the statements made by the other witnesses. The active principle is believed to be tetrahydracannabinol, but much about the pharmacology is not yet known, mostly because research involving this drug has been discouraged and inhibited by existing legislation. The many myths associating the drug with crime, insanity, sexuality, and addiction have become more intense since that time. Laws have lumped cannabis with narcotics, and penalties for using, possessing, and selling it have steadily increased. Cannabis is taken for euphoria, reduction of fatigue, and relief of tension. It is available at moderate costs (50¢ to $1.00 a cigarette) and grows easily in a wild state. It is probably used by several hundred thousand people in the United States, including many from the middle class. Small to moderate doses also increase appetite, distort the time sense, increase self-confidence, and, like alcohol, can relax some inhibitions. The only comprehensive scientific clinical and sociological study of the drug was done by a New York City mayor's committee in the early 1940's. The committee found that cannabis drugs were used extensively, mostly by Negroes and Puerto Ricans, to create feelings of adequacy. The drugs did not lead to addiction; did not lead to narcotics use, juvenile delinquency, or crimes; and were not widespread among school children. Publicity about the catastrophic effects was held to be unfounded. The drugs caused no mental or physical deterioration, although there was some transient adverse effect on mental functioning; there was no change in personality structure or reaction time. Much of the crime associated with the use of marijuana is, of course, crime by edict or definition rather than actual antisocial behavior. Anxiety and physical distress can be produced by larger doses, but, basically, cannabis has low toxicity and, to some extent, a built-in control because most users have found that they get a better "high" by stopping when they achieve the desired effect rather than by taking more. Experiments in the past both with marijuana and with synthetic marijuanalike substances (pyrahexyl or synhexyl) showed possible usefulness of the drug as an antidepressant. There are also antibiotic actions which may be of value. The mayor's committee found some usefulness for the drug in treating the withdrawal symptoms of narcotic addicts. Thus cannabis is a valuable pleasure-giving drug, probably much safer than alcohol but condemned by the power structure of our society. Smoking one marijuana cigarette can lead to many years in prison, while the alcohol user drinks with impunity despite the many dangers to himself and society.

OPIATES (NARCOTICS)

The term "narcotics" should be reserved for opium, its derivatives, and the synthetic opiatelike drugs. It should not be misused to include any of the other families of pleasure-giving drugs. The earliest known medical and, probably, nonmedical use of opium goes back some three thousand years in Asia. The active principle of the opium poppy is the alkaloid, morphine which was isolated in 1800. Diacetylmorphine (heroin) was produced in 1898 and for a time was thought to be non-addictive. It was, in fact, used as a cure for morphine addiction. It is no longer available for medical use in the United States or most other countries, but it is the drug of choice of illicit narcotic users in America, Japan, Hong Kong, Thailand, and other countries, in large part because of the quicker and more intense "high" effect which it produces (which increases its addiction liability). The development of the hypodermic needle in the 1840's led to considerable injection of narcotics during and after the American Civil War, and this, along with extensive self-prescription with patent medicines and tonics and the importation of opium by Chinese immigrants in the mid-1800's, led to considerable use of narcotics in the United States (no exact figures are known). In the twentieth century codeine and numerous synthetic narcotics have been discovered and widely prescribed. The first National Food and Drug Law in the United States was passed in 1906. A so-called tax law, The Harrison Narcotic Act, was passed in 1914; as Eldridge has said, it "set out to control the non-medical use of narcotics and evolved into the prohibition of non-medical uses and the control of medical uses." Medical use of narcotics is controlled mainly through a system of triplicate prescriptions which doctors are required to use and which are checked by state and federal agencies. The present number of known illegal addicts in the United States is around one hundred thousand, the majority of them young adults of Negro, Puerto Rican, and Mexican descent, products of large urban slum areas, discrimination, broken homes, and deprived cultural backgrounds.

The American system of handling illicit narcotics and cannabis use has been one of criminal sanctions, with steadily increasing penalties; the taking away of judicial discretion in sentencing, including prohibitions against probation, parole, or suspended sentences; and continual claims that this system is effective and the only possible way of dealing with the situation. In addition to illicit heroin addicts, there is an additional, probably significant, amount of dependence on narcotics among middle- and upper-class individuals, who, on various pretexts, obtain the drug, usually one of the synthetic narcotics, from physicians or who are themselves physicians, nurses, or pharmacists with ready access to the drugs. There is also an extremely large consumption of numerous cough syrups containing narcotics, particularly codeine, which can be purchased without prescription and which often also contain significant amounts of alcohol. Some glaring inconsistencies exist even within the framework of the legal prescribing of narcotics as, for example, cough syrups or a synthetic narcotic which is presently exempted from triplicate prescriptions due to very extensive lobbying efforts by its manufacturer.

Ordinarily medically used for analgesia, the narcotics are sought for euphoria and relaxation by illicit users. More rapidly than any of the other pleasure-giving drugs, they produce drug dependency, habituation, and addiction, followed by serious withdrawal symptoms (though less severe than with alcohol or barbiturate withdrawal). In contrast to the immediate effects of the other types of pleasure-giving drugs, the depressant action on the brain produces drowsiness or quietude in most people, temporarily impairing judgment and intellectual functioning. If addiction develops, however, it is usually accompanied by anorexia with emaciation, constipation, and impotency (sterility in the female), all which are reversible, unlike the physical effects of alcoholism, when the drug is discontinued.

As with the other drugs, many myths exist, and have been deliberately created, about illicit narcotics use. To counter a few of these: there are no permanent physical or mental changes from narcotic use; sexual drives are depressed rather than stimulated; addiction is spread from user to user rather than by the aggressive salesmanship of peddlers; some, not all, addicts in the United States were involved in crime before their narcotics use or addiction; the illicit narcotics traffic and profits from Southeast Asia (Thailand, Burma, Laos, China), Mexico, and the Near East (Turkey, Afghanistan, Syria, Lebanon) are as great (or greater) than ever despite the prosecution and persecution of illicit narcotic and cannabis users, with few of the major traffickers ever being apprehended; at least half of all "addicts" can be rehabilitated when the presently rare comprehensive hospital and outpatient treatment programs are provided.

The reports and statistics kept on narcotics addiction and the laws dealing with it lack uniform standards or terminology, are incomplete and confused, and are full of distortions and oversimplifications. Although little is actually known about detailed public attitudes toward the pleasure-giving drugs, there is some indication that many consider narcotic addiction worse than rape or murder, and in some respects the law deals with them in a harsher manner.

The data are not now and never were available to assess the extent of narcotics traffic and use in this country or in other countries, the social or psychological reasons for such use, and the success or failure of control methods. The grossly inaccurate estimates of the Federal

Bureau of Narcotics indicate that there are forty-eight thousand addicts in the United States. Even the more realistic and accurate figure of one hundred thousand (California alone, by more precise statistical determination, has approximately fifteen thousand addicts, as compared to the Federal Bureau of Narcotics estimate of some seven thousand) would make this a minor public health problem, especially as compared to alcoholism, barbiturate addiction, or cigarette smoking. From a social standpoint, however, the heroin user, and, to an increasing degree, the illicit sedative and stimulant user, is involved in a large number of crimes against property and, for the female, in prostitution. This crime represents a drain on the economy and leads to vast expenses for vice officers, jails and prisons (where up to one-fourth of the prisoners in such states as California are there for violations involving narcotics), welfare programs, probation and parole programs, chemical testing for the presence of narcotics, and so on. How much of this is cause and how much effect is difficult to assess, but certainly a significant amount of the crime occurs to obtain money for purchasing narcotics, and the present means of dealing with this has failed, in large part because it fails to reflect an understanding of the complex social and psychological forces involved in narcotic addiction and the intensity of the craving.

LSD-TYPE DRUGS

Peyote (peyotl), the dried top of the cactus *Lophophora williamsii,* and its major active principle, mescaline, are the oldest known members of the LSD family of pleasure-giving drugs, possibly having been used since two thousand years ago by the Aztecs and other Indian tribes of the United States and Mexico. Strangely enough, some states, such as California, include peyote under their narcotic laws and prohibit its use even in the traditional religious ceremonies of the predominantly Indian Native American Church. Federal law, however, does not include the drug as a narcotic. The contemporary situation is an interesting parallel to the efforts of Spanish missionaries and administrators to suppress peyote consumption after the conquest of Mexico, seemingly because they considered it an intoxicant dangerous to the individual and society; they felt that it increased courage and resistance to fatigue and hunger in the tribes which they had difficulty conquering and they considered it pagan. More recently, in addition to its cult and mystical uses, various tribes have also used the drug for such quasi-medical (and probably also mystical) purposes as a cure for snake bite, arthritis, tuberculosis and as an intoxicant.

Another naturally occurring drug of this family is psilocybin (and its analogue, psilocin), also called teonanacatl from the "sacred" mushroom *Psilocybe mexicana,* which has been used for some four hundred years in various areas of Mexico to produce visions as a part of religious rites. It was brought to public attention by Gordon Wasson in 1953 and was isolated and synthesized by Albert Hofmann, who in 1943 had discovered the hallucinogenic properties of d-lysergic acid diethylamide (LSD-25), thus precipitating a current of interest which has produced approximately eleven hundred scientific and pseudoscientific articles on every aspect of LSD's pharmacological and psychological effects.

Other drugs of the LSD type are ololiuqui, bufotenine, harmine, and numerous others, but none of these are so widely used or studied as the three described above. Recently there has been some use of morning glory seeds, after it was found to contain amides of lysergic acid.

The LSD drugs are currently used in legitimate channels for research on brain function, personality structure, and schizophrenia; for accelerating the course of psychotherapy; for the treatment of alcoholism; for religious rituals; and for consciousness-expansion and improvement of creativity. Because of their publicity and their psychological effects—visual hallucinations, changes in body image, disturbances in space and time perception, and euphoria—the drugs are sought by some college students, artists, and middle-class Americans who obtain them from black-market sources or from experimenters who have legitimate supplies.

The LSD-type drugs are not currently listed by the Expert Committee of the World Health Organization in the drug-dependency category, but this probably reflects the relative newness of scientific attention to their properties. Pharmacologically they have a mixed effect—part depressant, part stimulant—on the central nervous system. They impair the time sense, coordination, and judgment, and they, particularly mescaline, can bring on nausea and vomiting. Not infrequently they cause anxiety and depression. There is no sexual stimulation; in fact, an anaphrodisiac effect occurs. There are no permanent physical effects. Persistent (for weeks or months) psychotic reactions occasionally occur, probably only in prepsychotic people, and sometimes there is an accentuation of deviant behavior. There is sometimes concurrent use of other pleasure-giving drugs, but this is in no way a consequence of LSD use. It is the use for thrills by borderline individuals which most bothers medical and lay editorialists, as well as others who seem to be overestimating the extent of the use and harmfulness of these drugs. On the other hand, there have been greatly exaggerated unscientific claims and misuses of the drugs by both medical and non-medical investigators, such as Timothy Leary.

It should be recognized that the LSD-type drugs differ both qualitatively and quantitatively from the other pleasure-giving drugs. The euphoric and other effects are inconsistent, often less intense, and slow in onset compared to the other drug families. For these and other reasons, they would not be generally popular with the user of such drugs as narcotics or marijuana. Most use is intermittent and occasional, perhaps even a one-dose thing. The drugs are not addicting, although habituation and a type of dependence, along with some tolerance, can occur when regularly used. Each of the LSD-type drugs produces similar effects, but they differ in terms of dosage, intensity of reaction, and duration of effects. Mescaline and peyote are uncontrolled in some states and prohibited under narcotic laws in others. Psilocybin and LSD are currently overcontrolled by the federal Food and Drug Administration investigatory regulations and the procedures of the Sandoz Pharmaceutical Company, which holds the patent on them, making them available only to investigators with federal or state research grants. They are not available for prescription by physicians, and they are not presently under narcotic or dangerous-drug criminal ordinances, although this has, unfortunately, been suggested by some doctors and policemen.

Greatly influencing individual reactions to these drugs are the physical surroundings, the emphasis of the experimenter or other individuals present, and the personality and expectations of the subject. When deleterious reactions occur, they can be controlled, if necessary, by administration of one of the phenothiazine tranquilizers.

CONCLUSIONS AND RECOMMENDATIONS

The above comparisons should indicate to the unbiased observer that both the dangers and benefits of the LSD-type drugs have been exaggerated and distorted in a manner paralleling the evolution of social and legal attitudes toward marijuana. It should be noted, however, that mostly the emphasis on the dangers has reached the public, and this will probably continue because of the deficiencies of the mass media and their monopolization by the preservers of the *status quo*. Emphasis on the dangers also seems to predominate in the medical literature and, to a lesser extent, in the social science literature, but here we find somewhat more balance since a number of articles on the real and imagined benefits have also appeared.

As I suggested earlier, this book, although of great value in presenting precise and comprehensive studies of the LSD drug movement, is paradoxical in giving so much attention to the LSD-type drugs rather than to several of the other families of pleasure-giving drugs which represent far more serious and extensive social and health problems.

It is interesting that several recent articles and pseudo-articles condemn LSD studies for their lack of controls and the absence of follow-up evaluations, without apparent comprehension that such techniques as psychotherapy have been widely used for more than fifty years on thousands of people, many of whom were not helped and some of whom were, indeed, harmed or made dependent—all this without any short-term or long-term objective evaluation.

Combined with the overreaction of the Sandoz Company, the artificially created hysteria, generated by certain irresponsible studies and the overblown account of the press, is now discouraging legitimate investigation and stimulating political efforts to place LSD-type drugs under ever stricter laws. It seems highly probable that greater and excessive controls of legitimate medical and scientific use, exaggerated statements, increasing illicit use, and discouragement of scientific research will occur in the coming years despite the relatively small percentage of people who have suffered toxic effects from LSD-type drugs and the absence of proof of menace to society.

Considering both the wide range of inter- and intra-individual reactions and the possible benefits and dangers, the only justifiable and rational control at present would be to require a physician's prescription to obtain the drugs and to have their consumption directly supervised by physicians, although certain exceptions would be necessary and desirable, particularly in the case of the religious use of peyote. This course should be combined with a program of public health education to inform potential users of the possible dangers of the drugs.

The causes of drug dependency are many and involve sociological, psychological, biological, and chance factors. These factors include such things as availability and promotion of the drug through thriving licit (alcoholic beverage and pharmaceutical) industries and illicit (narcotic-smuggling) businesses. To be properly understood and responded to by society, the use and abuse of any pleasure-giving drugs must be seen in the total context of pleasure-giving drug use and the society in which this use has occurred. The use of these drugs serves as a barometer of human society, reflecting the underlying social illnesses. The drugs are used and abused in democracies and dictatorships, Communist and capitalist societies, and varied cultural settings. Anthropologists have helped to elucidate some of the complex cultural factors influencing the use of these drugs, especially alcohol and peyote. The major factors involved are the extent to which the society produces inner tensions in its members, the attitudes toward the use of the drug which the culture disseminates, and the extent to which the culture provides satisfactory alternate means to pleasure.

These drugs offer unique opportunities for research on the functioning of the mind and brain, and they seem to offer greater potential for good than for evil. If this potential is to be realized, we must shift the Establishment's present emphases in order to allow maximum individual freedom and to correct the underlying social conditions leading to abuse of the drugs. Their use by individuals for pleasure, thrills, or euphoria should not unduly concern society. What should concern it are such things as drunken driving, loss of vocational productivity, impaired creativity, deterioration of mental and physical health (bearing in mind that some of the pleasure-giving drugs and with some people these are improved rather than impaired), disruption of family life, crime, and so on. In many instances the cure is costing more than the disease, as Spinoza so wisely predicted.

Users of the pleasure-giving drugs may or may not be problems, but, in giving maximum emphasis to individual freedom, we can at the same time legitimately provide factual information to drug consumers by labeling and describing the drug's potency, effects, and dangers, indicating that it can be habituating, addicting, and the like, as the case may be. We can prohibit advertising which encourages the use of the drugs, and we can seek to encourage individuals to find constructive solutions for problems rather than escaping from them with drugs, television, hypersexuality, and so on. Those who do abuse the drugs in the sense of actually harming themselves or society should be made aware of available treatment resources—which need to be provided— and, when necessary, civil commitment under medical control, rather than imprisonment and condemnation, should be instituted. Physicians and social scientists have defaulted leadership and responsibility in dealing with the pleasure-giving drugs, and law-enforcement agencies and legislatures have far exceeded their legitimate areas of concern. An added consequence of present procedures with all the drugs but alcohol is to create in the illicit user a negative self-image and added difficulty in finding employment, which perpetuates and intensifies any pre-existing social alienation.

Rather than rush into print with more publications or hurriedly pass more unwarranted and harmful laws, we should be willing to spend a small proportion of our vast public budgets on systematic statistical and sociopsychological research on the use and abuse of pleasure-

222   JOEL FORT

giving drugs, thereby providing a rational foundation for future public
policies toward them. Finally, as we rapidly approach the world of
1984, with our outer-directed status seekers and organization men, we
might well ask ourselves why more people are not using the pleasure-
giving drugs rather than why so many are.

BIBLIOGRAPHY

AMERICAN BAR ASSOCIATION and the AMERICAN MEDICAL ASSOCIATION JOINT
COMMITTEE ON NARCOTIC DRUGS. *Drug Addiction: Crime or Disease?*
Bloomington, Ind.: Indiana University Press, 1961.
ATARACTIC AND HALLUCINOGENIC DRUGS IN PSYCHIATRY. Geneva: World
Health Organization, 1958.
CARLSON, E. T., and SIMPSON, M. M. "Opium as a Tranquilizer," *American
Journal of Psychiatry,* CXX (1963).
CHOLDEN, L. *LSD and Mescaline in Experimental Psychiatry.* New York:
Grune & Stratton, 1956.
COHEN, S. "LSD Side Effects and Complications," *Journal of Nervous and
Mental Disease,* CXXX (1960).
COLE, J. O., and KATZ, M. M. "The Psychotomimetic Drugs," *Journal of the
American Medical Association,* CLXXXVII (1964).
DeROPP, R. S. *Drugs and the Mind.* New York: Grove Press, 1960.
EBIN, D. *The Drug Experience.* New York: Orion Press, 1961.
ELDRIDGE, W. B. *Narcotics and the Law.* New York: New York University
Press, 1962.
FARNSWORT, D. L. "Hallucinogenic Agents," *Journal of the American Medical
Association,* CLXXXV (1963).
FORT, J. "Narcotics: The International Picture," *California Youth Authority
Quarterly,* XIV (1961).
———"Narcotics and the Law: A Review," *California Law Review,* L (1962).
GOODMAN, L. S., and GILMAN, A. *The Pharmacological Basis of Therapeutics.*
New York: Macmillan Co., 1956.
GRINKER, R. R., SR. "Bootlegged Ecstasy," *Journal of the American Medical
Association,* CLXXXVII (1964).
Hearings on taxation of marijuana, 75th Cong., 1937.
HUXLEY, A. *Brave New World Revisited.* New York: Harper & Bros., 1958.
ISBELL, H. "Historical Development of Attitudes Toward Opiate Addiction
in the United States," in *Conflict and Creativity,* ed. S. M. Farber and
H. L. Wilson. New York: McGraw-Hill Book Co., 1963.
"Law and Contemporary Problems: Narcotics," *Duke University School of
Law Review,* XXII (1957).
McCARTHY, R. G., and DOUGLASS, E. M. *Alcohol and Social Responsibility.*
New York: Crowell Co., 1949.
The Marijuana Problem in the City of New York. Tempe, Ariz.: Jaques
Cattell Press, 1944.
NYSWANDER, M. *The Drug Addict as a Patient.* New York: Grune & Stratton,
1956.
"Peyot," *United Nations Bulletin on Narcotics,* XI (1959).
*The President's Advisory Commission on Narcotic and Drug Addiction: Final
Report.* Washington, D.C.: United States Government Printing Office,
1963.

Proceedings of the White House Conference on Narcotic and Drug Abuse. Washington, D.C.: United States Government Printing Office, 1962.

ROUECHE, B *Alcohol.* New York: Grove Press, 1962.

SCHUR, E. *Narcotic Addiction in Britain and America.* Bloomington, Ind.: Indiana University Press, 1962.

SEEVERS, M. H. "Medical Perspectives on Habituation and Addiction," *Journal of the American Medical Association,* CLXXXI (1962).

SINCLAIR, A. *Prohibition: The Era of Excess.* Boston: Little, Brown, 1962.

SLOTKIN, J. S. *The Peyote Religion.* Glencoe, Ill.: Free Press, 1956.

TAYLOR, N. *Narcotics: Nature's Dangerous Gifts.* Boulder, Colo.: Delta, 1963.

TERRY, C. E., and PELLENS, M. *The Opium Problem.* Bureau of Social Hygiene, 1928.

Treatment of Drug Addicts. Geneva: World Health Organization, 1962.

UNGER, S. M. "Mescaline, LSD, Psilocybin, and Personality Change," *Psychiatry,* XXVI (1963).

WAKEFIELD, D. *The Addict.* Greenwich, Conn.: Gold Medal, 1963.

WIKLER, A. *The Relation of Psychiatry to Pharmacology.* Baltimore: Williams & Wilkins, 1959.

POLICE VIEWS ON DRUG USE

[XII]

Richard Blum, with Jeanne Wahl

There is considerable variety of opinion among drug users about police attitudes toward users of nonaddictive but illegal drugs such as marijuana, peyote, and mescaline. (See Chapter III.) Thirty-four per cent of the ninety-two persons in our sample who had had LSD believed the police to be hostile toward such persons, and 17 per cent believed the police to be ignorant of the (relatively benign) effects of these drugs and consequently unable to distinguish between their users and narcotics addicts. Eighteen per cent of the sample held that the police had no particular attitudes or feelings and were, quite properly, just doing the job society had assigned to them. Four per cent went beyond that neutral acceptance to say they heartily approved of police efforts to stamp out the use of such drugs and to punish offenders. As for police attitudes toward LSD use, the majority would not hazard a guess. Among those who did, 19 per cent believed the police to be hostile toward LSD users, 7 per cent believed the police to be ignorant and confused about LSD, and 11 per cent believed the police to have what they considered a perfectly reasonable approach, one characterized by a wish to prevent abuse and excess but not to interfere with legitimate employment.

Who was correct? What are police views toward the users of various kinds of drugs, including LSD? To find out, we approached, or tried to approach, eleven law-enforcement agencies holding federal, state, city, or county jurisdiction. In each we hoped to interview all officers working the narcotics and dangerous-drug detail, the men with the greatest knowledge of and experience with persons who used drugs. Five departments allowed us to conduct our inquiries. The range of cooperation from men working on narcotics or vice squads in these five departments ranged from 100 per cent (three agencies) to only 13 per cent.

In addition to the sample of thirty-one cooperating policemen (out of one hundred and nineteen working narcotics and dangerous-drug detail in the five agencies), we approached two parole agencies and were given permission to submit a questionnaire to those men who had supervised drug-user parolees (marijuana, methedrine, narcotics, and the like). A sample of seven agents was obtained. It was our purpose to compare parole agents with policemen to see if any differences in views obtained, presumably as a function of their somewhat different training and orientation to crime control.

BACKGROUND OF THE OFFICERS

The majority of the drug-control officers in the sample have been in law enforcement for sixteen years or more; most are between thirty and forty-nine years of age. About one-third are college graduates, several with law degrees, and one-third have only high-school diplomas. The remainder have had some college. Half the sample have been involved in narcotics and vice work for less than five years; half for more. One officer has been in drug control work over thirty years. Nearly all are deeply involved in their work and enjoy it fully. Our observations suggest that they are, for the most part, very loyal to one another, closely identified with the police group, and very much an in-group which feels itself set apart not only from the community, but to some extent even from other police personnel.

GENERAL VIEWS

The majority of officers believe that illicit drug use represents only a moderate law-enforcement problem in their localities. About one-third see drug abuse as a major problem. Asked to describe the outstanding personal and social characteristics of illicit drug users, the officers most frequently mention "moral and physical degeneracy," unwillingness to work, untrustworthiness and dishonesty, insecurity and instability, pleasure orientation, inability to cope with life problems and associated inadequate personality, weakness and dependency, aimlessness, and susceptibility to being led or manipulated by others.

The majority of officers (68 per cent) see the personality traits of the drug users as similar to those found among other persons who come to the attention of the police. Most frequently said to be much the same as drug users are social nonconformists, burglars, shoplifters, till tappers, prostitutes, and alcoholics. Among these, it is the alcoholics who are most frequently cited as having traits like drug users; one-fourth of the sample lumps them together.

DRUG EFFECTS

Officers were asked to describe the major effects of four drugs: heroin, marijuana, mescaline, and peyote. The following are the most common observations offered:

> HEROIN produces: addiction, depression, euphoria, passivity, sedation, organic physical inefficiency and defect, and habituation.
> MARIJUANA produces: habituation, recklessness, stimulation, intoxication, hallucinations, enhancement of sensations, release of inhibitions, and time-sense distortion.
> MESCALINE produces: hallucinations and color visions, wild behavior, and intoxication. (Half of the respondents said they did not know what effects mescaline had.)
> PEYOTE produces: hallucinations and color visions, stimulation, intoxication, and wild behavior. (One-third of the respondents indicated they did not know the effects of peyote.)

Reviewing these observations, it is apparent that most of the officers reporting did, in fact, distinguish between the effects of heroin and the other drugs. They see mescaline and peyote as producing the same effects and these are, in turn, much like those produced by marijuana. More officers associate marijuana use with irrational and criminal behavior, and they describe more varied effects for it, including occasional personality change, highly individualized response, defiance, enhanced sexual desire, unpredictability, and the like. This greater variation in described effects is no doubt partly a function of the greater opportunity for officers to have become familiar with marijuana and to have noted individual responses to it. The hallucinogens are obviously less familiar to them; nevertheless, what they have seen puts these drugs in the class of marijuana. We would suggest that the recklessness and criminality associated with marijuana use is a function in part of the kinds of marijuana users who come into contact with the police, just as it is possible that the wildness attributed to the hallucinogens also reflects an interaction effect between the drug, the kind of people who use it and become exposed to the police, and the kind of behavior users were exhibiting at the time of arrest. In other words, the police come in contact with a highly selected sample of users.

PERSONAL DRUG EXPERIENCES

It is not impossible that police officers number drug users or experimenters among their friends as well as among their clients. We asked if this was so. Among the thirty-one officers, all denied having friends who had experimented with opium, its derivatives and synthetics, or the hallucinogens. Three had friends who used marijuana; five admitted to having friends who employed stimulants. Taking the next step we asked the officers if they themselves had experience with any of these illicit drugs. One said he had taken marijuana.

THE ALCOHOL-MARIJUANA DILEMMA

Any thoughtful citizen can find himself hard pressed to explain or justify the legal prohibition against the use of marijuana or hallucinogens in a society which accepts alcohol use and all its attendant woes. Historians and cultural anthropologists may shed some light on the origins of this double standard, but the law-enforcement officer who works with drugs may nevertheless be troubled by what seems to be incompatible with his sense of fairness or, indeed, nonsensical in terms of the demonstrable dangers arising out of alcohol use as opposed to the more questionable dangers associated with marijuana use. How does the officer come to terms with these inconsistencies? What evidence does he bring to bear either to justify or to condemn the laws which he must enforce?

Among the officers in our sample, the following positions were most often set forth in response to our question about the difference between alcohol and marijuana use:

(a) Both are intoxicating, but marijuana creates criminal tendencies.

(b) Unlike alcohol, marijuana use, itself not dangerous, leads to the use of heroin.

(c) Both the drunk and the marijuana user are befuddled

by intoxication and may lose the capacity to distinguish
right from wrong. But the drunk is made helpless and incapable of action by alcohol, whereas the marijuana user
remains physically able and, further, may be impelled to
criminal acts by the stimulation of that drug.

(d) Alcohol has a number of benign effects; it tastes good,
it stimulates the appetite, it facilitates social interaction so
that it is pleasant to take as well as being capable of moderate use to produce only pleasant results. Marijuana has
no such inherently benign characteristics; it is not pleasurable *in itself,* but can be used only to achieve an end state
for which the means, smoking "pot," is merely instrumental.

(e) There is no difference except the social facts: alcohol
is acceptable and legal; marijuana use is rejected by those
who set social standards, and it is illegal.

(f) Different types of persons choose to use marijuana and
alcohol; primarily those with psychopathic or antisocial
trends select marijuana.

(g) The use of marijuana necessarily puts the user in association with persons operating illegally, for he depends upon
them for a source of supply. Consequently, the user is exposed to a group which is likely to be immoral or unethical,
and he runs the risk of adopting their dishonesty and bad
habits. This exposes him to a criminal career just because
of his marijuana habit.

(h) Marijuana use is associated with unpredictability of
behavior, whereas alcohol use leads to predictable behavior.
The marijuana user himself may not know how he will respond to the next stick; the alcohol user knows quite well
what a drink will do. Furthermore, those who live or deal
with the marijuana user not only are faced with uncertainty as to what he will do, but they have no way of knowing that he is under the influence of a drug. The alcohol
user, either by smell or action, is clearly identified as being
under its influence, and the persons with him can anticipate
what he will do and can adjust their actions to their predictions. The marijuana user on a "high" cannot be identified by those around him (unless he tells them or has taken
it with them), and so they are unprepared for irrational or
reckless behavior and can do nothing to protect themselves
or even the user.

(i) Alcohol is worse than marijuana by any measure of pharmacological effect. It produces more bizarre behavior, it produces more physical damage, it produces hangover, and so on.

(j) Both alcohol and marijuana are potentially dangerous and addictive; neither necessarily so. Social and personality factors must be considered in anticipating effects.

Many of the officers see no pharmacological difference between the drugs, except that marijuana has less certain effects. The stress is on the unpredictability of marijuana. Tigani el Mahi's hypothesis[1] holds that making a drug illegal and failing to institutionalize its use through controls and sanctions produces in itself adverse psychic effects and bizarre behavior when the drug is taken. One may suggest that the bizarre acts and criminality observed by officers are a consequence of the social circumstances of use rather than the pharmacological nature of the drug. Certainly the suggestion of criminal association due to dependency on criminal suppliers recognizes a social rather than pharmaceutical determinant of marijuana effects. On the other hand, the observation that criminally predisposed persons may choose to take marijuana, in that way opting for more association with rebellious or psychopathic or criminal users, indicates that factors influencing one's choice of drugs must be assessed at the same time one considers the consequences of taking such drugs.

One of the most interesting observations has to do with the notion that the alcohol user gives a warning signal which enables those about him to recognize his condition and respond appropriately, while the marijuana user gives no such warning and thereby puts those who deal with him at a disadvantage, for they do not anticipate the reckless or socially inappropriate, intoxicated behavior which emerges. This is an extremely important point; it affirms the need of the marijuana user to conceal his condition from unsympathetic outsiders, but at the same time it presumes his inability to fully control his behavior and make it conventional at all times. The alcohol user, on the other hand, because he is engaging in an approved form of behavior, need not be secretive about it. It is also the case that the paraphernalia of alcohol use, bottles and glasses, are more easily recognized and ordinarily less transportable than is a stick of marijuana. Finally, the smell of alcohol enables the immediate detection of the user, whereas it is unlikely that the ordinary citizen can recognize a marijuana odor.

Reviewing the substance of the police views of alcohol and mari-

230 RICHARD BLUM AND JEANNE WAHL

juana difference, we may say that the social consequences, based on existing law and values, loom most large. Some consider alcohol pharmacologically worse; others marijuana. Most would appear to agree that marijuana use puts the individual in risk of criminal associations, arrest, and social rejection. Only a few officers (16 per cent) believe it also places the user in jeopardy of graduating to the use of heroin or other narcotics. The infrequency of mention of this "steppingstone" hypothesis is noteworthy in view of the apparent widespread public acceptance of the notion that the first puff of "pot" is a first step down the inevitable road to perdition. We trust that it is quite clear to most narcotics officers that narcotic opportunities and addiction need not follow marijuana use.

USER CHARACTERISTICS

An early question provided for the spontaneous description of the traits of drug users. A more detailed adjective check list allowed the officer to check as many of twenty traits as he wished to describe each of three groups of users: opiate users, marijuana users, and hallucinogen users (peyote, mescaline, LSD). In an attempt to exclude ratings that would merely reflect general negativism or disapproval of users, each trait was paired with its opposite so that, although a rater could check both, he would realize his inconsistency in doing so. For example, Item 1 is "self-indulgent" and Item 2 "self-denying." Every trait listed is pathological or at least undesirable at either extreme—for example, "engage in deviant sex practices" or its paired opposite, "engage in no sex at all."[2] In consequence we may take the total frequency of traits checked as an indication of the extent of undesirable deviation thought to characterize users of each family of drugs. Employing this nondiscriminating over-all measure of things-wrong-with-users, we find hallucinogen users regarded as much less deviant or sick than either marijuana or opiate users. An average, per officer, of 3.2 negative traits was checked to describe hallucinogen users, while an average 5.2 traits was checked to describe marijuana users and 5.6 to describe opiate users. On this measure alone, we may say that police officers do, in fact, discriminate between the users of hallucinogens and the users of other illicit drugs.

Now let us rank the most frequently employed descriptions of drug users in the three groups. In parentheses appears the number of officers checking the trait.

One finds hallucinogen users characterized in much the same way as marijuana users. They are seen to share disrespect of authority, self-

TABLE IV

Users of

Opium, it derivatives, or synthetics	Marijuana, hashish	Hallucinogens
Self-indulgent (22)	Disrespectful of, rebellious toward authority (21)	Disrespectful of, rebellious toward authority (13)
Greedy and insatiable (18)		
Exploitative of others (18)		Self-indulgent (9)
Easily exploited by others (17)	Exploitative of others (17)	Profess "superior" moral ideas (9)
Morally degenerate (16)	Self-indulgent (17)	Engage in deviant sex practices (9)
Engage in no sex at all (14)	Abuse sources of pleasure (14)	Abuse sources of pleasure (8)
Abuse sources of pleasure (13)		
Disrespectful of, rebellious toward authority (13)	Engage in deviant sex practices (14)	

What are the least frequent descriptions of users in the three groups? They are as follows:

TABLE V

Opiate users	Marijuana users	Hallucinogen users
Calculating sadists (0)	Self-denying (0)	Engage in no sex at all (0)
Pathological aversion to dirt, mess, squalor (1)	Engage in no sex at all (1)	Unable to enjoy anything (1)
Brutish, cave man type (1)	Unable to enjoy anything (2)	Pathological aversion to dirt, mess, squalor (1)
Engage in deviant sex practices (1)	Effeminate and lacking in manliness (2)	
Profess "superior" moral ideas (1)		Self-denying (2)
	Helpless target for sadist's cruelty (2)	Greedy and insatiable (2)

indulgence, sexual deviancy, and hedonism. One major difference is ideological; hallucinogen users are recognized as propounding special values in their drug use—values which set them apart from the common herd and which, we infer, are hardly shared by the police. The opiate users are passive and inert in contrast to the active hedonism of marijuana and hallucinogen users. One-third or more of the officer sample agree all three groups are rebellious, self-indulgent, and abusive of pleasure sources.

Another approach to the data is to compare the proportions of paired opposites rated. This gives a picture of disagreement within the police group and elaborates the pattern of traits believed to exist in users per se. The following table presents those data.

TABLE VI

PROPORTION OF PAIRED OPPOSITE ITEMS

CHECK FOR EACH GROUP OF DRUG USERS

Paired opposite traits	User group and ratio of ratings		
	Opiate	Marijuana	Hallucinogen
Self-indulgent: self-denying	22/4	17/0	9/2
Engage in deviant sex practice: engage in no sex at all	1/14	14/1	9/0
Morally degenerate: profess superior moral ideas	16/1	14/5	4/9
Greedy and insatiable: controlled and ascetic	18/2	6/4	2/6
Effeminate and lacking in manliness: brutish, cave man types	6/1	2/10	4/3
Easily exploited by others: exploitative of others	17/18	11/17	6/5
Helpless target for sadist's cruelty: calculating sadists	6/0	2/6	3/4
Abuse sources of pleasure: unable to enjoy anything	13/10	14/2	8/1
Pathological enjoyment of dirt, mess, squalor: pathological aversion to dirt, mess, squalor	6/1	5/3	6/1
Disrespectful of, rebellious toward authority: aggressive and power-hungry authoritarians	13/2	21/6	13/3

It is apparent that there is no single police image of any drug-user group. It is also clear that the greatest agreement for all three groups is found on ratings of sexual behavior and self-indulgence.

COMMUNITY MENACE

Another scale asked officers to rate each of seventeen criminal, drug-user, or social-action groups in terms of the menace they posed to the community. Ratings were of serious, moderate, or no menace. Twenty-seven officers did this rating. Two kinds of data were obtained from this rating. One is an individual menace score which was obtained for each officer by giving an arithmetic value to each of his ratings: 3 points for "serious menace," 2 points for "some danger," and 1 point for "no menace or danger at all." The maximum menace score was 30, and the minimum score was 10. The second is a group menace score. The maximum menace score was again 30, and the minimum was 10.[3] A high score reflects the opinion of the police sample as a whole that the group in question presents a serious menace to the community. Below are ranked the seventeen groups in order of the group menace scores obtained:

TABLE VII

GROUP MENACE SCORES FOR EACH OF 17 GROUPS

	Score
United States Communist Party	27
Heroin addicts	26
Syndicate (organized gambling rackets)	25
Professional burglary rings	25
Confidence men	24
Marijuana users	24
Mafia	23
Black Muslims	23
White supremacists	22
"Fast buck" real-estate promoters	22
LSD users	20
City Hall demonstrators (students and others involved in disturbances at San Francisco House Un-American Activities Committee Hearings)	19
"Gay crowd" homosexuals	18
CORE (racial integration demonstrators)	18
John Birch Society	16
Peyote cultists (Indians in the Native American Church)	15
American Civil Liberties Union	14

The order of listing confirms the discrimination made on personality-trait ratings to the effect that heroin use, marijuana use, and hallucinogen use are, in fact, not considered similar phenomena. LSD users are seen as more threatening, on the average, than Indian users of peyote. We surmise that the latter are already viewed as a culturally distinct group whose peyote use is integrated with its separatist culture; LSD users are, on the other hand, "our own kind" who are rebelling, and who would dictate a new set of values to challenge the existing order. The same may be said of the group who receive the average menace score most like that assigned to LSD users—the San Francisco City Hall demonstrators. That group, certainly not criminal in any sense, aroused considerable police distress by their noisy challenge to the Un-American Activities Committee.

IDEAL PUNISHMENTS

Another way to understand the role of the drug user in the hierarchy of comparative criminality presumed to exist within the minds of police officers is to learn what punishments the officers would mete out to typical offenders from a number of groups. We tried to accomplish this through a questionnaire listing twenty criminal or social types which the officer was asked to sentence "with complete freedom to sentence as you think right." Two kinds of scores were derived. One was a punishment score for each individual officer in which each sentence was coded for severity on a scale of 0 to 8.[4] The sum of the twenty sentences constitutes an individual's punishment score. The highest possible score would be 160, indicating an extremely punitive position (death for *all* offenders); the lowest possible score would be 0 (all offenders released).

The other score was an offender punishment score based on the average sentence decreed by the law-enforcement sample completing the scale. Twenty-four officers completed it. The highest score possible is 80 and the lowest is 0.[5] A score of 80 would mean that every policeman sentenced that typical offender to death. Below are listed the offenders in the order of their group punishment scores. Average sentence as represented by the score is also shown.

Again we see that there is great discrimination between the classes of drug users insofar as ideal sentences are concerned. The drug peddler would be sentenced to an average six to ten years (which is a considerably more lenient sentence than federal law stipulates); the marijuana user is ranked with minor sexual offenders and petty larceny types and would receive a county jail sentence. (Again the lawmen are more lenient than federal law; present federal law sets a sentence of two to ten years for a first offense of conspiracy to transport or un-

TABLE VIII

Typical offender	Average punishment score	Average punishment
Murderer	77	Death
Drug peddler	51	
Rapist	51	6–10 years
Armed robber	48	
Burglar	41	
Con man (grand larceny)	41	
Bad-check writer	36	1–5 years
Communist (unregistered)	35	
Income tax evader	33	
Auto booster	33	
Marijuana user	31	1 day to 1 year
Prostitute	26	
LSD user	24	
Beatnik (on "vag" charge)	23	
Homosexual	23	
Speeding driver	22	No time served
Adulterer	21	
Common drunk	21	
Mexican wetback	18	
Litterbug	11	Individual treatment

lawful acquisition or possession of marijuana.) The LSD user ranks with the minor nuisances and would be put on probation by the average drug-control officer.

The offenders about whom there was least agreement are the Communists. They receive the widest range and the greatest variety of sentences: from release to twenty years in prison. They are followed by homosexuals, who would get the same variety of sentences, and then by LSD users, with sentences ranging from individual treatment through six to ten years.

The relative mildness of the punishments recommended by the police officers deserves comment. In contrast to the federal law, which does call for harsh sentences, the police recommendations are very gentle. It may be, of course, that those cooperating with us on the study were not representative of the larger law-enforcement group. On the other hand, one gets the impression that many narcotics officers are sympathetic toward users and their problems. In undercover work, where they themselves must talk and dress as users, they have ample opportunity to become acquainted with and, in adopting their outward habits, even to identify with users. Some officers speak frankly of this, indicating that they can be more comfortable with users than with many ordinary citizens.

As a group the police do not show any enthusiasm for what is commonly called "rehabilitation." The litterbug is the only one whose average punishment score places him in a recommended treatment group. That is somewhat misleading. Some officers do recommend something besides release, probation, or incarceration. Let us see how many officers suggest rehabilitation per se and for whom. Table IX lists all those offenders for whom treatment rather than more traditional disposition is recommended.

TABLE IX

RECOMMENDATIONS OF TREATMENT FOR OFFENDER GROUPS
BY NARCOTICS OFFICERS

Offender group	Number	Per Cent
All offenders	6	20%
Homosexuals	7	23
Drunks	6	20
LSD users	3	10
Prostitutes	1	3
Communists	1	3
Marijuana users	1	3
Persons committing crimes against property or person	0	—

The 20 per cent recommending individual treatment for all offenders is not included in those making specific treatment recommendations for particular offender groups. Had it been, one would find that nearly half of the officers would recommend treatment for homosexuals (43 per cent) and drunks (40 per cent) and about one-third (30 per cent) would recommend it for LSD users. It is for these groups, then, that narcotics officers are most convinced of the appropriateness and efficacy of either medical-psychological care or re-education (outside penitentiary walls). It is curious that homosexuals more than prostitutes are seen as benefiting from such intervention and that LSD users slightly more than marijuana users are so perceived. We suspect that treatment efficacy beliefs are linked to the absence of criminal associations for the offenders in question and probably to middle-class, as opposed to lower-class, membership.

Treatment is obviously not considered as appropriate for persons who commit crimes against property or person, except by that 20 per cent police minority who are rehabilitation oriented. As a sentencing principle it would appear that these police officers are more likely to recommend treatment for those who hurt only themselves but not for those who hurt others. Perhaps this is because such offenders are seen as sickest, most likely to be motivated for cure, or because with them there is no conflict in sentencing between rehabilitation and the desire, through punishment, to deter others from crime, to extract vengeance, to require penance, or to protect society by isolating the offender.

PERCEIVED PUBLIC REACTIONS

Each officer was given a check list which set forth possible reactions in the "responsible public" to the use of illicit *but nonaddictive* drugs: "marijuana, peyote, mescaline, and like drugs." On the check list were three groups of six key phrases (see Table X). One set presented adverse public reactions, for example, "disgust over the presence of such practices," one set described neutral or ambivalent responses, for example, "disinterest in the drug problem," and one set presented approving views, for example, "sympathy for the motives of users." Below are listed each set of phrases and the number and percentage of officers in the sample affirming each as a public reaction to nonaddictive stimulating or euphoric drugs.

As we see from the table nearly all of the officers perceive the responsible public as fearful of the spread of drug use. Nearly half of the officers see the public responding to drugs with disgust and revulsion. Practically none of the officers describe the public as in any way pleased with or accepting of nonaddictive drug use.

We shall venture four speculations about the perception of public response which these officers convey. We begin by noting the views of nonaddictive drugs, of police practice toward users, and of present narcotics legislation as presented by the controls used in our LSD study.

TABLE X

Opposing	Neutral	Approving
Disgust over the presence of such practices (N=13;42%)	Disinterest in the drug problem (N=0)	Sympathy for motives of the users (N=4;13%)
Anger at self-indulgence of the users (N=10;30%)	Lack of information about the drug problem (N=21; 68%)	Approval of persons who are doing what they want to do (N=0)
Fear of the spread or contagion in the community from users to nonusers (N=28; 90%)	Emotional detachment about drug issues (N=2;06%)	Satisfaction that people are enjoying themselves with drugs (N=0)
Revulsion over the consequences of use (N=13;42%)	Confusion over what to think of drug use (N=13;42%)	Acceptance of drug use as long as no one is harmed (N=1;03%)
Despair over present trends to increased use (N=10;30%)	Neutrality between proponents of freedom to use drugs and proponents of legal controls over drug use (N=0)	Encouragement to users to have new experiences through drug use (N=0)
Hopelessness about controlling such human problems (N=7; 23%)	Objective interest in appraising the problem (N=4;13%)	Happiness that some people are finding personal expansion through drug use (N=0)

These controls constitute, by our definition, one segment of the responsible public; they include government administrators, social workers, professors, physicians and psychiatrists, a priest, and a journalist. We cannot contend that our sampling was representative; we venture the guess that the views of our controls were not unlike those of many persons in medicine, university life, the arts, and the communication media. Their views probably are more intellectual and liberal than those of businessmen and other traditionally conservative people. The controls show little or no evidence of fear, revulsion, or disgust, nor do they seem uninformed. Only a few seem to have any strong negative reaction to the idea of nonaddictive drug use, just as only a few seem to wish for stricter controls for narcotic drugs; many are opposed to present punitive narcotics-control practices and are disapproving of what they believe to be the hostility of police toward drug users. In these attitudes, the controls are little different from the users themselves.

We suggest, that the police either misperceive the opinion of this segment of the public, regard this segment as not "responsible," or prefer to limit their observations to only one sector of the "responsible" public, namely, a sector whose drug views provide justification to the police for the work which the police must do. We conclude that police views are selective and at least partially erroneous. Just as we have found the user sample to misunderstand police attitudes and knowledge, we now find that the police misunderstand at least some sectors of important citizen opinion.

We do not think that misunderstanding in this instance is a result either of accident or ignorance. We think it represents: (a) selective public contact through which the police have little opportunity to become acquainted with the views of the professional and intellectual community, but may be exposed to the views of more militant and conservative citizens; (b) selective, need-determined perception, which serves to support and justify the police role as protagonists in a cultural drama, a role which is, in fact, subject to much public abuse. The police are not unaware of their own role as a minority group which is discriminated against and are not oblivious to their rejection by many citizens. Retreat to a mutually supporting in-group is one response; justification of their endeavors is another. Insofar as the public is believed to be distressed over drug use, the public is then in need of the kind of service which the police, in doing their jobs, must perform. Occupational and personal esteem is enhanced, for slaying dragons in the public service is ennobling work. (c) The projection of private feelings about drug use which, denied in direct inquiry, are expressed by being attributed to "responsible" persons. Projection implies that some police officers have strong emotional investments in their work, investments that arise from personality dynamics in which the ideas or symbols surrounding drug use play a salient role. Our assumption is that, on the private, personal level, drug use is associated with a challenge to control, to order, and to the defense systems erected to cope with impulses threatening this required control and order.

Let us give an illustration of that kind of emotional response on the part of a bright and capable officer working in a well-respected department.

> I tell you there's something about users that bugs me.
> I don't know what it is exactly. You want me to be frank?
> OK. Well, I can't stand them; I mean I *really* can't stand
> them. Why? Because they bother me personally. They're
> *dirty*, that's what they are, filthy. They make my skin crawl.

It's funny but I don't get that reaction to ordinary criminals. You pinch a burglar or a pickpocket and you understand each other; you know how it is, you stand around yacking, maybe even crack a few jokes. But Jesus, these guys, they're a danger. You know what I mean, they're like Commies or some of those CORE people.

There are some people you can feel sorry for. You know, you go out and pick up some poor chump of a paper hanger [bad-check writer] and he's just a drunk and life's got him all bugged. You can understand a poor guy like that. It's different with anybody who'd use drugs.

On the psychodynamic level, we think that this officer's intense reaction against the "dirty" user and the significance of drug use for some "pot" smokers reflect two sides of the same concern. Revulsion and repression occur. For the policeman, the drug user becomes the prototype of the enemy. For the "pot head," drug use and the values associated with it can signify (but need not) rebellion against authority, controls, and the neatness and lack of spontaneity associated with being "square."

Because discussion of the projected emotional reactions against drug use requires understanding of the significance of use, we shall comment further. Interviews with some users of LSD, marijuana, and the like, especially those in the informal black-market group, reveal the importance to them of being spontaneous, creative, and uninhibited. These are values which some express in ways which can only be rated as rebellious and anticompulsive. Some of their art work consists of disorganized finger-painting smears; some of their apartments are truly a housekeeping nightmare: jumbled, uncleaned, sprawling, messes with clothes strewn about, beds with sheets so covered with dirt they must be termed a "velvet grey," and plates and food containers from meals of days and weeks standing about uncleaned. It does not require a psychoanalytic orientation to conclude that these individuals, all of whom are from "proper" middle-class backgrounds, are something more than casual; they're trying too hard for that. Now, although many social scientists might reject out-of-hand the psychoanalytic notion of compulsivity as arising out of toilet training done too soon or too harshly, we think it unwise to ignore the obvious. The people we describe—and again we stress they are but a very few of the user sample—*are* dirty. And "dirt" in our society is a concept not unrelated to toilet training. And what do these people call their pleasure? They call it "pot." The symbolism of that is hardly to be ignored, and it suggests a simple hypothesis: that some do, in fact, equate drug use with the overthrow of compulsive or orderly restraints imposed upon impulse expression, beginning with the childish impulse expression of defecating at one's own pleasure instead of when and where others have ordained it. To support our hypothesis, we asked *these* users a simple question: "Is there any other name besides 'pot' which you use for marijuana which is something like 'pot' in its meaning?" The answer was "yes." And what was their other word for marijuana? The reply: "Shit." And that really *is* another word some of them use.

We suggest that the projecting police officer—or citizen—is, in fact, threatened by his quite accurate but partially unconscious understanding of what some users do mean or intend by their drug use. That threat mobilizes the individual's feelings about past trauma of his own, trauma experienced at the hands of parental authorities during the difficult stages of learning order and suppressing impulse. These individuals respond with disgust, anger, revulsion, and fear, and "cleanse" themselves by the standard human ploy of making the enemy external, that is, of scapegoating. What is an inner problem is externalized; a private issue is added to a public one. If these be the dynamics, one must conclude that police involvement in drug control—for some—is a central personal issue in which stamping out drug use is symbolic self-policing as well as the performance of a public duty. The emotionally aroused police officer who calls these users "dirty" and hates them for their "self-indulgence" is quite an accurate diagnostician, even though the diagnosis is in the service of his own defense system.

The Russells[6] have discussed a psychodynamic mechanism much like the one envisioned here. They ascribe the punitiveness of adults to the past punitiveness of their parents. The hostile behavior of parents is said to be directed to the reduction of the child's comfort and to the suppression of his needs. As a consequence, the child learns to control his urges in a compulsive "quasi-instinctive" manner, instead of understanding his bodily processes intelligently and directing them rationally. To appease his parents, the child will emphasize cleanliness; should he rebel, he will do so through squalor. Neither preoccupation is voluntary; both are automatic, inflexible, and unadaptive.

The Russells believe that addictions and phobias are related; both contain powerful elements of attraction and compulsion; both involve unawareness of parental behavior and of one's own irrational responses thereto. Reasoning from the Russells' theory and our own prior speculations, one would expect to find a relationship linking feelings of disgust and discomfort to expressions of vindictive moralizing, combined with sentimentality. There will also be repression of spontaneity and exploratory drives and the presence of considerable hostility toward oneself and others, especially toward those dangerous others who are comfortable, spontaneous, or freely exploratory. A strong sense of menace and punitive attitudes should also be part of the pattern, as should actions which are cruel, repressive, and destructive, albeit rationalized in terms of morality and sentiment.

One would also expect that the ones more fearful of drug use, for example, and most disgusted by it would be most closely related in psychological dynamics to those addicted. In both there is the seething push-pull of attraction and repulsion which is beyond the control of understanding of the conscious mind. One would expect both addicts and fearful antiaddicts to be playing hide-and-seek with drugs and with the people who give drugs. One might also expect both groups to be cliff walkers, coming close to the edge of the precipice to test their ability to take or not to take the feared-desired substance. And one would think that some in both groups would be avid missionaries, the addict converting others to drugs, and the phobic trying to convert others to his cruel system of avoidance.

Lest the foregoing discussion be misunderstood, the theoretical personality dynamics are not thought to be characteristic of policemen nor of LSD users per se. What is suggested is that there will be individuals, within and outside police work, people who do or do not take LSD and other drugs, who will demonstrate the kinds of behavior which the theory predicts. Insofar as they do, it will be easier to understand the stresses and strains inside them, and the intensity and irrationality of the behavior which would otherwise be incomprehensible to the observer.

POLICE GUESSES ABOUT THE
CONSEQUENCES OF LSD USE

Each officer was given six statements about the possible consequences of LSD use with which he was to indicate his agreement or disagreement. Three statements favored unrestricted use of LSD; three were opposed. The statements were introduced with the statement that we wished to learn the "best guesses" of the officers about "the dangers or advantages which might be involved in the widespread nonmedical use of such a powerful substance as LSD." Thirty-one officers responded.

The majority of officers (84 per cent) consider the extension of LSD without medical supervision to constitute a public health hazard and further believe (90 per cent) that it is inviting trouble to allow youth to be exposed to yet another source of excitement. Most of the officers (90 per cent) do not feel that LSD use is a private matter which is the business of the individual as long as it is done in his home, nor do they feel (90 per cent) that the LSD will contribute to creativity or social advancement among those employing it. Most officers (70 per cent) indicate that one of the potential dangers to free access to LSD use would be the development of unconventional attitudes among user groups.

There is only one area in which the near unanimity of narcotics police officers is disrupted. Almost half of the sample, responding perhaps to some extent to the remarks introducing this scale, agreed that among the potential benefits of LSD is its capacity to aid in the psychological development of the user. We may conclude that most narcotics officers in our sample are opposed to the nonmedical use of LSD because they believe it to be a menace to public health, the conventional social order, and the well-being of youth. Most do not believe LSD to have any beneficial potential for creativity or social values, but nearly half indicate that it may be an aid to psychological development.

Viewing the replies to this scale, coupled with general comments during our interviews, we would suggest that officer response to new "soft" drugs (as opposed to "hard" narcotics) is predictable. Some will accept the opinion of medical authorities, as presented by the mass media and in legislative hearings, that such drugs have medical or psychological values. Others, their antagonism toward euphoria-producing substances more fixed, will reject medical opinion which favors such drugs. Some will be willing to allow the medical community the right to use these substances; others are suspicious of psychiatrists and are unwilling to accept their opinion about anything. The police view of a new drug will be based not only on the pharmacological characteristics of the drug itself, but on its social and psychological meaning. For instance, a drug need not be addictive to be considered a danger; it does need to produce pleasure to be so considered. There is no general concern about the "rights" issue involved in policing private use of such substances in private homes; there is a great concern over the fact that the use of such drugs becomes a focal point for the evolution of groups who espouse unconventional views. There is no advantage seen in a drug which "frees people from old ways and enables them to see things differently," but there is value in a drug which aids in individual psychological growth.

We surmise then that individual health is a value and that drugs which are reputed to contribute to health, whether physical or psychological, will be granted their place in the medical armamentarium.

But drugs which are claimed to contribute to unorthodox personal pleasure or social change are disapproved. The user claims are for movement toward artistic expression, aesthetic enhancement, mystical religion, "internal freedom," spontaneity, love, or perhaps orgiastic sexuality. These ends are espoused by groups already likely to be tagged by police as "liberal," "left wing," "beat," "bleeding hearts," or correctly recognized as confirmed drug users (as with some informal black-market users). For these people to move in such directions is not the ordinary officer's idea of the Pilgrim's Progress.

We conclude that most of the officers stand for health, for the existing social order, and, if need be, for the protection of the individual against his own impulses toward indulgent pleasure and rebellion. So long as the individual's private experimentation with drugs is, in fact, a social activity which is contagious—and we agree with the officers that there is evidence of such contagion—their position is that individual rights must be subordinate to the public good. In this case, the public good implies self-control, maintenance of the *status quo,* the avoidance of exploitative relationships, respect for authority, regard for the person and property of others, and the pursuit of only those pleasures which are institutionalized and widely acceptable. Thus it is that marijuana, LSD, homosexuality, "gang bangs," dirt, and mess are unacceptable, while alcohol and heterosexuality are acceptable.

A COMPARISON OF POLICE AND PAROLE OFFICERS

We thought it likely that persons working in law enforcement whose jobs required they take a different position vis-à-vis the offender would have somewhat different attitudes toward drug use and drug users. For this reason we explored the replies of a small sample of parole officers. We expected them, by reason of their work with offenders, to be more moderate in their views. We saw two parole departments; from those departments, seven men cooperated in the study. Comparing the parole officers to the narcotics-control policemen, we find the following apparent differences (to be subjected to statistical test when larger samples are available).

For success in their work, parole officers emphasize the need for personal characteristics of tolerance, understanding, and firmness more than do police officers. They also more often describe the drug user in psychological terms, implying his illness and the officer's understanding. They emphasize his "weak ego" and "dependency" in contrast to the greater frequency of moral judgments and behavior descriptions offered by peace officers. Like peace officers, parole officers see the drug user as most resembling the alcoholics among all types of offenders with whom the officer must deal.

More parole officers than police officers report knowledge of friends who have experimented with dangerous or narcotic drugs and more admit to having experimented with marijuana. Any percentages would be misleading because of the small sample size. We presume that the differences reflect somewhat greater freedom to explore among the parole officers and, coupled with greater emphasis on accepting others, a greater willingness to admit drug experimentation on their own part. Parole officers report less knowledge about the use and effects of the hallucinogens and are reluctant to describe the users of those drugs. In describing the characteristics of marijuana users, the parole officers are less likely than police officers to describe them in psychopathological or disapproving terms.

Parole officers differ from peace officers in their notions of the degree of menace which various groups pose to the community, as measured on the menace scale. Parole officers view the following as considerably less menacing than do the police sample: CORE, the Communist Party of the U.S.A., Black Muslims, homosexuals, the Mafia, the ACLU, and the student HUAAC City Hall demonstrators. On most other groups, the parole and police officers agree. We conclude that parole officers are less concerned with threats to the social order from various political groups or from sexual deviants. They are, in general, more tolerant of political extremism, but not any less concerned than the police about the social dangers of drug use or economic crime.

Parole officers are more lenient than peace officers in the sentences they would dispense for typical offenders. Most of the latter decree death for the murderer; none of the former would execute a criminal. Parole officers are also dramatically less punitive with reference to adultery.

It is curious that, despite greater emphasis on psychological factors in drug use and a more moderate approach to menace and punishment, there are no dramatic differences in emphasis on treatment or rehabilitation outside of prison. Parole officers are much more likely to call for probation or no sentence, but they are not any more likely than peace officers to stipulate hospitalization, psychological-psychiatric care, or re-education per se. It may be that these approaches are implicit in their notion of probation, but they are not made explicit. Indeed, such treatment is stipulated for drunks, homosexuals, LSD users, and prostitutes no more often by parole officers than by the police.

With reference to the perceived reaction to nonaddictive drug use by the "responsible public," parole officers are much less likely to attribute emotional reactions to that public. Less than half see the public as responding emotionally and never with "disgust," "revulsion," "anger," or "hopelessness." More often parole officers, compared with peace officers, describe the public as neutral or "emotionally detached." No parole officer describes public acceptance of or sympathy toward nonaddictive drug use.

With references to "best guesses" about widespread nonmedical use of LSD, the parole officers take about the same position as narcotics officers. The majority see it as a public health hazard and contributing to unconventionality. All of them agree its use by youth would invite trouble, and all indicate they see no beneficial creative or social consequences from its use. They are more skeptical than the police about its psychological benefits as well.

The comparison of parole and narcotics officers suggests that the former, as befits their training and job requirement, do have a more psychological or case-work orientation to the drug user. The parole officers appear to be less disapproving of the nonaddictive drug user as a person, but that does not mean they are more sympathetic to the LSD drug movement. They do not differ from narcotics officers in their evaluation of the community menace posed by the drug movement, even though they are considerably more tolerant of extreme political ideologies or of sexual deviancy. Similarly they are much less punitive than peace officers in the recommended sentences for most crimes; but this is not the case for sentences called for in the case of use of LSD (averaging a one day to one year county-jail sentence). Parole officers do not see the public as responding emotionally to nonaddictive drug use; there is little or none of what we infer to be the role justification and projection of strong negative feelings found among narcotics officers; nevertheless, the former are, if anything, even more skeptical than the police of the claims made by LSD enthusiasts for its artistic, psychological, and social benefits. They are just as opposed to its nonrestricted use as are most of the police.

We conclude, from our limited samples, that parole officers take a milder view of drug use and drug users, but that their general orientation to the purposes and administration of criminal justice is not different from that of their peace officer colleagues. As case workers, they are closer to the offender in a relationship that is no longer, as it is with the police, a matter of the hunter and the hunted. We find them in a position in which overt conflict has been subordinated to institutional relationships maintained by a number of edicts and forces. The parole officers are more removed from the din of battle and have less emotional investment in maintaining the social order or their own psychological bastions. We presume that their personalities, their training, and their work lead to less personal involvement in the struggle between "good" and "evil." Because of this, the parole officer need not, as warriors do, limit his definitions of the social world to those who are friend and those who are foe. It is clear that in the absence of intense feelings about drug use, it is still possible to oppose unrestricted use of mind-altering drugs. Thus we may suggest that opposition to the drug movement need not—although it may—reflect one's own personal conflicts and psychodynamic defense systems.

DOGMATISM AND ATTITUDES TOWARD DRUG USE

In addition to the psychodynamic formulation which has been proposed to account for the vehemence of revulsion felt by certain individuals when faced with the fact of drug use, a more general relationship between personality and attitudes was hypothesized at the beginning of the study. It was expected that feelings of menace, as measured by the menace scale, and punitiveness, as measured by the punishment scale, would be associated with the presence of dogmatic-authoritarian personality trends.[7] The reasoning was that the more rigid person, suffering from a lack of flexibility in discriminating various segments of his environment and penalized by his own personality structure so that he more often experiences distress due to maladaptiveness, would feel more endangered by his environment and would respond with more intense generalized hostility. A positive relationship between menace scores and dogmatism scores, using the Rokeach scale, was hypothesized, as was a positive relationship between dogmatism and punishment scores.

The results do not provide any firm support for these expectations. A product-moment correlation of $r = .28$ (P.E. $= .12$) was obtained for the relationship between dogmatism and severity of punishment recommended and an $r = .11$ (P.E. $= .13$) for dogmatism and felt menace. It is apparent that factors other than dogmatism account for the attitudes expressed on these two scales, alhough there is some relationship between personal dogmatism and punitiveness scores. What these other variables may be constitutes an area of inquiry for future investigation.

SUMMARY

Thirty-one police officers with experience in the control of narcotics and dangerous drugs were asked their views of drug use and drug users. The characteristics most frequently attributed to the illicit drug user were moral and physical degeneracy, unwillingness to work, untrustworthiness, insecurity, pleasure, orientation, inadequacy, and openness to exploitation. Drug users were often seen as similar to alcoholics in personality. Among all specific criminal types, only drug users were conceived as "natural enemies of cops."

Officers were well aware of the differing effects of various classes of drugs. Those who did not know said so and did not make any assumption of similarity with narcotic drugs. Hallucinogens were considered to produce special social behavior: "wild" or "intoxicated."

Only one of the narcotics officers said he himself had experimented with illicit drugs; but several have friends who have done so.

There was considerable disagreement within the sample about the danger of alcohol versus other drugs, but many saw similarities; the notion of the greater predictability and recognizability of alcohol use figured importantly, as did the social consequences of use.

Users of hallucinogens are regarded by officers as much less deviant or sick than are marijuana or opiate users. Most often officers consider hallucinogen users as rebellious toward authority, self-indulgent, professing superior morality, abusive of pleasure sources, and sexually deviant. They share many attributed traits with marijuana users, but differ importantly in being seen as espousing a superior morality.

There is no single police view of drug users; many different opinions are found among the officers. There tends to be least agreement on hallucinogen users, which reflects least experience with that group. On conceptions of menace, the average rating is that LSD users pose some menace to the community; they are ranked about the same in this as "fast buck" real-estate promoters, homosexuals, and student anti-HUAAC demonstrators.

The average punishment which officers would mete out to LSD users is probation without incarceration. The same sentence is recommended for vagrant beatniks, prostitutes, and homosexuals. All officers considered LSD use to merit some action by the law; the most extreme demand was for a sentence of six to ten years for possession. Treatment or rehabilitation for legal offenders as a group is not much stressed by officers; when it is recommended, it is for persons who harm themselves rather than for offenders against property or person. Homosexuals, drunks, and LSD users fall in the group recommended for treatment by about one-third of the officers.

The majority of officers perceive the public as fearful of the spread of the nonaddictive drugs and as reacting to drugs with disgust and revulsion. There is some clinical evidence that some officers may project their own reaction on the public. These projected police reactions are sensitive to the actual significance of drug use for some of the rebellious persons among the users. Most officers are opposed to the spread of use of LSD and anticipate that it would precipitate a number of hazards. They are not concerned with any civil-liberty or privacy issues in the imposition of controls on drug use. They do not see LSD as providing any social or artistic benefits, although half do believe it is a psychotherapy adjunct. For that reason, there is less objection to its medically controlled use. The sample seems split on whether or not they will accept psychiatric opinion with reference to drug effects and benefits. The police sample tends to value drugs with demonstrable physical or psychological health benefits, but discount or disapprove those which are claimed to produce pleasure, artistic or religious changes, or are associated with radical social change.

Seven parole officers with experience with drug users were found to view things differently than their law-enforcement colleagues in police work did. Parole officers have a more psychological orientation, in contrast with a judgmental, moral one, toward the handling and evaluation of drug offenders. Nevertheless, they agree with narcotics officers in perceiving the drug user to be like the alcoholic.

More parole officers admit to experimentation with drugs and to having friends who use (nonaddictive) drugs than do police officers. Although parole officers join the police in using disapproving terms to describe the narcotics addict, they are much less critical of the marijuana user than are the police.

Parole officers less often see political or socially deviant groups as a community menace; they agree with police in evaluating criminal elements as a menace. Parole officers are more lenient in the sentences they would hand out to offenders; none would use capital punishment, whereas most police officers would.

Parole officers are much less likely to perceive the public as responding emotionally to the use of nonaddictive drugs. They see the public as neutral but share the police view that the public is not sympathetic toward or approving of the use of nonaddictive drugs. Parole officers take the same position as police in seeing the extended use of LSD as a health and social hazard. They are more skeptical than the police about its therapeutic potential.

Parole officers are, in general, less conservative and less emotional about social deviancy and about drug use than are police. Their similar disapproval of extended LSD use suggests that conservatism or emotionality per se do not account for negative view of the drug movement.

There is a slight correlation (r = .28) between personality dogmatism and punitiveness, but practically none (r = .11) between dogmatism and opinions about the extent of menace from various groups.

The beliefs which intellectuals hold about the police, imagining them to be ignorant of the difference between hallucinogens and other drugs and sadistically hostile toward any form of drug use, are not in keeping with the facts about police opinions. If the police can be persuaded that a mind-altering drug has health benefits, they are prepared to accept its medically supervised use. On moral and social grounds, the average narcotics officer does disapprove of LSD use for the purposes for which most drug-movement people wish to use LSD; nevertheless, the punishments which these officers would mete out for unsupervised LSD use are not severe.

NOTES

1. Tigani el Mahi, "The Use and Abuse of Drugs," World Health Organization, Reg. Off. Eastern Mediterranean, EM/RC12/6, XVI (1962).
2. The assumption of equal negative valence for each choice among the paired opposites cannot be made for one of the trait pairs, "controlled and ascetic" versus "greedy and insatiable."
3. To arrive at individual menace scores, the procedure was to sum the total number of points each officer received on his ratings, divide the sums by the number of groups actually rated (some officers did not rate every group on the scale), and multiply the resulting quotient by 10. The higher the menace score, the more listed groups the officer checked as being a serious menace. A second score, the group menace score, was obtained by multiplying the number of times each group listed on the scale was checked in each of the three categories of menace by the total officer sample. The product was divided by the number of officers making the rating and the quotient multiplied by ten. This gives a maximum menace score of 30 and a minimum of 10.
4. The following are the scores assigned per sentence. Release of the offender with no action, 0 points. Individual treatment required, 1 point. Disposition without treatment but without incarceration (that is, probation or the like), 2 points. Incarceration without stated duration—county jail from one day to one year or state prison without time stated—all 3 points. One to five years, 4 points; six to ten years, 5 points; eleven to twenty years, 6 points; twenty years or more, 7 points; death, 8 points.
5. The average punishment score was calculated by multiplying the number of officers checking that frequency by the scale weight of that frequency (0 through 8); dividing by the number of officers indicating a sentence for that offense; and multiplying by 10.

6. Claire Russell and W. M. S. Russell, *Human Behavior* (Boston: Little, Brown, 1961).
7. T. W. Adorno, Else Frenkel-Brunswik, D. J. Levinson, and Nevitt Sanford, *The Authoritarian Personality* (New York: Harper & Bros., 1950); Milton Rokeach, *The Open and Closed Mind* (New York: Basic Books, 1962).

A POLICE ADMINISTRATOR COMMENTS ON THE DRUG MOVEMENT

[XIII]

Edward Comber

The preceding chapter offered an analysis of the views of a number of working police officers assigned to narcotic and vice investigations. In general, these officers were found to disapprove of persons who resort to the use of drugs—including LSD—without benefit of legal prescription. They disapprove of the use of drugs solely for personal pleasure, and they are concerned about the undesirable effects on the community that follow increased consumption of such pleasure-giving substances. These views seem to be a fair assessment of the opinions of the majority of policemen. The views did not, however, present some of the underlying issues which the drug movement poses to the police administrator, nor did they clarify some of the points of dispute which arise between those who propose and those who oppose freer access to pleasure-giving drugs. It is the purpose of this chapter to discuss some of these issues.

Most police officers would contend that the view of the person in the drug movement is essentially personal and subjective. The law-enforcement officer feels that his own position is impersonal and therefore more likely to be impartial. The drug user seeks license for the unrestrained employment of substances which serve *his* needs and feelings. Regardless of his claim for interpersonal effects—being more loving or understanding—his object is to attain temporary internal satisfactions. That his experience may be only a transitory delusion of well-being productive of no tangible social gain is discounted. What he seeks is the privilege to attain his private ends. The law-enforcement officer, on the other hand, has no interest in particular drugs because of what they can do for him; he is concerned, rather, with his responsibility to the community as that responsibility is set down by laws and custom. Detachment rather than involvement characterizes his approach, and it reflects the philosophy inherent in the just enforcement of law. His views will tend to reflect the predominant morality of the society as it is declared by statutes. He serves as a public officer to provide a service demanded by the public. In that public service he must avoid the exercise of personal prejudice or self-seeking. His efforts, when ideally practiced, necessarily will aim for the public well-being. When arguments arise over drug use and drug effects, the law-enforcement officer's attitude will be conditioned by his position as dictated by law, by his responsibility as set forth by administrative directive, and by his experience with elements that threaten public welfare. He will tend to see his own position as morally right, objective, and benefiting the greater public good.

Police efforts to control drug use are only a small part of the many duties imposed on a law-enforcement agency. Narcotic squads as special operating units are of recent origin. In many departments the investigation of narcotic and dangerous drug cases is only a part-time assignment that involves a small number of officers. In the experience of many agencies, important sectors of the public consider present efforts far from adequate and demand greater vigor in the suppression of the drug menace. Whatever the criticism of those citizens who oppose police efforts to control illicit drug use, a larger number of citizens demands greater enforcement. This demand, however, may not be accompanied by the provision of adequate funds and facilities for increased drug control.

Some critics of law-enforcement practices cry out that the officer should display more understanding of the individuality of the user and should overlook private experimentation with pleasure drugs in those cases where the user accepts the risk to his health or well-being. These persons are, in essence, asking for preferential treatment. Yet the same citizens may condemn any arbitrary police actions which smack of differential enforcement of the law, actions in which the letter of the law is not observed and in which one group of persons may be subject to police intervention while another is ignored.

It would be interesting to know how many of the people described in the present study, the ones arguing for personal privilege to employ drugs, support the idea that disabled drug-dependent persons be given rehabilitation. One gathers that most of them would support treatment programs designed to change and improve the user. But if rehabilitation is a valid concept, then one must accept the fact that the use of pleasure-giving drugs produces harm, a harm which one seeks to remedy. If that is so, then it would certainly follow that these people should support prevention, for prevention is most certainly less wasteful of individual and community resources. Yet if one does accept the notion of the prevention of the harm which comes from drug abuse, must one not then support laws which seek to control the distribution and use of dangerous substances? Is not the enforcement of these laws the obligation which society itself has placed on law-enforcement personnel? How can the thoughtful citizen oppose these efforts? The law-enforcement position does not appear unreasonable; it seeks to achieve reasonable regulation of those substances which, if unregulated or diverted to unlimited selfish use, would in fact create unnecessary risks to the individual and would waste the human and financial resources of the community.

Any extended discussion of drug abuse leads to the consideration of the need for controls and the definition of the scope of legal regulation. The practical control of drugs remains an academic matter until some instruments for implementation of control are applied. The results of control efforts will depend on the delicate balance of several factors: (1) the extent to which society understands what various drugs do and the major forms of distress which drug abuse poses; (2) the establishment of standards for the proper and healthy employment of drugs and the provision of legitimate means for their proper distribution and consumption; (3) an effective and consistent body of law proscribing improper drug use (drug abuse, as it is usually called) and providing means for the control of abuse; (4) the provision of agencies and persons charged with control and accountable for the proper exercise of their authority; (5) adequate means for the rehabilitation of those who are identified as victims of harmful drug effects.

Success in the over-all effort to control drugs requires that each of the foregoing conditions be met. Failure to meet any of these conditions disables the entire program and means, in effect, that some individuals will become victims of drug-induced harm, others will fail to receive the benefits of potentially health-giving substances, others will be denied rehabilitation, and the community will suffer not only unnecessary cost and needless loss, but will also experience the distress of knowing that its efforts to maintain a harmonious and benevolent social order are not successful. It will be easier for the citizen, lay or professional, to become aware of the system's failure than it will to identify the focal point or the reasons for failure. The citizen who is dissatisfied with the apparent inadequacy of drug control may vent his wrath at one element, the police. He is not likely to appreciate the inability of any one element to achieve a good result unless the entire social effort is complete and coordinated. The fact is that drug abuse is one of the most talked about and least understood topics of the day. Too many people are responding emotionally without having the facts at hand; too many are critical of one or another element in the control effort without having an overview. The result can only be increased dissension rather than a sensible effort at improvement.

One of the many problems encountered in the use and abuse of drugs, LSD included, is semantic. Words like "intellectual," "religious experience," "loving," and "pleasure-giving" all invoke reactions, but we cannot be sure that the speaker and hearer have the same things in mind. This is true for the word "police" as well. In this book there are at least three uses. For some, the word "police" means a law-enforcement officer; to others, a law-enforcement organization; and to others, the entire establishment concerned with the administration of criminal justice (police, courts, prisons, and so on). It is difficult to agree on the role of the police if definitions are not made clear at the outset. Even when the meaning of the word is established, there are no guarantees on agreement on roles. Failures to understand the domains of operation still exist. One contributor to this volume, for example, implies that the police are prime movers behind all oppressive (punitive, restrictive) drug legislation. The insinuation is not only incorrect, but also fails to comprehend the legislative process and the limited role of law-enforcement personnel therein. In advocating legislation, law-enforcement personnel are primarily concerned only that proposed laws include workable provisions that are intelligible to all interested citizens and organizations, that they are laws that permit implementation and the meeting of police responsibilities without resort to extralegal procedures and without confusion arising from conflicting applications and interpretations.

Because of the failure of individuals to have an overview of drug-control problems, because of the emotionality and the paucity of facts, because of the limited private rather than broader public concerns, because of the confusions over what the police are and what they do, many people have criticized law enforcement not only for its admitted inadequacies, but also for the failures and conflicts generated by other agencies, by the body of law, and by the uncertainty and conflict in society itself.

Everyone must keep in mind that the police can never do more than enforce the existing law within the limitations of actual public support. Should the public will be ill-defined, should various vocal segments of the body politic oppose one another, should partisan emotion rule, the chances are that the police will be the scapegoat for that which is unresolved. One segment of the public sees a seductive drug peddler beside every park bench and near every school playground. They demand unrelenting police action, even if the nature of the menace is unclear. Another segment proclaims that each person has the right to seek his own pleasure as long as no overt injury occurs to another. They hold that the police should not interfere. A third group may be identified among certain healing professions which are convinced that the drug user is sick and must be treated medically. The police may provide a service by locating and identifying the sick victim, but, once segregated from society, he is to be left to the correctional effort of the experts. The fact that there have been few cures that offer any assurance of success does not diminish the experts' enthusiasm. Lost in the contention of vocal interest, the average citizen remains apathetic, showing little interest in his own society's problem of drug abuse. That apathy is not jarred by the fact that a significant portion of the criminal offenders of most penal institutions has been charged with committing crimes associated, directly or indirectly, with drug abuse. Should one include the alcoholic offender in the statistics, one finds that an immense number of arrests and commitments are associated with the use and effects of mind-altering drugs.

It is with reference to new drugs that some serious law-enforcement problems emerge. A legislative body may declare certain acts to be in violation of law and charge the police with regulation. Rarely is simultaneous provision made for implementing that responsibility. As a result, the law-enforcement agency must live through an awkward period of adjustment as it attempts to execute its duty with limited tools. It can also happen that the compromise which the legislative process represents cannot be enjoyed at the practical level. The wording of the statute may be precise, but the area of action remains fluid and uncertain because of the subtle semantic attempts on the part of lawmakers to join the competing demands of the public. The officer's duty may be set forth, but what remains unspoken is the delicate balance of powerful opposing forces. On paper, the office is given a charge; in fact, he is asked to serve several competing masters. The enforcement program is mediated at legislative, judicial, and administrative levels. It is further complicated by shifts in ideology, political power, social change, and public incidents set forth in the press.

Still another problem, one which may be inferred from the comments of people interviewed in the present study, is found in the citizen's conception of the nature and scope of police power. It is seen through a magnifying glass; the citizen easily attributes greater freedom of action and greater power than an officer legally possesses. Some think of policemen as gruff despots whose authority should be curtailed. They assume that police failures to control human conduct can represent only a failure to apply power wisely; they may even assume a desire on the part of the officer to condone rather than to suppress vice. They fail to realize how limited police power is and how it is subject to continuous redefinition through changes in penal law, rules of procedure, court decisions, and, very importantly, the will and temper of the supporting community.

A source of disagreement between the police and medical or behavioral scientist is to be found in the different situations vis-à-vis the drug user in which each group finds itself. The police look to the scientists for knowledge which is essential, especially in drug control, to their work. Yet they must also require appreciation on the part of those scientists of how differing experiences give rise to differing points of view. The physician or scientist deals with the drug user in a context of cooperation and quiet mastery. The observer uses no restraint, requires no unwilled acts, and represents no feared authority. The scientific or medical worker has a selected sample which would not be with him unless its members were already in favor of the professional's goals. Not so with the police. They gather an involuntary "sample" which is hardly cooperative—a sample which may differ in behavior, characteristics, and goals from that seen by the physician or scientist. The latter finds his clientele friendly and cooperative; the police officer finds his not only uncooperative, but very likely to be pathological in the psychological and social sense.

No wonder that a professional whose contact with drug users has been pleasant can deprecate the opinion of the police officer who insists that drug offenders show undesirable behavior and suffer from antisocial tendencies. Sometimes the contention is that the police see only the castoffs at the bottom of the social scale and that these are hardly a cross section of persons using drugs for pleasure. The question is an interesting one and requires further study both of the kinds of samples seen by both groups and the kinds of behavior demonstrated by the same drug user in two situations—one with a physician or social scientist, the other at the time of arrest by a police officer. It is certainly the impression of narcotics officers that the offenders they see do come from all levels of society, that many of them are involved in criminal violations apart from those of drug use itself, and that most who come to police attention have passed the experimental stages of drug use and have considerably modified their lives in order to adjust to and maintain their drug dependency.[1] From the standpoint of the observing officer, the tragedy of drug effects seems undeniable and consists of reduced personal adequacy and an inability to maintain one's obligations to society.

Those persons who regularly use LSD and whose views are reported in this volume would no doubt deny the risks to their own personal and social function which are to be observed among persons who are dependent on other drugs. Yet as one reads the LSD regulars' comments, learning of their increased inner orientation, their lessened interest in competition, status, and work, and their admitted occasional disruption of marriage, one wonders whether these changes might not preview a progressive surrender not unlike that found among users of other drugs. As Dr. Killam noted in Chapter VI, there appear to be parallels between the evolution of the LSD-using social group and the evolution of groups using illicit drugs. One presumes very different pharmacological effects, but what is of interest is the similarity in interest and attitude and the possibility of induced disability. Neurochemistry seems to be only part of the drug-dependency story. The social situations, the interests of the group, the personalities of the individuals —all these play an important part, so much so that similar social responses can occur to quite different pleasure-giving drugs. It has also been established, as in the present study, that people having similar social backgrounds and interests nevertheless report divergent responses when given identical drugs. Both of these phenomena are of concern to the law-enforcement officer and are important to his understanding of the drug user. It is also quite clear that by no means every person who uses any "psychotropic" drug is going to become dependent on it or to develop an ethnocentric or antisocial point of view. Obviously, society's problem in preventing undesirable responses to drugs must deal with social and psychological factors as well as with drug supply itself.

There are those who would contend that the control of drug supplies through law enforcement is only a minimal contribution to the prevention of undesirable human reactions to drugs. Some professionals may believe that even without drugs people predisposed to their abuse and to subsequent disability will find a way to express their discontent and maladaptation and that, consequently, attention should be paid to the people at risk rather than to drug distribution itself. Some even say that the law and the resulting police constraints cause the ill effects observed. Certainly for disadvantaged individuals from socially disorganized areas there can be no doubt that social-psychological prophylaxis is part of the larger job of social control in which the police are necessarily involved. On the other hand, reading the "natural history" of LSD use in this book, one must conclude that, as a consequence of having had the opportunity to take LSD, groups who display no psychological inadequacy or social disadvantage do begin to expand their drug use, some of them ultimately becoming disabled. It is difficult to argue that the elite here studied would have gone astray in any event; their drug use and its bad results do reflect certain psychological and situational predispositions, but a necessary condition is the opportunity to take LSD or some other mind-altering drug. If that opportunity had been prevented, that portion of LSD users who did have what the physicians call a "bad result" would be in better shape today.

On a different matter, one finds a number of people accusing the police of being unrealistic about drugs. Many such accusers are themselves drug users—LSD proponents included—who demand the right to use drugs in order to escape reality. It is odd that people who are escaping reality accuse those who are not of being unrealistic. Since the final decision about what is reality rests on social agreement, it is well to note that the LSD proponent has come to his opinion about the desirability of inward-turning through processes which are concealed in the inner workings of his brain. These processes, from all the available evidence, incorporate the LSD effects of distortion of sensation, hallucination, euphoria, and, from what one is told of neurophysiological experiments, interference in the synaptic transmission of nerve impulse. These are some of the central nervous system events that are associated with the thinking that leads the member of the drug movement to conclude that the police are out of touch with reality. In contrast, the police position is openly arrived at. The subjective thinking of individuals does, of course, constitute the basis, but it is thinking which is objectified in the statutes, directives, public hearings, legislation, and records of public bodies and agencies and which is open to public review and inspection. It is a system that utilizes a plane of reference external to and independent of the individual officer. Documentary evidence must be prepared in support of all policy positions taken. Operations are exposed to scrutiny and debate in the public forum and are, in the final examination, expressions of social consensus. Which process, then, and which position—that of the police or that of the drug movement—is the less exotic and the more realistic?

There are a few other points which should be made. One is recognition of the limited and sometimes conflict-ridden base which constitutes the social consensus on which all police efforts are based. The fact is that many citizens are not of one mind when it comes to the suppression of certain compelling or hedonistic impulses. Drug abuse, like other vices, stems from the individual citizen's wish for gratification. Psychologists will eventually learn what is meant by that term; it certainly includes compulsions of despair such as gambling fully as much as orgiastic delight, simple animal lust, or the maintenance needs of the "main line" heroin user. In any event, there are things which people secretly want but which they publicly proclaim to be immoral. Too often the citizen does not resolve that hypocrisy in his own mind but, rather, asks the police to take responsibility by being his official conscience while he is then free to engage in the very conduct he has denounced. On a larger scale one may think of much of what goes on in the vice arena as a dramatic enactment in which the police, offender, and tempter are the dramatis personae for a spectacular morality play —a play enacted daily in the newspapers and courtroom. Although the police are to be rigorous in their dramatized public actions, the hidden demand is that they, too, be permissive in private. They are solicited to give their private blessing to the discreet sinner at the same time that they are cheered for cracking down on the scapegoats. The citizen can then simultaneously indulge his pleasure, his inconsistency, and his morality. So it is, as other chapters in this book have made clear, that the use of pleasure-giving drugs is one of those publicly proclaimed "vices" which tempts as much as it repels. The consequence for the police is that any action they take is likely to be the object of the displeasure of one side of the citizen's own conflicting desires.

Another element to be considered is that of risk. In a society which stresses the rights of individuals for self-direction and assumes responsibility for free and rational choice, much is made of the right of an individual to decide for himself whether he will engage in activities which endanger himself but not others. With reference to pleasure-giving drugs and LSD in particular, a person may think it is his own business. Why not take a chance if the potential gain is so great? One pays the price of psychosis or loss of job or family in those rare cases when one loses, but isn't that one's own choice? Is it? To be sure, the individual suffers, but it is the community which pays for the mental hospital and it is his wife and children who lose the support of the breadwinner and/or are deprived of normal family life. This study shows that divorce occurs if the wife will not go along with the husband's conversion to the drug movement. When that happens, it is the wife who suffers the risk as much as the husband. One must conclude that the community itself has rights, rights to protect the well-being of all its members, rights to protect itself from unnecessary expense, danger, trauma, or undermining forces.[2] Whatever the talk of alienation, the fact is that none of us are alone and what we do does have consequences for others. That fact underlies all legislation for the control of narcotic and dangerous drugs, and it would be well for those who propose free access to pleasure-giving drugs to keep their community importance and community obligations in mind.

There is another risk in drug abuse which may be overlooked. The experience of the police in dealing with drug-dependent persons, alcoholics included, shows that these people are vulnerable to attack or injury from others. Much of the present practice of arrest is based on a desire to protect the disabled drug user from others who would rob or brutalize him. In the case of a user with a habit—and it is likely that some LSD users have a habit—the craving for drugs opens the way to systematic exploitation. Indeed, much of the relationship that the police observe between addicts who peddle to one another is that of mutual exploitation and deceit. One must not ignore that the community must protect its individual members from their own folly and from the evil of others; one must not ignore the fact that evil does exist and is manifested when human beings take unkind advantage of one another. One must consider whether or not drug use increases the opportunity for evil to be enacted. The good intentions and high ideals of a particular LSD enthusiast do not suffice to remake the world; along with others, he, too, may be in jeopardy insofar as his judgment is clouded and his dependency so great that he can no longer protect himself from those others—proselytizers, salesmen, cultists—on whom he becomes dependent. The argument here is for recognition of the individual and social hazard and for sufficient controls on those who dispense drugs to be reasonably assured that abuse in drug distribution will not flourish.

With reference to the "shadow side" of men, there is a curious thing about the choice of language of the user of pleasure-giving drugs. That argot is presumably enjoyed because of some titillation with the arcane, because it is part of the new LSD self, and because it is part of the mutually supporting camaraderie of the "pill heads." The fact is, however, that much of the language used is criminal cant, some of it admittedly antiquated. One wonders whether the choice of language is strictly fortuitous or whether it reflects some special interest, some toying with a psychological identification with elements which are dubious—that is, criminal. One suspects that the parallels between

LSD social patterns and those associated with the more dramatically illicit drugs are not simply a response to repressive law, as some would contend, but reflect an initial motivation on the part of the drug user. There may be pleasure not only in drugs, but also in playing with the notion of a criminal self. If that were the case, it would follow that, if pleasure-giving drugs were legally dispensed, the reason to use them would be reduced.[3] On the other hand, it would also follow that those who use them for reasons of rebellion, identification with criminal elements, or expression of their disdain for conventional society would surely seek another way of misbehaving, perhaps one with more serious consequences, for with drug use at least most of the effects do not bring direct harm to nonusers.

Members of the drug movement can dismay a police officer when they profess a superior morality as part of their LSD interest and when they affirm their social concern and ennobling self-change. As one reads this study, one finds these claims ringing rather loudly from those who have been initiated in special LSD centers. Of course, most people will modestly admit they are noble, but the test is what they do. Some of the doings among the drug movement have a familiar ring to the police officer. One finds some of them trying to sell LSD at $10,000 a bottle, others hustling it for smaller but more certain fees, and some smuggling it across the border; no doubt, there are others hawking aqua pura with an LSD label on it. These by no means exhaust the range of possibilities; the techniques of bilking for fun and profit are limitless. What must be remembered is that, as long as LSD or any other drug is heralded as a good item in very short supply, there are smart operators who are going to make an unconscionable profit.[4]

The final point to be made is more philosophical. As people discuss LSD-like drugs and other mind-altering substances, some will make judgments which will *not* be based on an evaluation of effects, intents, or correlated behavior. In contrast to the foregoing pragmatic considerations, judgments may be made of individual acts and people of and for themselves. That constitutes the moral or absolutist position, and it is derived from ethics, idealistic philosophy, and religions which postulate a God-given morality. It may also be secondarily derived from personal points of view which assume that what is given, or what is, is right, sacred, and incontrovertible, whatever its purposes or origins.[5] Sometimes the absolutist evaluation of acts has roots which can be primitive as well as profound—for instance, the taboos which prohibit incest, masturbation, sexual perversion, or murder. Whatever their roots and whatever the philosophical sophistication of the person making the judgment, it is the case that people do judge acts on the basis of their inherent good or evil. With reference to the use of drugs, the historical origins for its consideration in the moral framework are evident in the New Testament: "They which do such things [drunkenness, revelings] shall not inherit the kingdom of God" (Gal. 5:21), ". . . make not provision for the flesh, to fulfil the lusts thereof" (Rom. 13:14), and

> It is good neither to eat flesh, nor to drink wine, nor any thing whereby thy brother stumbleth, or is offended, or is made weak. . . . Happy is he that condemneth not himself in that thing which he alloweth. And he that doubteth is damned if he eat, because he eateth not of faith: for whatsoever is not of faith is sin (Rom. 14:21–23).

The scientist or humanitarian who tends to weigh acts in a pragmatic light will differ fundamentally from those who view acts from the moral, absolutist standpoint. Many police officers, legislators, and religious people will be found in the latter camp. Their approach to LSD is likely to reflect the view that pleasurable drug use in the absence of medical necessity is, in itself, wrong. Other contributors to this book have condemned such an orientation; nevertheless, it is a fact of life and one which is supported by much in our culture and our quest for certainty. Those who favor the scientific approach take refuge behind selective theories and demonstrations which they can manipulate, yet they admit doubt and uncertainty in other areas of knowledge and experience. This writer can accept the occasion to question the validity of a moral concept, but one must keep in mind that limitations on the ability to perform a suitable demonstration—that is, to empirically prove there exists a God-given law—do not of themselves prove the moral position invalid. The debate which is occurring in society and which will expand as the drug movement expands will be clarified— although not resolved—by recognition of these basic philosophical differences.

NOTES

1. *Proceedings of the White House Conference on Narcotic and Drug Abuse* (Washington, D.C.: United States Government Printing Office, 1962).
2. Some proponents of "rights" try to discount the demands of society; however, they seem to ignore the fundamental fact that any individual acts which are in defiance of the structure and strength of society are assaults on the instrument that grants the protester his freedom to protest.

3. After this chapter had been written, a book appeared which takes a very strong position on a number of these subjects. In the first chapter of *The Road to H,* there is a discussion of opiate use as partly arising from the "attractiveness of the forbidden" and the "glamor of defying authority." The authors also write, ". . . the most dangerous consequences of addiction to the individual were a direct outcome of the existence and enforcement of the law" (Isidor Chein, Donald Gerard, Robert Lee, and Eva Rosenfeld, *The Road to H* [New York: Basic Books, 1964], p. 7). It is well to keep in mind that alcohol is a pleasure-giving drug which is legitimately accessible. The dramatic evidence about its use, a use which is analogous in some ways to the employment of other mind-altering substances, does not provide support for the idea that free access reduces the individual and social problems involved.

4. *Proceedings* . . ., *op. cit.*

5. Jean Piaget, *The Moral Judgment of the Child* (Glencoe, Ill.: Free Press, 1948).

CONCLUSIONS AND COMMENTARY

[XIV]

Richard Blum

What has been learned? What social issues are involved? What may be suggested? It will be the purpose of this section to respond to these questions. To begin with, these are the facts, at least the facts as they now appear, until revised by more adequate studies yielding more certain knowledge.

REPORTED LSD EFFECTS

The study confirms prior observations.[1] LSD-25 in the range of dosage employed by sample members (25 to 900 micrograms) has powerful effects on the minds of those taking it. There are a very few exceptions. For example, one person taking about 200 micrograms became psychotic; another taking 200 micrograms claimed only that his eyes were blurred so that he found it harder to watch television that evening. The range of effects is nevertheless predictable. The physical consequences described are incapacitation, nausea, numbness, cramps, exhaustion, and changes in facial musculature. The major mental effects are sensory changes, including alterations in intensity in attention, imagery, and hallucinations; transient feelings of anxiety, excitement, despair, power, terror, release, calm, intoxication, euphoria, or detachment; new perspectives about oneself, including insights, recollections, redefinitions, acceptance, or rejection; new views or emotions about others, including felt objectivity, closeness, withdrawal, loathing, and lovingness; changes from prior chronic states, including reduction of tension, anxiety, or anger, reduced competitiveness, or increased depression; shifts in interest, including reduced work interests and goal striving, increased artistic or philosophical concerns, greater preoccupation with internal events and self, and greater interest in drugs per se; and new integrative experiences which may be culturally acceptable, psychotically delusional, or mystically religious.

Most persons taking the drug reported both pleasant and unpleasant effects, the pleasant ones more often being recalled as significant. Distortions in recall occur as the result of apparent memory loss, present euphoria, repression, need-determined perceptions, or learned interpretations of an ambiguous experience. The majority of persons taking LSD would like to take it again; many have done so; a few (one-sixth) have become regular users. Among the regular users, the majority, but not all, report increasing dosage and frequence. Differing effects are reported by the same person from one experience to the next when dosage is held constant. Cross-tolerance is reported by some heavy alcohol drinkers. Most regular LSD users report a failure to experience the most dramatic initial effects with repeated similar dosages; that is, they report tolerance of the drug. The number of persons in the sample who meet the criteria for being habituated is 10 per cent or greater, assuming the accuracy of self-reports.

LSD use is associated with extended use of other mind-altering drugs. Although there is a slight difference between those who have taken LSD and those who have not in the amount of mind-altering drug experience (excluding alcohol and tobacco) had prior to taking LSD (12 per cent of the controls have taken mind-altering drugs, whereas 24 per cent of the total LSD-accepting sample had had such experience), after LSD the picture changes rapidly. Either as a consequence of planned administration of other drugs by LSD institutions or informal use, the majority of persons accepting LSD had also taken other drugs by the time of this study. The use of LSD is also associated with the regular use of mind-altering drugs; whereas only 6 per cent of the controls were regular users, one-third of the LSD-accepting sample used such drugs with some regularity.

There is no uniformly adverse reaction to the regular use of one or several mind-altering drugs—"multihabituation."[2] Nevertheless, some regular users do demonstrate reduced work effectiveness and gross psychological disorder. These opinions of the observer are not shared by the regular users themselves, who tend to see their performance as unimpaired and their psychological adjustments as satisfactory. This disagreement raises the possibility of bias, of inadequate assessment methods on the part of the observers, or poor judgment and euphoria in the regular users. The study does present evidence that regular users tend to show poor judgment insofar as they are overly trusting and euphoric. Again these evaluations pit the "pathological" orientation of the observer against the felt tranquillity or mystical joy of the LSD user.

EPIDEMIOLOGY

The means employed here for identifying cases do not allow any estimate of the incidence of LSD use in the normal population nor of the prevalence of cases of regular users in the two metropolitan centers where data were gathered. The populations of users and controls sampled here certainly are not representative of the total populations in the two metropolitan centers. On the basis of the information available it appears that LSD use is most likely to occur among psychotherapy patients whose psychiatrists have themselves had LSD, among middle-class persons living in areas where LSD institutions make the drug publicly available, among artists and professionals having informal equal-status contacts with mental-health professionals who do have access to the drug, among volunteers for drug experiments in institutions, and among active social groups of younger persons already using other drugs, whose interests or career training in the arts and professions expose them to LSD information and sources of supply among professionals. There are, however, a large number of potential or actual users who have no contact with professionals and have access to LSD only through black-market sources: homemade or imported LSD and homegrown or purchased morning glory seeds.

At the present time, LSD use would appear to be confined to a limited social strata of intellectuals in the twenty-one to fifty age group, primarily male, or the wives or girl friends of such males; they are white, often Anglo-Saxon, Protestants. It is a phenomenon concentrated among respected, conforming, successful persons with socially favored backgrounds and careers.

The diffusion of the drug has been primarily through informal social contacts among such groups, or through formal role relations of doctor to patient, teacher to student, or investigator to experimental subject. Respect and dominance relationships facilitate diffusion—husband to wife, employer to worker, and so on. Future diffusion is more likely to be through institutions as LSD use becomes organized, formal, and controlled.

Of interest is the presence in four separate groups—LSD users, controls, narcotics officers, and parole officers—of unexpectedly high incidence of the use of mind-altering drugs. Such experimentation does not imply continued use, but at least 10 per cent in each sample except the police have used drugs other than those prescribed by physicians or available in pharmacies. Drug availability and predispositions to use cannot be considered unusual phenomena; the use of illicit drugs to alter consciousness is compatible with the more widespread employment of prescribed drugs (tranquilizers, energizers, and the like) and alcohol in the American culture.

Although a rate of incidence of 10 per cent for the illicit use of mind-altering drugs among adult metropolitan populations appears immensely overestimated, what is strongly suggested is the need for genuine epidemiological studies in the use of mind-altering substances. Such studies must attend to patterns of diffusion, the natural history of use, the correlates of use both behaviorally and sociologically, and the effects of use. It will be important to learn whether any more adverse effects from the use of illicit nonaddictive drugs are to be observed, as the el Mahi hypotheses would indicate,[3] than from the use of sanctioned or prescribed drugs. To venture a guess from the present study, comparing reduced work efficiency and psychosis in this sample with general estimates of the consequences of alcohol, tranquilizer, or barbiturate use, no such effects would be predicted, providing the definition of effect was medical, that is, physiological. On the other hand, for social effects, for example, reduced conformity, a more adverse response would be predicted.

LAW ENFORCEMENT

It is clear that the use of unprescribed or illicit drugs is by no means confined to criminal, deviant, or lower-class groups. A number of otherwise law-abiding citizens experiment with, and some habitually use, drugs such as marijuana, peyote, and methedrine with little apparent risk of association with criminals or of engaging in offenses against either property or person. They also appear to run little risk of detection and arrest. There is no evidence that such illicit drug use among successful and older intellectuals is associated with sexual deviancy, overt rebelliousness, degeneracy, or untrustworthiness. Furthermore, there is no evidence of interest in or likelihood of any "steppingstone" sequence from any illicit mind-altering drug to the use of the addictive drugs. By virtue of their greater drug interests, willingness to experiment, and trust in those initiators (respected friends or professionals) who give drugs, this group is theoretically in some risk of using any dangerous or narcotic drugs. This would be especially true for the less well-controlled, more naive, habitual users of potent mind-altering substances, since their judgment may be impaired. But at the present time, one may rule out concern over narcotics use as an actual risk for these persons.

Whether or not laws should be changed or law-enforcement effort directed more toward this group is a question that will necessarily be raised. Given the occasional occurrence of psychotic reactions and the presumptive evidence for a few persons showing reduced efficiency or effectiveness, there seems little doubt that LSD use does present hazards for those taking the drug. Whether these hazards are any greater than, or indeed as great as, those which are posed by other permissible drug activities, alcohol use, tobacco use, or use of prescribed tranquilizers, energizers, sedatives, and the like is a very important question. The evidence from this study suggests that the controlled institutional use of LSD is associated with the least extension of LSD-taking to other drugs or to the informal (unsupervised) and sometimes illicit use of LSD. Institutional safeguards do not appear, however, to exclude any of the risks of immediate psychological or physical bad results, regardless of the claims of institutional personnel to the contrary. Except to control the drug effect hazards, there would appear to be no reason to direct law enforcement toward this otherwise eminently law-abiding sector of the population.

Implicit here is the acknowledgment of differential law enforcement—because of the nature of police intelligence operations, because of conceptions of criminal dangers associated with drug use, because of limited police personnel, and because of certain privileges of upper-income and educated groups to engage in illicit activities, as long as these are discreet and conform to certain norms of the "acceptably illicit." Differential enforcement is not compatible with the democratic ethic, even though it is compatible with the facts of the structure of power and prestige in our society. Perhaps one solution is not increased enforcement against the elite, but a reappraisal of the laws governing the use of mind-altering drugs so that at least drug use which is relatively harmless in and of itself (excluding now the reactions to the drug which are a result of the expectations of the user and the demands of the group)—marijuana and peyote, for example—be excluded from legal concern. Such a move would be consistent with Vollmer's belief that drug use should not be a police problem. Unacceptably deviant behavior by members of groups which use these substances will no doubt emerge in other forms and can be dealt with under other laws.

Much rests on the judgment of pharmacological harmlessness and on the amount of risk that the individual is allowed to assume for himself before society intrudes to prevent or control use. In LSD, for example, the risk exists but will be balanced against the notion of the individual's rights to choose for himself or to have private experiences, even if these are publicly disapproved. Such a debate is a continuing one in our society and extends beyond the use of illicit drugs to alcohol, tobacco, and acts of sexual deviancy in private and between consenting adults. As Myrdal[4] observed, Americans have a number of problems in reconciling individual rights and the public good and also in deciding whether or not laws are enacted to be enforced or merely as expressions of ideals or devices to encourage discretion.

The evidence from this study does show that law-enforcement officers are well informed about drugs but may not be so well informed about the opinions of important sectors of the public. They are dedicated to their work, but because of their essentially moral position may exclude from consideration tools which might help them reduce the volume of that work, specifically psychological- and medical-treatment techniques applied to offenders. The effectiveness of those techniques has not been so well demonstrated as to make this a pressing current problem, but one may anticipate advances in the near future which would make it worthwhile for police officers to consider the usefulness of such methods. At present, the question of the extent to which conventional morality can allow the "amoral" (nonpunitive or nonpenitential) handling of the offender is one by no means confined to the police.

The study also suggests the advantages which may accrue to the police and the citizenry at large from a more trusting relationship between police and professionals in medicine and social science. We see distrust on both sides, and the intellectual community appears to err grievously in its assumption of generalized hostility and ignorance among policemen. Again the value positions of the two groups are different and, although these no doubt reflect differences in social background, training, and temperament, they also reflect the different positions of the two groups with respect to their responsibilities for maintaining the present distribution of power and the control of deviant conduct in our society.

SOCIAL ASPECTS

Sociologically it is clearly demonstrated that LSD use is a social phenomenon. The drug is given by one person to another along predictable lines of association and role relationship. It is usually taken in the presence of several persons—friends, relatives, and associates other than the initiator. Afterward, those who continue the use of or interest in the drug do so in association with like-minded persons and do form social groups based upon the shared experience and developing interests. Out of some of these informal associations there have emerged formal institutions devoted to the public ends symbolized in the drug movement. The institutions composing the movement engage in mass communication and political action and, internally, suffer the same problems of factionalism and strain associated with competing professional roles or differing stands on traditionalism versus innovation that other artistic, religious, or mental-health organizations experience.

Persons in the drug movement occupy different roles with associated variations in power and tasks. Those in leadership positions may find it necessary to pretend conformity with movement rituals and values while at the same time actually behaving appropriately to the demands of those outside the movement. Implicit is that commitment to the movement and identification as a user, "swinger," or perhaps a "guru," which by no means rules out the necessity for flexibility in interpersonal behavior nor accommodation to roles in social systems external to the movement. When users speak of "playing the game," they acknowledge their intention to participate in and play act conformity to the ordinary world while at the same time enjoying detachment and the commitment to the private sphere of drug use and nongame, sincere interaction with fellow believers. Insofar as they do "play the game," their actions are no different from others who act appropriately to the roles they hold in a social system.

It is apparent that the insider-outsider dichotomy which Howard Becker[5] applies to the musician-marijuana user is not generally applicable to the LSD accepter. Some but not all LSD users conceive of themselves as in-group members and, at the same time, since they are sensitive to the hostility of others, can feel themselves to be outsiders. On the other hand, since most of the sample members are successful, conforming professionals and artists whose daily work keeps them in contact with colleagues, most of whom are not personally antipathetic to drug use as it is carried out by the LSD user, the insider-outsider dichotomy need not always emerge, except as a function of personal ethnocentric predisposition or a necessary group formation around sources of supply. One of the curious aspects of proselytism is the means by which it prevents a fixed in-group from forming. As long as movement members are dedicated to converting others, much of their time will be outside-oriented. Similarly, as they succeed in conversion, the in-group continues to expand, sometimes so rapidly that there may be very few social contacts in the user's ordinary circle who have not, with him, become LSD initiates. The fluidity and lack of hostile out-group contacts reduces the opportunity for group consciousness or self-identification as a "drug group" per se. Proselytism also serves, by its very success, to reduce feelings of guilt or defensive in-grouping which would occur if movement enthusiasts were met by an unbreachable wall of social disapproval. Again the fact that readiness to take mind-altering drugs seems so common, at least among the circle of potential converts, tends to emphasize the similarities among one's acquaintances rather than to lead to a strong "we-they" categorization. In Everett Hughes's terms,[6] LSD use may not be a master status trait but only an auxiliary one in determining self-conceptions.

Even the notion of the "square" or the "worldly man" is not really an identification of nonusers. It is an ideal, a stereotype, which may fit a few but not all of the nondrug social contacts in the user's life. Nor is it applied indiscriminately, for sympathetic interaction takes place on the basis of shared values even though one person is and the other person is not an LSD user. Thus it has been shown that, once initiated into a drug group, some people continue as highly acceptable members without taking drugs again. Conversely the drug-taking *rite de passage* is not sufficient to ensure in-group status should the convert disagree on other fundamental propositions of action or opinion.

Robert K. Merton's[7] notion of "retreatism," attributed to persons in a disadvantaged social position lacking either legitimate or illegitimate means for achieving culturally sanctioned ends, is clearly irrelevant to the LSD phenomena. While one may think of the convinced LSD user as retreating, it is certainly not because he has failed to achieve at least some of the glories of this world, nor does he lack institutional means to secure more of these ends should he so desire. And whatever retreat does occur is not a withdrawal into a dismal emptiness or shadowy world of despair. As described, it is a retreat from competition and strife but also toward something felt to be positive: tranquillity and personal or religious exaltation. The retreat, then, if that is what it is, is more along the lines of "privatism,"[8] an antimaterialistic emphasis on a reliable inner world in the face of an unreliable outer one. A retreat of that order is what Max Weber[9] refers to when he speaks of the "self-deification" accompanying the inner needs of the "world-fleeing" intellectual; it is an attempt by the intellectuals, who have lost political power to bureaucracy and the state, to endow their lives with a meaning and significant order which cannot be found through empiricism and worldliness.

PSYCHOLOGICAL ASPECTS

There are a number of variables, intrapsychic and interpersonal, rational and nonrational, which predispose some persons to take LSD and, among those taking it, predispose a minority to become regular users of it and other mind-altering drugs. The decision to accept or reject the drug is influenced by the kind of information one has about its effects and about how one feels about his life circumstances and directions at the time the drug is made available. If one's life is unpleasant, if one conceives of most of the distress to be due to some lack, need, or problem in oneself, and if one believes the drug to produce personal benefits, then the chances are that one will take LSD. If one's general motivation is curiosity and excitement-seeking or is directed toward the inner life, one is predisposed to take the drug. If, on the other hand, one is ready to blame external sources for one's distress, if one's motivation is toward known rather than unknown sources of stimulation, if one distrusts foreign substances or drugs in general, if one is holding the line against change, or if one is informed that the drug's effects are transient, superficial, or unpleasant, then the chances are that LSD will be rejected.

Those who are already more interested in the active social world maintain that interest, continue their upward climb and/or competitive striving, and do so at the cost of continued tension, perhaps resorting to sanctioned relaxers and restoratives in the form of alcohol or overeating. These persons are unlikely to take LSD and are certainly unlikely to become regular drug users. The LSD accepters, especially the continuing users, appear more willing to withdraw from striving and to abandon worldly goals; as this occurs, they become more relaxed, more preoccupied with themselves, and more euphoric. Their level of anger goes down and is replaced by more affectionate feelings. There are very great differences between accepters and rejectors in how the drug and those who use it are perceived. The accepters, especially the regular users, evaluate the effect of the drug on themselves and their acquaintances as highly beneficial. Rejectors see LSD's effects on their acquaintances, often the very same people, as harmful or nonexistent. Accepters see LSD users in a very favorable light and attribute either psychopathology or stodginess to those who refuse the drug. Rejectors are less emotional about the typology of takers and refusers; they are less self-praising and also less critical of the one who is different, in this case the user.

Those who continue to use LSD regularly are likely to become deeply involved socially with other LSD users, to be ethnocentric, to be overtrusting, and to demonstrate undercontrol in ego function. There is some reason to believe that those who have discontinued the use of the drug had—and remember—an unpleasant initial reaction to it or had a more complete experience, either in terms of relief, lasting anxiety reduction, or the absence of tantalizing *presque vu* phenomena. Regular users more often have an enjoyable initial experience followed by many felt benefits, but there is the suggestion that the experience is incomplete or that anxiety is only partially alleviated, so that repetitive behavior may be induced.

There are some subtle indications that the LSD rejectors may be better able to withstand anxiety, that they find more satisfaction in competitive striving, that they are more extroverted, and that, whatever their protestations of tolerance—which they can afford as a comfortable majority behaving in accordance with antidrug morality—they do disapprove of drug use and users on moral grounds, that disapproval sometimes lending itself to pleasant feelings of superiority. It may be that these intellectuals, schooled to accept deviancy, allow the police to be their projected conscience. Externalized, that conscience can then be criticized as well as secretly approved. Implicit is the fact of a moral conflict over the use of drugs both in those who use them and those who do not use them. That conflict is projected to beliefs about police and public reactions to drug use. This conflict is interpersonal as well as intrapsychic. Various groups are in strenuous opposition with reference to the evaluation of the dangers, menace, and benefits of drug use, and with reference to the need for control or moral suasion through punitive devices. But what is not to be overlooked is the likelihood that, the more intense positions people take and the more passionately they invoke principles, sentiments, and morality in the name of freedom or repression—mass conversion to drugs or mass imprisonment of users —the more the observer should be alert to intrapsychic conflict and defense in these expostulators. Their conflicts are likely to center on the handling of physiological and developmental needs—especially those connected with sex, defecation, exploration, and oral satisfactions; with attitudes of rebellion or overconformity toward authority, and, in general, with matters of comfort, spontaneity, and pleasure for which drug use has much symbolic significance.

The significance of drug use for some users merits special attention, especially those real groups of younger persons who use a number of mind-altering substances and for whom such use is symbolic of revolt against constraints—psychic and social—and is an affirmation of anti-compulsive, anticonservative spontaneity. This same emotionality is to be found in those who react to these users with intense disgust, their reaction being a fear of overwhelming menace, and enlist noble sentiments in the cause of punitive repression. As Fritz Redl[10] observed, a temptation which is repressed at great effort may be handled through reaction formation and the outpouring of hostility on the scapegoat caught doing the tempting deed. The Russells[11] and other psychoanalysts have observed similar dynamics and have pointed to the distortion in early childhood of the various urges to seek comfort and to explore which, as they emerge in the child, set off the parents' anxiety and hostility. What might otherwise be naturally evolved behavior with un-emotional rational direction becomes a matter of parental manipulation and childhood conflict. One side of the conflict appears conscious, but, as the Russells point out, not intelligent. The child becomes compulsive and espouses the punitive morality of the parents. Any threatened breakthrough of the disapproved behavior leads to disgust and depression; therefore great effort is spent to prevent these urges, now caged and warped, from getting loose. Cleanliness, control, and self-denial are exaggerated at the cost of inner comfort, personality growth, and intelligent self-understanding. Interpersonal relations are equally distorted as the behavior of others is continually evaluated in terms of whether or not they are behaving as oneself has been forced to do. If they are not, various pressures are brought to bear to force conformity. A generalized social sentiment emerges among those who share such upbringing which ill conceals phobias and tendencies toward addiction and the temptation of the forbidden in just those areas where unresolved pushes and pulls remain. Subsequent social behavior by such individuals or groups may be cruel, hypocritical, exploitative and may include a psychodynamic ritual of seduction and rejection of the person so seduced. To proselytize is, for some, that seduction. To then betray, exploit, or disdain is the rejection.

It is in a psychodynamic light that one can view the compulsion against pleasure which pervades the Puritan sentiment and which produces such a harsh response to conduct that is "self-indulgent" or "abusive of pleasure." Say this first phrase and immediately one can invoke the picture of the greedy and indolent child stuffing himself with food and omnipotently devouring the world; say the second and evoke the secret sin of the masturbating child, the lascivious woman, or the yellow-toothed, lecherous old man. The sexual component is apparent, but should not be so prominent to make one overlook the more general restrictions placed upon pleasure, spontaneity, or the antirational. The constraints which the several place around the one, constraints not only on how he shall act, but on what he shall feel, where he shall turn, what he shall believe, and how he shall grow, are the essence of the taming and the civilizing of the not-yet-human animal by his parents. That same constraining action is re-enacted wherever the more powerful deal with the less powerful to convert the latter to the values, and generally to the advantage, of the former. It is in that public re-enactment of the familial scene that one encounters the conflict over individual rights versus the public good. The several continue to constrain the individual, for reasons of altruism and self-interest, and for reasons rational and irrational. In turn, the individual struggles for reasons equally selfish or grand, and for reasons intelligent or instinctual, to command his own self-direction and advantage.

ANTHROPOLOGICAL ASPECTS

There are several areas of anthropological interest which are suggested by the data from the study. One is the peculiar pattern in which proselytizing follows kinship lines but in which, unlike the more typical diffusion of LSD use from the dominant to the subordinate, children initiate their parents. "You've never seen such a loving family; X 'turned the whole crowd on.' It was the highest Thanksgiving ever." That is most certainly a reversal of the usual parent-child pattern of instruction and introduction to new experience and suggests, for those families in which it occurs, an implicit recognition by the parents of the "togetherness" which the drug conversion symbolizes. Rather than be different or stand outside the children's activities, the parents avow their interest in being incorporated into the peer group of their children. This is, of course, very "permissive" and "democratic." It also implies an effort to prove nonconservatism and youthful orientation on the part of the parents, which is not surprising in a culture which values youth so highly and which, publicly at least, proclaims its faith in scientific progress, pills included.

The culture of drug user is another aspect of interest. J. S. Slotkin[12] has described in *The Peyote Religion* the relationships between drug values and practices and the social-historical position of the Menomini Indians vis-à-vis the whites. Becker has described the subculture of the jazz musician-marijuana user; Harold Finestone[13] has reviewed the place of drugs in the life of the "cat," the frustrated young urban Negro interested in music and kicks, who lives solely within his own achievement-blocked social group to fashion a new kind of status which represents an indirect attack upon conventional values. For the "cat," drug use is a renunciation and rebellion, a subtle accommodation avoiding confrontation or attack, a way of finding status and self-identification, and a means to pleasure and aesthetic satisfaction. G. Morris Carstairs[14] compares the Brahmin's acceptance of hashish and rejection of alcohol with the Western world's acceptance of alcohol and rejection of hashish and the opiates. The latter drugs are productive of a quiescence compatible with values of meditation and the turning-wheel-of-life ethos of the religious man of the East. Alcohol is incompatible with that, but is, in its effects, compatible with the Western aggressive interpersonal ethos; it is the intoxicant of the warrior, the Kshatriya.

These observations point out that the pharmacological effects of a drug will affect its selection or rejection by a culture, the requirement being that, for general sanction, employing the drug must not produce effects opposed to the predominant ethos of the culture. On the other hand, drugs rejected by the culture at large may be selected by dissident subcultural groups just because they do symbolize the rejection of that larger ethos and because the effects produced are compatible with the interests of the dissident subculture. Some drugs may not be intimately linked with the ethos because of the recency of their innovation, their unavailability, or the unimportance of the subgroups employing them. In those cases, the acceptance of a drug, ignored or disdained by the larger culture, may not symbolize rebellion or the conflict of power and values, but may reflect more moderate dissent—a desire to fashion new images, myths, or identifications or to experiment with values accepted but not encouraged in a pluralistic society. The use of hallucinogens is best seen in that light.

It is also apparent that, just as a drug, whatever its modal effect, produces varying effects among different individuals, so too may different groups seize upon the use of the same drug to achieve or symbolize diverse ends. Hashish may be chewed by fanatic assassins or smoked as *bhang* by placid Brahmins; while its cousin, marijuana, is blown by boisterous beats or quietly used at the day's end in place of a cocktail by some successful professionals in metropolitan America. And this is the case with LSD; for some groups, it produces the "king of highs," and for others it reveals the infinite mystery of self. Among those real groups which employ LSD, one of those two themes is predominant; the younger up-and-coming intellectuals seek artistic ends, excitement, and euphoria; the more settled and established pursue self, love, and God—and sometimes, not surprisingly, a new kind of power.

GENERAL COMMENTS

The consideration of the determinants, correlates, effects, and significance of the drug movement cannot be limited to the relatively narrrow focus of any one of the life sciences. The use of mind-altering drugs is a human phenomenon and must be considered in the greatest possible breadth. Although there is most certainly a place for data analysis and theory construction at any one level of analysis, that is, within the framework of any one discipline, the time has passed when biological and behavioral scientists could enjoy provincialism and at the same time hope for any sense of completeness in developing a picture of human behavior. The preceding portion of this chapter has attempted to summarize, by various disciplinary approaches, some of the pertinent features of LSD use. The following portion abandons any such disciplinary focus and will range rather generally over some of the more interesting and significant aspects of the drug movement.

Inward and Outward Direction

In pursuing the matter of cultural themes and drug effects, one comes again and again to a dichotomy: inward-turning versus outward-turning. There are those who are in and of the world and those who are not; and as with any simple typology, there are those who fall somewhere in between. In psychology, the words are introversion and extroversion; in sociology, inner-directed and other-directed.[15] In anthropology, the words are more diverse: cultures of contemplation and cultures of action or Dionysian cultures of ecstasy and Apollonian cultures of moderation. And in religion, there is a division between the mystics and the ascetics—and, unfortunately for the typology, the majority who are neither, or those who become one to achieve being the other.

But when one does encounter the inward-turning individual, especially one who, by cultural dictate, is never to be more than part-time mystic, the constant correlates are there. They are individual ecstasy, group orgies, the use of drugs, of music, and of art; the primacy of eroticism, of magic, of spirituality, and of direct experience; the presence of spontaneity, emotionalism, and irrationality. The experience itself, as William James[16] said, is ineffable, noetic, transient, and passive, but also glorious: it is the "anesthetic revelation" induced by drugs, a cosmic consciousness-inducing meaning, unity, and unanimity denied to the empiricist; it is the delicious optimism of grace. But also, as James saw, the experience can be or can produce stupefaction, intellectual enfeeblement, helpless passivity or, in what he brilliantly called "diabolical mysticism," the power, desolation, and dread of the paranoid psychosis.

The roots of mysticism? For William James they were, empirically, internal—to be found in the subconscious, in the unification of a discordant self through conversion, and in the biologically necessary interest of man in his private personal destiny. "Religion," he wrote, "in short, is a monumental chapter in the history of human egotism." But to James, mysticism had roots beyond biology and psychology; it had observable social and aesthetic sources in a reaction against the "flat" evangelism of Protestantism, that "almshouse" of "naked gospel," compared to the richly artistic and emotional quality of Catholicism. He also saw in the uncertain content of mysticism its intellectual infidelity, its dalliances with the heroes of each age—"alliances with material furnished by the most diverse philosophies and theologies, provided only they can find a place in their framework for its peculiar emotional mood." But James, a religious man, saw roots beyond the cold abstractions of empiricism; quoting the mystic al-Ghazzali, he saw that "knowledge about a thing is not the thing itself." James affirmed that the religious experience was reality; the rest was only symbols. "The axis of reality runs solely through the egotistic places. . . . The world . . . the intellect contemplates is without solidity or life." Religion, mysticism at its base as the strongest of feelings, not only has function and utility, but *is* being alive.

Max Weber expanded the history, circumstance, correlates, and consequences of mysticisim as opposed to asceticism. His was the delineation of the Protestant ethic and the evaluation of the ascetic Protestant quest for salvation through worldly work alone. Taking this organized asceticism, together with the history of Christianity, capitalism, and the evolution of the modern state, what are the predominant "givens" in the Western world which Weber describes? We list them as follows: inner worldly asceticism; rationalism; a sober and dominant bureaucracy; the ideal of order and security; the ideal of alertness and self-control; the exaltation of commerce and vocations with a power distribution to maintain them and military force to protect and facilitate them; the proliferation of the apparatus of the state; indifference to religious feeling and the emphasis on institutional religious forms accompanied by suspicion of the independent religious seeker; the rejection of personal ethics and personal loyalties or feelings as dictating modes of economic and bureaucratic intercourse; and success in business as the proof of favor with God, as proof of salvation, and as the finest fruit of a rational way of living. The dominant modes, as Weber saw them, are anti-intellectual, antiromantic, antimagical, anti-irrational, antierotic, and antiaesthetic. Politics devotes itself to the dominant interests of the state and to realism; it is opposed to every residue of the religious ethic of brotherhood, just as are the economic institutions.

What is the outcome? The world as we know it in all its progress, efficiency, and rational smoothness. But for individuals who accept the heritage of mystical religions, or who regenerate that heritage in their own experience, there can be a sense of loss. Humility and brotherly love are gone. There can be a sense of guilt, a "secret anguish" Weber calls it, as men are compelled to act in spite of their spiritual propensities and to experience "godless sin" as they participate in an eminently impartial, intrinsically honest, and overwhelmingly well-organized system. There can be, among intellectuals especially, but also among the middle class or aristocracy who have lost their power to bureaucrats and the military, a reaction against the entire system. The reaction is "apolitical emotionalism," a revulsion against the perfection of rationality and impersonal manipulations—in essence, a revolt against a system which works but which does not gratify. The direction of the revolt? As long as it is apolitical, then it must turn inward, and that flight is into mysticism.

Parsons,[17] in discussing Weber, rightly notes that one modern term for the disaffection of men for the impersonal social system in which they find themselves is "alienation." The nature and effects of that social system have been the subject of continuing sociological discourse the last decades. Whyte's *The Organization Man*,[18] for example, shows the business system molding its participants; *Crestwood Heights*[19] has described how the system prepares the young for the rational control of their own peronalities as saleable commodities; Stein[20] has documented *The Eclipse of Community* in the anonymous urban monolith, and others have discerned how difficult it is to identify oneself as something special when so much of one is controlled, constrained, and molded for the market place.

Sociological theory, beginning with the brilliant symbolic interactionism of Mead[21] and expanded by current writers[22] has taken role theory quite beyond the business of attributes and "as if" behavior and has moved from attending to the forces shaping social behavior to social forces shaping personality. As this has occurred, role has slowly been converted into "self" and social status into "identity." The play is reality, and persons are only actors, players, masks, or other outward-oriented, feelingless entities. There are no more persons, merely personae.

Such theories reflect the natural evolution of social-science theory keeping pace with the commodity market in mass-produced personalities. It is apparent that the theory not only describes but *reflects* a rational culture of interchangeable, emotionless, and completely meaningless and nonspontaneous parts. Inner experiencing and idiosyncrasy are discounted; the person has come to be described as the product of interacting social forces alone. These theories reflect the reality of the world Weber described. But they also reflect the experience of the contemporary social scientist, for the limitations on the vision of man must be a function of the limits of the vision of men, in this case social theorists. And any one who has worked in a modern university will not be surprised that the scholars therein have themselves been molded to the modern view, seeing man as rational, adaptive, conforming, vocationally oriented, and psychologically empty. Such theories reflect, in our own generation, the triumph of Protestant asceticism. The theory itself, however accurate, is alienated from the feeling, experiencing, and uniquely responsive man.

CONTROLS AND ACCOMMODATION

The drug movement provides a framework for the intellectual apolitical rebel. It is his revolution, a quiet revolution with no thundering rage. Its participants are too well acculturated and have benefited too much from the good thing of our society to have the audacity or the ingratitude to overrun the ethic itself. Like the violence-eschewing "cat" of the Negro ghetto, the LSD-using white professional is too committed to the values of the larger society and, in his case, too well rewarded for his good conduct to think of overturning a social order which is exactly what a properly reared citizen must think it should be: efficient, fair, honest, healthy, secure, charitable, and rational. The bind is on. He is what the society would have him be, eminently hard-working, successful, honest, and all the rest. The controls are built into his personality—indeed over controls, as the evaluation of ego control and distrust showed. Such a man cannot actively rebel. But the constraints which negate an active protest do not prevent him from experiencing emotions of reaction against that kind of a life and world. These are the feelings expressed by the words "unfulfilled," "tense," and "anxious," which most LSD users, and most of the controls as well, use to describe themselves.

The response to these symptoms is biologically determined by a desire to escape from pain and, culturally, by that optimism and activism which permeate the myth of progress: the belief that one need not accept things as they are and that one can change things, oneself included, for the better. So it is that LSD use remains consonant with the Western articles of faith; cure is possible, there are better worlds beyond, and science does provide a means for control—in this instance, one more pharmaceutical miracle.

The notion of control is an important one. This is a control-oriented society; technology and the whole apparatus of rational endeavor work to control nature and to control men. But that effort, one which is usually considered beneficial to man's comfort and security, has generated instruments so ponderous that the individual can lose all hope of controlling the instruments themselves. The state, organizations, and the various forms of collectivity are Frankenstein monsters, for they have moved from being instruments in the hands of men to being instruments which hold men in their hands. This is the nature of bureaucracy and the culmination of an efficient technological revolution.

For some, especially those who refuse to take LSD, the challenge of life in the machine age is met with some optimism. There is enough gratification found in remaining with the mainstream, seeing just how far one can swim against the current, seeing what eddies and backwaters one may turn to advantage, or, for many, the heady pleasure of plunging ahead, swimming with the current in full confidence that where it is taking one is exactly where one wants to go. For others, especially those who use LSD regularly, there is disinterest in remaining in those turbulent waters. Some are not optimistic about any benefits to be accrued, for the cost in malaise is great enough to annul the worth of any ends. For some, the awareness of the hopelessness of trying to control any part of oneself, once it is committed to the real world's torrent, looms uppermost. Others are discouraged because they fear they will not reach the goals they wish, a failure which will cost them dearly in self-esteem. Rather than seek and fail, they renounce those ends and seek new and easier glories. Their ambition is converted but not lost. For them, there is success achievable in the approval of friends or, for those who have become gurus, in the admiration of their disciples.

Individuals who have lost interest in or hope of controlling themselves and events in the real social world may try to control that area that can be controlled, the inner life. Appropriately enough, the devices employed still reflect their commitment to the world outside, for self-control is not achieved by oneself alone; it is achieved with a technological boost from the world of pharmacy.

Individuals sold on the system itself, sold on the self that is part of the system and yet still miserable, do not question the fundamental values, but seek only to alter that reality which can be changed without encountering direct and massive disapproval. Real revolutionaries are shot; illicit drug users are jailed, but LSD users are law-abiding people who behave in proper ways. They choose a pill in a society which advocates pills. They are initiated by one of the elite of that society—a doctor or sometimes an executive or engineer. And they use a drug which was or was believed to be perfectly legal to use at the time and under the circumstances when most of the professionals who were seeking the approved ends of personal benefit and improvement took LSD. The perfect regard for propriety characterized not only the use, but the reaction to the drug of the entire sample of legitimate users.

That regard for propriety was much less evident among the younger people who used LSD in the black-market setting. They had already taken other drugs illegally, they took LSD without benefit of medical supervision, and their response to the drug was erotic and orgiastic. No legitimate user of LSD engaged in orgiastic eroticism after taking the drug. But regardless of his greater immediate unconventionality, the black-market user's revolution is also a quiet one. He is willing to enjoy himself, but he is by no means attacking the world, nor is he reacting against the broad ascetic ethic. He has no intention of renouncing his career goals nor that wonderful, active, beckoning, big wide world. Obviously the life situation and propelling motives of the black-market user cannot be interpreted as symptoms of suffering which are to be relieved by a flight into contemplative mysticism. The use of LSD by the black-market group is associated with unconventional response, but not with mysticism and not with any withdrawal from commitment to the external world. Their short-term active unconventionality does not forebode any long-term unconventionality. The professional and legitimate LSD user, on the other hand, initially proper in use and response, may nevertheless be suffering, and that suffering may move him to mysticism and a long term of quiet unconventionality.

LSD BENEFITS EXPERIENCED

For the older, more successful people who are in need of lasting change, LSD does provide relief. It does not change basic personality structure nor the external world itself; it does change relations to that world by altering feelings, beliefs, and actions. The "anesthetic revelation" establishes contact with a lost inner psychic world—and William James would say with real and grander worlds of religion and God as well. For the user who does move in the direction of contemplative

mysticism, there is a fleeing from the world and the re-establishment
of the ethic of brotherhood, symbolized in becoming more loving. But
as with most brotherhoods, and certainly as with many fellowships of
the mystery religions, brotherhood and the personal ethic is limited to
the elect, to spiritual kinfolk. And so, demonstrating the pattern of
personal ties and clan loyalties which have characterized the "little
communities"[23] of tribesmen and peasants, the LSD user's brotherhood
is confined, ethnocentrically, to those in the drug movement and, indeed, because of the factionalism therein, only to some in that movement.

Having become "loving" is one of the most important changes
which the regular LSD user reports in himself. It is real because it is
felt to be real. But it is also inferred in the warm reactions of others to
some of these people. That lovingness arises not just because of the
regeneration of the ethic of brotherhood, but also because of the biological, psychological, and social fact that human beings have the capacity
to love, a capacity which does grow[24] as one makes peace with oneself
and as one has intense emotional experiences with others during critical periods. Certainly the LSD initiation, fraught as it is with anxiety,
uncertainty, danger, symbolic affirmations, great hopes, and group support, is one of those critical periods. Indeed, under some LSD institutions' procedures, that initiation is planned so as to maximize anxiety
and dependency ties which are then molded to a special form of "lovingness."

The balance of lovingness also rises as the heavy weight of tensions
and hatreds fall. As the individual does move even a bit away from
the exhausting competition with others and the never-ending striving
for goals that are always one step ahead, his aggressiveness and social-
ized anxiety, which have been in the service of vocational gain, and his
hostility in response to the competitive threats posed by others recede.
Thus what is felt as a new lovingness is partly the result of the dimin-
ishing of strife and hatred.

This lovingness need not be manifest to others. For one thing, the
mystically oriented person may not be actively benevolent. He may be
disinterested in those overt forms of charity and aggressively helpful
intervention of those who subscribe to the conventions of philanthropy
and humanitarianism. These acts are themselves part of the other-
directed motifs of an ethical and rational society. Thus, what the LSD
user feels to be loving and what the observer requires as "proofs of
love" are quite different. Second, it is to be recalled that Morimoto,[25]
in observing normal persons under LSD influence, found them to seek
support from others, but not to be brotherly. Since the drug incapaci-

tates the user, he does, in fact, rely on others for assistance and for reassurance. He becomes physically and psychologically dependent upon the initiator. Most initiators accept that and encourage dependency with warmth and understanding. The background of most of the LSD users is one which has discouraged dependency. "Self-reliance," "stand on your own two feet," "bear your pain in manly silence"; those are the watchwords. But the LSD experience alters that, encouraging intense • interrelationships, dependency, and, psychoanalytically speaking, regression. What a luxury and relief it must be! To indulge in that relaxation and to be allowed it. One feels loved and is allowed to love in return. That accepted dependency and resultant interpersonal tie may be the root of the LSD lovingness and would account for the absence of reciprocal, brotherly conduct, as observed by Morimoto. That dependency might also account for the feelings of protectiveness sometimes reported by observers; it and the earlier lack of active benevolence can account for the discrepancy between the observer's impression of a few users as simply passive, unconcerned, or selfish and the users' description of their own lovingness.

Persons who take LSD often claim they are more "open" now. They were "closed," they say, before, and they see those who reject the drug remaining closed as they themselves once were. To the observer, this openness may not readily be apparent, especially as the convictions associated with the drug movement are heard again and again, like the monotonous roll of melody from a player piano which is never turned off. That the rank and file of the initiates should say the same things is no surprise; the careful teaching of the meaning of the experience and the conveying of a language about that experience is essential to the growth of real social groups centered about the drug. But how can people, with such set convictions and ethnocentrism— and one refers especially to those who have taken the drug under some LSD institution's auspices—conceive of themselves as open? It is because their point of reference is their former selves. These are engineers, physicians, professors and the like who were once committed to a point of view which was certainly in keeping with that of their colleagues. But in accepting LSD, they set out on an adventure of the mind and spirit. They opened themselves to a new way of acting and to new beliefs. Viewed in this light, one can understand the liberation which being open implies.

MALE AND FEMALE ATTITUDES ON LSD

It is men who most often take LSD, and it is men who become repeated users. That is understandable, since men, more than women, are directly immersed in the impersonal striving interaction that characterizes the Protestant ethic. The life of the woman, at least the non-working woman, is much more restricted. Her daily social contacts are far fewer, and the proportion of those contacts which are personal and emotional, contacts with husband and children, is far greater. Even if she does work, the woman is biologically committed to family ends, and she is likely to measure her own status position in terms of what her husband's position is and how that affects the family position. Her biological commitments to child care provide her with "real" experiences in James's sense; the demands upon her because of that nurturing role are so very strong and so satisfying that it is a rare female who will consider any kind of desertion from those responsibilities and pleasures. Given these circumstances, it is no wonder that women rarely seek out LSD, and, when they do take it, it is so often in response to the urgings of their husbands. That acquiescence is less in the interest of internal experience than in maintaining a relationship upon which the security of the nest is based.

But there is another aspect of the husband-wife relationship generated by LSD, and that is the disapproval which women may voice about their husband's LSD interests, regardless of whether or not the woman has temporarily pleased him by being initiated. As pragmatists, necessarily self-controlled for reasons different than any religious asceticism, they are aware of the threat which LSD can pose to the controls and commitments of their mates. One may tolerate a husband's experimentation, but not if it jeopardizes family security by leading the husband to quit his job. Should the wife be status conscious, a status which depends upon her husband's success, it does not take a job change to evoke her concern. She need only sense his reduced interest in achieving or anticipate some threat to social position because of society's adversity to LSD use per se. For these women, the successful husband is betraying his wife by renouncing the status escalator just as he nears or even reaches the top. Her own investment in that goal, perhaps many years of encouragement or pushing, is in danger of being wasted.

Not only are conventional and comfortable daily habits threatened with change—the husband's sexual impulses, for example, may be expanded to trouble the wife's conventionality—but his interest in discarding the old may immediately be assessed by the wife in terms of the marriage itself. She may fear that, as the husband renounces one set of unsatisfactory institutional conventions, he may generalize to another. Having jettisoned the dull cargo of work, he may seek to break the chains of yet another form of institutional slavery. In some cases, this wifely fear has been justified: the husband has renounced his wife along with his job.

COMMITMENT AND MODERATION

An important consideration is the extent to which LSD produces a full commitment to the inner life, that is, produces full-time mysticism. Only one member of the sample was a true mystic in the sense that he had renounced the world completely and was fully dedicated to seeking individual salvation and grace through the religiously irrational. But this man had been an Eastern mystic before taking LSD. He took the drug once, found it an interesting experience, and renounced its further use because "one cannot achieve the discipline of the spirit through drugs." No member of the sample who became interested in religious mysteries after LSD renounced the world. A few did quit their jobs or worked less effectively, but they did this not as a matter of disciplined spiritual choice but rather, according to our interpretation, because of disabilities associated with the untoward effects of the continual use of a number of mind-altering drugs.

Most LSD users stayed on the job and compromised their inner visions with the demands of outer world. That they have done so augurs well for their adjustment to that world, for there is no headlong flight from reality. The ascetic observer will approve and think well of the common sense of the LSD user. On the other hand, if one, longing for passionate commitments, hopes that it alone can make Dionysians out of molded Apollonians, he will be disappointed. The intellectuals who use LSD, with the possible exclusion of the younger black-market orgiasts, are incapable of altering themselves to such an extent that they go to any extreme. Should they try to achieve extremism through the continued use of drugs, they are more likely to suffer chronic drug effects rather than be transported to any state of ultimate and continuing enlightenment. It does not appear that LSD is a short cut to personality reconstruction or to nirvana.

The moderation of the sample and the absence of passionate extremism or an intensity of commitment to the inner way leads to another observation. Those who compromise, except perhaps the aforementioned true mystic, must adjust inner desires and outer demands. What these persons propose is to "play the game." One is to go through the motions of a vocation but to do so without conviction, enthusiasm, or the investment of personal feelings. It is in this that regular LSD users may differ most dramatically from most, but not all, rejectors.

The LSD user who proposes to play the game is in fact carrying the rational impersonal system to its logical next step. By proposing further to divest himself of feelings in his relations with other men, by proposing to analyze the system and play it exactly according to its rules, without feelings, without a personal ethic, but with a willingness to abide by external moralities, that man completes his alienations from society. He becomes the very model of modernity. Nothing could be more rational. That modern man, wrote Weber,

> performs his duty best when he acts without regard to the person in question . . . without hate and without love, without personal predilection . . . but sheerly in accordance with the factual material responsibility imposed by his calling, and not as a result of any discrete personal relationship.

It is ironic that the sensitive intellectual who seeks spontaneity and richness denied him by the cold and ungratifying outer world by turning to inner experiences which are drug-induced, that sensitive man who renounces "the slave goals" of success and status which are part of an "inhuman bureaucracy," can in fact become the epitome of that dehumanization in his worldly interactions. Not all who use LSD repeatedly would so evolve, of course. That some will is the inevitable consequence of the massive effects of having lived in that world too long, of taking a drug which reduces "with" behavior and which leads to the association with social groups which, as they espouse "playing the game," not only reflect the awareness of a need to compromise and a desire to turn inward, but which represent the triumph of alienation in their own motifs. The existentialists are concerned about commitment, about "being." So too are many LSD users—and their peers. LSD helps the user to feel more intense and alive, but whether or not it allows him "being" in the existential sense remains an open question. If commitment to private experience is sufficient, it does. If commitment must be as a human being with other human beings, that is, if the axis of reality also runs through shared experiences, if *being* alone is not sufficient and requires also *being together*, then one must wonder if LSD will provide lasting fulfillment.

The alienated man will be divorced from it all, a perfectly rational man acting impersonally in an automatic system. In that sense the euphoria produced by LSD and maintained, in regular users, by frequent use of mind-altering substances, is completely compatible with the evolution of an alienated society. The LSD user responds to alienation initially with despair, but then he makes an adjustment which is reportedly very satisfying, but which serves further to alienate him from that society and his own feelings about that society. The LSD rejector, on the other hand, suffering too, but in all fairness perhaps not so sensitively as the LSD user, is willing to continue to suffer rather than to abandon his emotional investment in the world. Lest the drug rejector's position be overly glorified, let it be made clear that he needs some escapes, palliatives, and restoratives too, and may very well guzzle alcohol, overeat, take sleeping pills, chew aspirin, use tranquilizers, or find his brand of ecstasy in a modified form of the "imperial madness"[26] by becoming—as some most certainly do—drunk on power.

The Religious Quest

Weber was wrong when he held that Christianity, in rejecting intellectualism, also rejected from the beginning the idea of ecstasy or the notion that God favors the visionary. Quite the contrary, the one who experiences such visions is especially blessed and may enjoy the knowledge of that favor along with the experience itself. Edward Gibbon[27] writes:

> The supernatural gifts, which even in this life were ascribed to the Christians above the rest of mankind, must have conduced to their own comfort, and very frequently to the conviction of infidels. Besides the occasional prodigies which might sometimes be affected by the immediate interposition of the Deity when he suspended the laws of Nature for the service of religion, the Christian church, from the time of the apostles and their first disciples, has claimed an uninterrupted succession of miraculous powers, the gift of tongues, of vision and of prophecy, the power of expelling demons, of healing the sick, and of raising the dead. The knowledge of foreign languages was frequently communicated to the contemporaries of Irenaeus, though Irenaeus himself was left to struggle with the difficulties of a barbarous dialect whilst he preached the gospel to the natives of Gaul. The divine inspiration, whether it was conveyed in the form of a waking or a sleeping vision, is described as a favour very liberally bestowed on all ranks of the faithful, on women as on elders, on boys as well as upon bishops. When their devout minds were sufficiently prepared by a course of prayer, of fasting, and of vigils, to receive the extraordinary impulse, they were transported out of their senses, and delivered in ecstasy what was inspired.

Thus the use of mind-altering drugs today is in keeping with the religious traditions of Western culture. Whether the visions of the mystical experience are true as well as real is a question which cannot be answered here, but which cannot be avoided in accounting for the varying reactions of people to LSD use and to the statements of those who have employed the drug. The question of the truth of the mystical vision, that is, whether or not it is a revelation of that which religion treats, determines, for some at least, the acceptability of the use of such substances. If this is the way to salvation or to God, they say, then how can the means be denied? If it be not the means to salvation or to God, then it is blasphemy or foolishness.

Many believe that the visions are true as well as real and that drug use must be permitted as a legitimate religious endeavor. Such arguments have been advanced only recently before the California legislature in the hearings over the use of peyote, now illegal, by Navajo Indian members of the Native American Church. Others, supporting efforts to repeal the illegality of peyote use in religious worship, have argued only that the religious motive is sufficient, that the observer cannot know the truth, and that Constitutional guarantees of freedom of worship prevent the skeptic from obstructing others' right to seek religious truth.

Some hold that there is no religious truth other than that revealed to the mystic. For them, the institutional church is but a trapping of the world and dogma is but the superstructure of intellect. Only the mystic is assured salvation or the vision of truth unfolding. This position, by no means unusual in the history of religion, is fundamental to a mystery religion and is linked, as Mircea Eliade[28] discusses, with the myths of some primitive societies. Eliade contends it is the myth of the return to paradise which is basic to the mystical experience. Such a belief, interestingly enough, emerges in the accounts of some LSD users who describe journeys back through time to "the beginning." That experience, if granted as truth, would place the LSD mystic in possession of a racial unconscious as well as mark him as one of the elect who are privileged to experience truth. Certainly any culture which valued revelations would be hard pressed to justify the exclusion of the means and accounts of such illumination.

There are, on the other hand, the skeptics who either discount the mystical experience as not containing any religious truth or go further to deny the existence of religious truth as such. Gibbon[29] writes:

> A state of scepticism and suspense may amuse a few inquisitive minds. But the practice of superstition is so congenial

to the multitude that, if they are forcibly awakened, they still regret the loss of their pleasing vision. Their love of the marvellous and supernatural, their curiosity with regard to future events, and their strong propensity to extend their hopes and fears beyond the limits of the visible world [led to the establishment of polytheism]. . . . So urgent on the vulgar is the necessity of believing that the fall of any system of mythology will most probably be succeeded by the introduction of some other mode of superstition.

One taking that position would certainly doubt the reports of LSD users and be prepared to prohibit the drug, should there be any evidence of its destructive effects or should evidence for its benefits to psychological health be inconclusive.

That the beliefs voiced by those in the drug movement constitute a mythology can hardly be denied. Whether the mythology be true is the subject of considerable dispute. But, as a mythology, it has a function. As Henry A. Murray[30] wrote:

Religions, myths, philosophies and systems of psychotherapy have been largely or partly devoted to the achievement of unifying resolutions, and to the degree that any of these systems succeeds in doing this—in preventing or relieving intolerable conflicts, curing "sick souls," people will trust it, cling to it, believe in it and conform to its prescriptions. Further, to the extent that such high evaluations are shared by the population at large, the system will serve as a cohesive force.

That there is a need for the drug movement is demonstrated by its emergence, granting the premises of functionalism. For the intellectuals from whose ranks the movement draws its recruits, perhaps the world does require a new mythology. Murray describes the current state of affairs in which there is

the senescence of the traditional religions and their present incapacity . . . to bring forth a new vision of a better world, to generate widespread passionate belief in their own doctrines, or in all sincerity, to guide individual self-development and conduct in the light of an acceptable ideal.

In the world of today, writes Murray, there is "the spread of existential anxiety, affectlessness, meaninglessness, spiritual loneliness, hollowness, alienation and regressive emotional drift." Given these curses of our time, no wonder Murray concludes that the world needs some new mythology, "radical and revolutionary."

The drug movement is an expression of that need. It is a dream, an idea; its converts, like all those aflame with their own convictions, have charisma. That is why the observer is so often drawn to convinced LSD users, for they *are* alive, and the observer must sense the strength of their convictions. It *is* contagious. For those who subsist on the jejune diet of social accommodation, Protestant rigor, and reason, the charisma emanating from ones who have conviction evokes a psychic tropism. The movement promises much—a return to paradise, a Utopia of the inner life—and so LSD-25 becomes, if one may be allowed a neologism, a "Utopiate."

Whether the movement fulfills its promise or whether it falters because of some insufficiency in its mythology, some undesirable side effects in its means, or the intensity of its worldly opposition, the need
• for *something* will be no less strong. It is this need which must be kept in mind. Whatever happens to the drug movement as such, drugs will continue to be used to alter states of consciousness. To the extent that ordinary consciousness remains in a state of reactive despair to the world of reality—or is empty of that experience which mind senses as its own potential—people will join together to seek new meanings in some mythology.

NOTES

1. Sandoz Pharmaceuticals, *Annotated Bibliography Delsyd LSD-25 (d-lysergic acid diethylamide)* (Hanover, N.J.: 1958), addenda 1–4.
2. Sidney Cohen and Keith S. Ditman, "Complications Associated With Lysergic Acid Diethylamide (LSD-25)," *Journal of the American Medical Association*, CLXXXI (1962), 161–162.
3. Tigani el Mahi, "The Use and Abuse of Drugs," World Health Organization, Reg. Off. Eastern Mediterranean, EM/RC12/6, XVI (1962).
4. Gunnar Myrdal, *An American Dilemma* (New York: Harper & Row, 1962).
5. Howard Becker, *The Outsiders: Studies in the Sociology of Deviance* (New York: Free Press of Glencoe, 1963).
6. Everett Hughes, *Men and Their Work* (Glencoe, Ill.: Free Press, 1958).
7. Robert K. Merton, *Social Theory and Social Structure* (Glencoe, Ill.: Free Press, 1957).
8. Nevitt Sanford, *The American College* (New York: John Wiley & Sons, 1963).
9. Max Weber, *The Sociology of Religion,* trans. Fischoff (Boston: Beacon Press, 1963).

10. Fritz Redl, "Contagion and 'Shock Effect,'" in *Searchlights on Delin-quency* (New York: International Universities Press, 1949), pp. 315–328.
11. Claire Russell and W. M. S. Russell, *Human Behavior* (Boston: Little, Brown, 1961).
12. J. S. Slotkin, *The Peyote Religion: A Study in Indian-White Relations* (Glencoe, Ill.: Free Press, 1956).
13. Harold Finestone, "Cats, Kicks and Color," in *Identity and Anxiety,* ed. Maurice Stein, Arthur Vidich, and David White (New York: Free Press of Glencoe, 1960), 435–448.
14. G. Morris Carstairs, "Daru and Bhang: Cultural Factors in the Choice of Intoxicant," *Quarterly Journal of Studies in Alcoholism,* XV (1954), 220–237.
15. David Riesman, Nathan Glazer, and Reuel Denney, *The Lonely Crowd* (New Haven: Yale University Press, 1950).
16. William James, *The Varieties of Religious Experience* (New York: Doubleday, 1954).
17. Talcott Parsons, Introduction to Weber, *op. cit.*
18. William Whyte, *The Organization Man* (New York: Simon & Schuster, 1956).
19. John R. Seeley, Alexander Sim, and Elizabeth Loosley, *Crestwood Heights* (New York: Basic Books, 1956).
20. Maurice R. Stein, *The Eclipse of Community* (Princeton, N.J.: Princeton University Press, 1960).
21. George Herbert Mead, *Mind, Self and Society* (Chicago: University of Chicago Press, 1934).
22. Erving Goffman, *The Presentation of Self in Everyday Life* (New York: Doubleday Anchor Books, 1959); Anselm Strauss, *Mirrors and Masks: The Search for Identity* (Glencoe, Ill.: Free Press, 1959).
23. Robert Redfield, *The Little Community* and *Peasant Society and Culture* (Chicago: University of Chicago Press, 1960).
24. Carl Rogers and Rosalind F. Dymond, *Psychotherapy and Personality Change* (Chicago: University of Chicago Press, 1954).
25. Kyo Morimoto, cited by H. A. Abrahamson, *Neuropharmacology: Trans-actions of the 2nd Conference* (New York: Josiah Macy Jr. Foundation, 1955).
26. Suetonius, *The Twelve Caesars* (Baltimore: Penguin Classics, 1957).
27. Edward Gibbon, *Decline and Fall of the Roman Empire* (New York: Heritage Press, 1946), I, 366–367.
28. Mircea Eliade, "The Yearning for Paradise in Primitive Tradition," in *Myths and Mythmaking,* ed. Henry Murray (New York: Braziller Pub. Co., 1960), pp. 61–75.
29. Gibbon, *op. cit.,* p. 389.
30. Henry A. Murray, "The Possible Nature of a 'Mythology' to Come," in Murray, *Myths and Mythmaking, op. cit.,* pp. 300–353.

INDEX

Addicts: barbiturate, 2–3; mutual exploitation by, 261; myths about, 208; narcotic, 147; rehabilitation of, 216; U.S. opiate, 215

Addiction, 2, 61, 147, 161, 206–207, 212; to alcohol, 209; dynamics of those prone to, 136, 239–242; to heroin, 65–66; to LSD-type drugs, 219; to marijuana, 214, 230; to opiates, 216; to tranquilizers, 211

Addictive drugs, willingness to take, 27, 35, 50–51, 66, 99, 269

Adjective check list: as description of drug-user traits by police, 230–233; as measure of felt LSD change, 26, 67, 78–79, 101

Administrative problems, of law-enforcement agencies in drug-control work, 255–257

Age: of five LSD-user subsamples, 28–29, 35, 37, 60, 267; of LSD accepters versus rejectors, 92–93, 115; of regular users versus discontinuers, 86; of Zihuatanejo group, 144

Alcohol, 1, 19, 30–31, 38, 67–68, 73, 90, 97, 99–100, 103, 148, 156, 197, 206, 208–210, 221, 268–269; compared with other drugs, 211–218; discussed by police, 227–230, 270, 273, 277, 289

Alcoholism, 30, 65, 67, 120–121, 146, 148, 209–210; compared with drug use by police and parole officers, 226, 244–245; use of LSD in treatment of, 218

Alienation: and LSD use, 288; and the modern disaffection, 280, 292; and religion, 194–197; and social responsibility, 261; in sociological theory, 280–281

ALPERT, RICHARD, 149, 160, 162–163, 169–170, 173

ALLPORT, GORDON, 176

Amanita mushroom, 7

American Civil Liberties Union, menace ratings by police and parole officers, 233, 245

American Medical Association, 212–213

Amnesia: experimentally demonstrated with LSD, 88; as factor in self-description, 103; and recall of LSD experience, 78; retrograde, 18

Amphetamines, 119, 206, 211–212; see also Benzedrine, Dexedrine, Methedrine, Stimulants

Antihistaminics, 211

Anxiety: about changing the setting of LSD use, 45; inhibition of in opiate use, 89; level at Zihuatanejo, 152; in LSD regulars and discontinuers, 78–80, 82–83; in LSD users and controls, 110; partial reduction of as a determinant of continuing drug use, 79–80, 82, 274; produced by LSD-type drugs, 218; produced by large doses of marijuana, 214; reduction in associated with LSD use, 166–167; in response to respiratory distress, 137–138, 284; in transpersonative personality theory, 149–150, 155–157; treated by sedatives and tranquilizers, 211

Apollonian culture, 6, 9, 59, 111, 278

Arrest: for alcohol-related offenses, 210; for dangerous-drug offenses, 211; drug offender's behavior toward police, 257, 266; drug offender's behavior with doctors and social scientists, 257–258

Attitudes: of citizens toward police, 255, 257; of doctors and behavioral scientists toward police, 257; of drug users toward authority, 230–232, 239–243; ignorance of public regarding pleas-